Helmut Determann

Gel Chromatography

Gel Filtration · Gel Permeation · Molecular Sieves

A Laboratory Handbook

With 40 Figures

Springer-Verlag New York Inc. 1968

Dr. phil. nat. HELMUT DETERMANN, Privatdozent

Institut für Organische Chemie der Universität Frankfurt am Main

Translated by Dr. phil. nat. ERHARD GROSS

National Institutes of Health, Bethesda, Maryland, USA

Translation of the German Edition of Determann "Gelchromatographie".

Title No. 1442

Foreword

The efforts spent on many a scientific book cannot be justified, no matter how many words are said about it. The opposite is true for this book and a few brief remarks upon its publication.

Within a short period of time, short even by all present standards, gel chromatography has gone through a development and experienced an acceptance that is unknown to any other method. From experience, the new and unique separation technique is today known and liked in all laboratories that are concerned with substances of high molecular weight; in others, the technique is known from hearsay, the least. Soon it became evident that a comprehensive coverage of the conceptual development, the theoretical principles, and the experimental technique of the new method would be desirable. This coverage is now offered by the book of an expert. Its author has personally participated in the development from its beginning and helped to promote it. He has made possible the gel chromatography, also of proteins, on thin layer plates; for lipophilic substances he has contributed considerably to the transition from water to organic solvent systems and developed theoretical concepts for a better understanding of the effects that are responsible for the separation. The book, so it appears to me, is pointing in new directions. The reader does not only expect a clear presentation of facts but also that of instructions for practical applications. Both these expectations have been met by the expert.

The text is concise and clear, nevertheless conducive to new thought and invites new developments and further advancements, as the interested reader will find. In these days of the transition from the chemistry of the solute to the regions of structural organization for which the water swellable gels may serve as models, this book may well mark the beginning of new orientation and of new concepts.

THEODOR WIELAND

Preface

Gel chromatography is a new method for the separation, purification, and analysis of mixtures of substances. The separation is based on differences in molecular size, thus gel chromatography lends itself also to the determination of molecular weights. The required equipment is simple and the technique easily applied. Within the course of a few years the method has been introduced in many chemical and medical laboratories. A sizable number of auxiliary and supplementary methods have been developed for the application of the method on a micro as well as on a preparative scale. In areas of overlapping interest between chemistry, biology, and medicine, gel chromatography has been developed to an important technical and manufacturing tool. What initially may have been considered a specialized biochemical laboratory technique has now become a standard chromatographic method. Gel chromatography is now applied everywhere where substances of different molecular size have to be separated and analyzed.

The large number of possible applications delineates the opportunity as well as the difficulty of this book. Reviews and bibliographical summaries have been published. However, they were restricted either to a special aspect or kept rather short. It appeared therefore timely to present this special technique and the accumulated extensive experimental data more comprehensively. The spectrum of substances separable by gel chromatography reaches from functional viruses, proteins, antibiotics, and lipids to synthetic polymers of high molecular weight. This multitude of results necessitated the restriction of the book to a guide for the application of gel chromatography to different problems. Within the frame work of the book it was not possible to cover all published results. The special properties of the different classes of substances require special experimental conditions; therefore the practical aspects of the application of the technique are dominant in this book.

A brief introduction and the historical survey are followed by the detailed discussion of the experimental technique. The theoretical principles of gel chromatography are as yet not firmly established; their discussion has therefore been kept brief. Outstanding examples have been selected for the detailed discussion of the various techniques and their potential application. The applications in biological chemistry are numerous. Only a limited number of selected separations could be described in detail. Other applications from this field have been organized by classes of substances and are discussed in the final chapter of the book.

It is the aim of this book to inform the reader about the methods, the potential, and the limits of gel chromatography and to encourage him to experiments in his own field of interest.

H. Determann

Frankfurt am Main, November 1967

Table of Contents

Chapter 1

Introduction

Separation by Molecular Weight Differences 1
   Dialysis 2
   Homogeneous Gels 3
Chromatography on Granulated Gels 4
   Illustrative Experiment 5
   Terminology 6
Historical Survey 8
   Ion Exchangers 8
   Neutral Gels 9
References 11

Chapter 2

Materials and Methods

The Gels 13
   The Preparation of Hydrophylic Gels 15
      Dextran Gels 15
      Polyacrylamide Gels 17
      Agar Gels, Agarose Gels 19
   The Preparation of Organophilic Gels 21
      Sephadex Derivatives 21
      Acrylic Gels 22
      Polystyrene Gels 23
      Aerogels 25
   Commercial Gels 26
      Sephadex 26
      Sephadex LH-20 28
      Bio-Gel 28
      Agarose 29
      Styragel 30
Equipment 31
   Columns 32
   Pumps 34
   Hose Connections 35
   Detectors 36
   Fraction Collectors 39
   Integrated Units 40
Experimental Techniques with Columns 42
   Packing of the Gel Bed 42
   Chromatography 43
      Sample Application 43

   Elution 46
   Analysis 47
  Extension of the Gel Bed 48
   Recycling Chromatography 49
 Thinlayer Gel Chromatography 51
  Preparation 51
  Chromatography 53
  Results 55
 Centrifuge Techniques 56
  Equipment 56
  Illustrative Experiments 58
   Desalting 58
   Concentrating 59
References 60

Chapter 3

Theory

Numerical Evaluation of Experimental Data 64
 Volumes in the Gel Bed 64
 Elution Parameters 65
Effectivity of a Gel Column 69
Approaches of Interpretation 72
 The Exclusion Principle 73
  Simple Geometric Models 73
  The Ogston-Laurent Gel Model 75
 The Principle of Restricted Diffusion 76
 Comparison of the Various Interpretations 77
 The Partition Principle 78
Affinity of Solutes to the Gel Phase 79
 Partition and Adsorption 80
 Hydrophylic Gels 82
References 84

Chapter 4

Principles of Application

Gel Filtration 87
 Desalting 88
 Group Separation 90
 Modification of Macromolecules 92
 Complex Formation 96
Gel Chromatography 99
Molecular Weight Determination 105
 Calibration 105
 Technique 111
 Molecular Weight Determination of Proteins 113
  Theory 113
  Results 115
  Association Equilibria 118

The Study of Polydisperse Systems 120
    General Principles 120
    Gel Chromatography 122
    Evaluation of Gel Permeation Chromatograms 123
    Results 125
Separation without Differences in Size 129
    Chromatography in Aqueous Media 129
    Chromatography with Organic Solvents 132
    Fractional Precipitation 135
References 136

Chapter 5

Results

Enzymology 141
    Isolation of Enzymes 141
    Enzymatic Reactions 144
Endocrinology 145
Chemistry of Plasma Proteins 148
Structural Elucidation of Proteins 152
Nucleic Acid Chemistry 155
    Nucleic Acids 155
    Oligonucleotides 156
    Virus Separation 157
Carbohydrates 158
Clinical Chemistry 159
Miscellaneous Applications 162
References 166

Bibliography 170
Author Index 171
Subject Index 188

Chapter 1

Introduction

Next to chemical composition, size and weight are the most significant properties of a molecule. The molecular weight is frequently the decisive parameter to distinguish two molecules. The difference in molecular size plays a role in all conventional physical separation methods. The higher homologues of a series show usually higher melting and boiling points as well as lower solubility than related compounds of similar structure. For all practical purposes these differences are overlapping with other properties such as polarity or electrical charge density which determine the behavior of a substance during crystallization, distillation, extraction and during most of the chromatographic methods of separation. Sorting by size is a very common ordering principle in the macroscopic world. At the molecular level it was applied relatively late and in only a few isolated cases. It is also true for separations which are based on differences in molecular weight that other factors than the difference in molecular size play a role.

Separation by Molecular Weight Differences

Two characteristic differences between molecules are of fundamental importance: sedimentation velocity and space filling. The differences in sedimentation are determined in the ultracentrifuge (1) which is capable of producing extreme gravity fields. It was the technique of ultracentrifugation that made it possible for the first time to determine the molecular weights of sensitive macromolecules. However, by its very design, the ultracentrifuge is not a tool applicable to preparative needs. Nevertheless a mixture of macromolecules may be centrifuged in a density gradient. Depending upon the weight, substances are sedimenting to zones of specific densities from where they may be isolated thus using the ultracentrifuge as a tool for the micropreparative separation of macromolecules (2).

Macroscopically, classes of molecular size are separated by sieving or filtering. In the separating medium are imbedded meshes or pores which are penetrated only by particles of up to a certain maximum size. The term *"molecular sieves"* is reserved for a group of crystalline aluminosilicates. These so-called *"Zeolites"* may differ in composition and structure (3). The Zeolites are found in nature. Today, however, they are also available synthetically (4). The network-structure of the SiO_4 and AlO_4-tetraeders is responsible for the formation of cavities in the interior. These cavities are connected by pores. The small diameter of the pores does not allow the penetration by large molecules. Small molecules are diffusing unimpaired. The "inner surface" and the penetrating substance are frequently interacting, thus causing the selective adsorption of polar substances of low molecular weight (5). Many Zeolites show considerable ionexchange capacity and the entire picture is rather complex. Zeolites are therefore only used as molecular sieves for special technical separations. The pronounced selectivity and the adsorptive capacity – even at high temperature – ascertain widespread application in this area (cf. 6). The term "molecular sieve" is only applicable to the surface of a Zeolite which – like a sieve – will only be penetrated by molecules which are below certain molecular size.

Dialysis

Semipermeable membranes are closer to the principle of a sieve at the molecular level. These sieves were made available first in the form of animal membranes (7). Today films of cellulose (Visking or Kalle) are used predominantly for dialysis. Such foils permit frequently the passage of small molecules only. For decades dialysis was the method of choice to desalt macromolecules in aqueous solution. Swelling in zinc chloride solution or mechanical stretching (8) increase the permeability of cellulose membranes considerably. Now proteins of molecular weights of up to 100000 diffuse within relatively short periods of time (8, 9, 10). Membranes of Agar or Agarose have been made which in the swollen state are partially permeable for proteins (11) and viruses (12). The measurement of the rate of diffusion through modified cellulose membranes of particular selectivity offers a clue to the spatial structure of sugars (13), of amino acids (14), and of peptides (15). CRAIG (16) has proposed for such subtle separations the term *differential dialysis*.

The difference in the rate of diffusion is naturally small and complete separation of molecules of different size must not be expected upon single passage through the membrane. Attempts have therefore been made to increase the separatory effect by placing in series membranes of increasing density. The direction of migration for charged molecules can be fixed by the application of an electrical field (9, 12, 17). – The low efficiency of differential dialysis can undoubtedly be increased by making the diffusate of the first step – eventually after concentration – the retentate of the second step (18, 19, 20). These multiple dialysis methods have the following in common: the biggest components are migrating the relatively shortest distance.

Homogeneous Gels

The sieve effect is much pronounced for substances which migrate within the membrane along the direction of propagation. MOULD and SYNGE (*21*) studied the electroosmosis of uncharged polysaccharides in a collodium membrane and were able to establish a quantitative relationship between the degree of polymerisation and the rate of migration. For the diffusion in homogeneous gels the relationship between the concentration of the gel-forming agent and the rate of migration has been clearly recognized (cf. *22*). This effect is of particular significance for the electrophoresis of macro-molecules in starch and polyacrylamide gels. SMITHIES recognized the relationship between gel concentration, molecular size and rate of migration when he introduced the starch gel (*23*). Later on he established the relationship quantitatively (*24*): under otherwise identical conditions, the distance of migration of a protein is inversely proportional to the concentration of starch; a coefficient can be defined which is solely an expression for the molecular size and not dependent upon charge or electrophoresis conditions. For explanation, SMITHIES refers to a "dynamic" model of the gel with thermally agitated polysaccharide chains. The more closely these chains are spaced the fewer times they will allow a given molecule to migrate via a pore of sufficiently large size. A completely different concept was developed by TOMBS (*25*) as a result of a careful analysis of the influence of the concentration of polyacrylamide on electrophoretic mobility. In his static model, TOMBS assumes a gel with fixed pores of different size the distribution of which is determined by the concentration. For a given ion a "limiting pore" is defined as one of such size that an ion can just pass through it. The mobility of the ions is then determined by the number of pores which are larger than the "limiting pore". Similar effects played a role in the discontinuous electrophoresis of ORNSTEIN and DAVIS (*26*).

By definition gels (*27, 28*) are made up of two components: the dispersed substance (here the gel forming material) and the dispersing agent (the solvent). The two components penetrate and stabilize each other. The coherence of both systems is characteristic for a gel, i.e. within the system one may proceed to any location without ever leaving the system. (If this condition is only met for the dispersed substance but not for the dispersing agent, we are then dealing with a foam). The coherence of the dispersing agent is demonstrated by the fact that small molecules diffuse with practically the same velocity like those in solution. The structures of the majority of gels are formed by macromolecules which are held together in "knots" and junction points or regions of junction points, respectively, depending upon the type of interaction between the predominantly linear molecules. In general secondary valence forces (hydrogen bond, dipol-dipol interaction, dispersion forces) or primary valence forces (ionic and covalent bonds) are the main contributors. The first type of cohesive force requires the participation of a large number of atomic groups to be effective. This leads to the formation of junctional regions. The latter forces are responsible for isolated junction points, i.e. the formation of "knots" (cf. *29*). Removal of the dispersing agent causes the gel structure to shrink to a *Xerogel*. Sometimes the original structure is maintained in the form of a rigid *Aerogel*. The type of dry gel is determined by the more or less pronounced rigidity of the elements of the gel forming substance. Numerous types of transition stages have been encountered. The preparation of gels and structural differences will be discussed in the second chapter.

Chromatography on Granulated Gels

The discussion of the behavior of molecules of different size in homogeneous gels (page 3) has made it clear that effective separation cannot be brought about solely by diffusion. The situation changes as soon as we consider the boundary between gel and solvent. The solvent will be identical with the dispersing agent of the gel (cf. Fig. 1). There will be no diffusion (cf. Fig. 1a) as long as the molecules of the solute in the solvent outside the gel are larger than the largest pores in the gel. With decreasing molecular size of the solute a point will be reached at which a certain number of the pores of the gel will become accessible for the molecules; diffusion equilibrium is characterized by the state indicated in Fig. 1b. The distribution of molecules is now a function of pore size (or of the gel density). For solute molecular

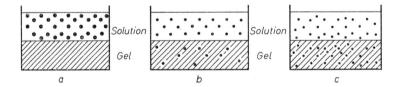

Fig. 1. In each one of three dishes is placed a layer of gel under solvent. In the solvent there are molecules which (a) do not penetrate the gel, (b) penetrate a portion of the gel, (c) freely penetrate the entire gel.

weights which are small with regard to gel density, the gel does not interfere with diffusion (Fig. 1c). In the state of equilibrium we find equal numbers of molecules in the gel and in the supernatant solution. A mixture of the three different types of molecules shown in Fig. 1 could be separated by an approach which is reminiscent of counter current distribution: the solution is allowed to make contact with the gel layer; after equilibrium has been reached the liquid phase is moved to a new gel layer, fresh solvent is being poured onto the old gel layer. The appropriate waiting periods have to be observed and the process repeated until complete separation has been accomplished. The slow diffusion would make such a procedure an elaborate one.

Much more effective separations are obtained with granulated gels by greatly increasing the interface area and reducing considerably the time required to reach equilibrium. The gel grains together with the solvent are poured into a vertically mounted glass tube. The molecules of different size in a percolating solution are separated upon washing with solvent. The process is shown schematically in Fig. 2. For reasons of simplicity only two molecular sizes (large and small dots) and the gel particles (circles) are indicated. Figure 2a depicts the state immediately after applying the solution to the layer of gel particles (gel bed). The gel does not interfere with the diffusion of the small molecules. These are distributed evenly throughout the entire cross section of the glass tube. The large molecules do not penetrate the gel. To them is only available the solvent between gel particles (outer volume) (Fig. 2b). Upon washing with solvent, only the molecules in the outer volume are transported. The *larger molecules are moving faster* than the smaller ones (Fig. 2c) which are retarded due to the temporary diffusion into the (stationary) gel phase. If the mixture contained also

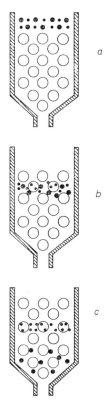

Fig. 2. Schematic representation of gel chromatography in three phases.

solutes of medium size, these would – in the state of diffusion equilibrium – enter only a certain portion of the gel phase (cf. Fig. 1b). The components of the solute mixture will leave the glass tube filled with gel particles *in the order of decreasing molecular weight* and corresponding to the hold-up time in the stationary gel phase, which in turn is dependent on diffusion.

Illustrative Experiment

The schematic presentation of the separation procedure will be illustrated by an example. The experimental approach will be described in brief. More detailed information can be found in Chapter 2 (page 42). *Soluble starch*, everywhere available, was chosen as high molecular substance, *glucose* as the small molecule. The gel consisted of Sephadex G-25, fine.

A glass tube of 2 to 3 cm inside diameter and a length of 50 to 20 cm had been strongly constricted at one end by flame shaping. A plug of glass wool was put into the constriction. The tube was mounted vertically. A piece of rubber tubing and a clamp served to close the tube. The tube was filled to one third of its volume with 0.5% salt solution. Sephadex G-25, fine (17 g) had been allowed to swell by adding the dry powder to excess 0.5% salt solution. This solvent will be used throughout the experiment. The tube was opened after 5 minutes to allow the gel to settle under flow. The effluent solvent is being replaced constantly by fresh solvent. The packed gel bed has an approximate volume of 87 ml and is ready for use. The tube was closed again and the supernatant removed, in order to be able to apply unperturbed the mixture to be separated. Starch (20 mg) and glucose (30 mg) were dissolved in 2 ml of salt solution and carefully applied to the top of the gel bed. The tube was opened to enable the solution to enter the gel bed. The top of the gel was rinsed with 2 ml of salt solution. The vacant space of the glass tube was filled with solvent and the elution continued. Beginning with the application of solution, the eluate was collected in a graduated cylinder which contained 1 ml of iodine/potassium iodide solution. The content of the graduated cylinder turned blue, indicating the presence of starch, after 32 ml had been eluted from the gel. The positive reaction for starch lasted for 12 to 13 ml and diminished rapidly thereafter. After a total of 66 to 67 ml had been eluted, the presence of glucose in the eluate was shown by heating an aliquot with Fehling's solution. The glucose was eluted completely after a total of 80 ml had been collected.

Due to its molecular weight, starch (the large dots in the schematic representation of Fig. 2) did not diffuse into the gel grains. Glucose (represented by the small dots), however, penetrated completely the swollen Sephadex. We have measured the volume at which starch was eluted from the gel. In doing so we determined the volume outside the gel grains, the only volume in which the starch is able to migrate. The elution of glucose, however, required the displacement of almost the entire volume of the gel bed. The experiment may be repeated without further preparation to demonstrate the reproducibility of the separation. The separation can be demonstrated very impressively with colored substances. A picture of the separation of a mixture of hemoglobin (large molecules) and DNP-aspartic acid (small molecules) on Sephadex G-50 is given in Fig. 3 approximately in the 3 stages of Figure 2 (from right to left).

Terminology

Several theories have been developed to explain what happens within the gel particle. These theories will be discussed in Chapter 3. For the moment we shall make the following statement: mixtures of substances may be separated on the basis of molecular size by passage over the bed of a granulated gel of suitable pore size. No doubt, this is a chromatographic process and chromatography is defined as follows: soluble substances are contained in a solvent and percolate an insoluble material, in the process of which they will be separated. There are principally two terms in use for chromatographic processes. Either, one refers to the support on which the separation

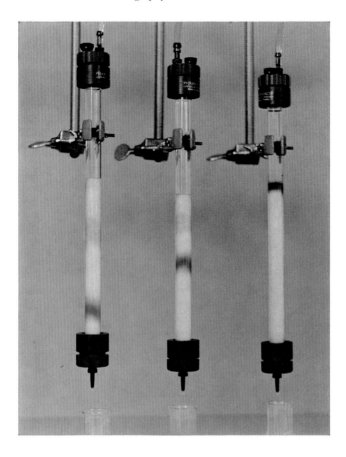

Fig. 3. Separation of hemoglobin (molecular weight 68000) and N-dinitrophenylaspartic acid (molecular weight 299) on Sephadex G-50 in three phases. The mixture was first applied to the column to the left, 10 minutes later to the column in the center, and immediately before exposure to the column to the right (Photograph by D. JAWOREK).

Table 1

Name	Year	Authors	References
Gel filtration	1959	PORATH and FLODIN	(30)
Molecular sieve filtration	1961	FASOLD, GUNDLACH and TURBA	(31)
Exclusion chromatography	1962	PEDERSEN	(32)
Molecular sieve chromatography	1962	HJERTÉN and MOSBACH	(33)
Gel permeation chromatography	1964	J. C. MOORE	(34)
Gel chromatography	1964	DETERMANN	(35)

is accomplished (e.g. paper chromatography) or one refers to the process which one assumes to be responsible for a successful separation (e.g. partition chromatography). Thus, one refers to the separation of ions on charged polymers by employing either of the two principles: Chromatography on Ion Exchangers and Ion Exchange Chromatography. The same is possible for the procedure described here. Table 1 contains the various terms which have been coined for the method. All these terms have their advantages and disadvantages.

In this monograph the term *Gel Chromatography* will be maintained. In doing so we shall be able to cover also separation techniques which are not solely based on sterical factors. This satisfies best the practical need of informing the reader – irrespective of the mechanism – about the applications of chromatography on porous gels and associated problems, the more so, since the following terms are too closely linked to restricted areas and are not generally applicable: "molecular sieve" with Zeolites, "gel filtration" with the dextran-gel Sephadex, and "gel permeation chromatography" with porous polystyrene gels.

Historical Survey

Gel Chromatography has a relatively short history. Ten years ago the technique was in its infant stage. Over the past six years the method has been developed at an amazing speed. – Paper chromatography had an early predecessor in Runge's capillary analysis. Similarly, observations had been made in the past that the structure of the support in a chromatographic tube was responsible for the separation of molecules by size.

Ion Exchangers

It has been pointed out already that differences in molecular size play also a role in separations which are based primarily on other properties of the molecular species to be separated. The chromatography on ion exchangers was studied systematically and the corresponding relationships were elucidated rather clearly. Already in 1944, O. SAMUELSON (*36*) reported that the anion exchanger Wofatit is not capable of adsorbing lignin sulfonic acids. Fragments of low molecular weight, however, are adsorbed. In similar fashion, clupein will not be adsorbed by the Wofatit cation exchanger (*37*). The hydrolysate of clupein will be adsorbed. In 1949 KUNIN and MEYERS (*38*) studied the relationship between the degree of crosslinking, swelling properties, and the capacity for large ions of a polystyrene anion exchanger (cf. Tab. 2). The authors concluded that the pores were too small and prevented the molecules from entering the network thus

Table 2. *Relationship between the degree of cross-linking and the capacity of ion exchange Resins (38)*

Relative degree of cross-linking	Increase in volume upon swelling (%)	Capacity (meq./g) for OH	for Penicillin
1	540	3.2	3.2
2	225	3.1	2.6
3	180	3.1	2.3
4	160	2.9	1.8
8	125	2.6	0.1

suppressing the exchange. The properties associated with the microstructure of ion exchange resins (*39*) were effectively utilized by R. W. RICHARDSON (*40*) in the purification of cotton dyes of relatively high molecular weight THOMPSON (*41*) succeeded in selectively binding amino acids to a sulfonated polystyrene resin, thus separating them from the residual protein from which they had been removed enzymatically. PARTRIDGE (*42*) explained this type of selectivity by the porosity of the resin. DEUEL and coworkers (*43*) studied very carefully the capacity of the anion exchanger Amberlite IR-4B for polygalacturonic acid and polyphosphoric acid of different chain length. The number of adsorbed molecules increases proportionally with decreasing molecular weight.

MIKES (*44*) showed in 1958 that the capacity of a strongly cross-linked polystyrene sulfonic acid can be increased considerably for large cations, if one carries out the polymerization in dilute solution. The author explained this unexpected porosity already in the sense of a particular type of cell structure (cf. below).

Not only ions, uncharged molecules may also be separated on porous ion exchange resins. The distribution coefficient on Dowex 50 for nonionic substances of low molecular weight as tabulated by WHEATON and BAUMANN (*45*) are related to the molecular weight in a rather limited way. CLARK (*46*), however, accomplished a perfect separation of sorbit, glycerol, and glycol on a column (2.5 × 240 cm) of Dowex 50 X-2. The substances were eluted from the column in the order of decreasing molecular weight, indicating a separation due to the principle of gel chromatography.

Neutral Gels

Porous substances without ionic groups (e.g. charcoal, metal oxides, and cellulose) have been used early in adsorption analysis (*47*). The observed sieving effects have been reviewed by DEUEL (*43*). In 1954 DEUEL (*48*) synthesized the first uncharged gel (a cross-linked galactomannan) which was used for the desalting of colloids. In the following year LINDQVIST and STORGÅRDS (*49*) studied the "sieving properties" of starch grains. LATHE and Ruthven (*50*) showed in 1956 that starch could be applied to the separation of neutral compounds in the molecular weight range of 100 to 1000. The undesirable ionexchange effects which they encountered with ionic substances were greatly reduced by the addition of salt. Starch grains which had been allowed to swell in warm water were suitable for the separation of polysaccharides and proteins of molecular weights of up to 150000. The authors developed then the concept which is still valid and explains the separation as follows:

> "It is suggested that columns of starch in water form a new type of partition system in which the volume of the stationary phase is determined for each substance by the depth to which it can penetrate the starch granules."

Polson (*51*) was experimenting in the same year with another natural product, namely agar-gel. He recognized also that the tendency of a protein molecule to diffuse into the agar-gel is a function of the diameter of the molecule and of the gel concentration. Many disadvantages, however, are associated with the natural products starch and agar and the application of the new technique was limited to the examples quoted.

In 1959 Porath and Flodin (*30*) discovered a universally applicable gel in the reaction product of soluble dextran and epichlorohydrin. The gel was soon manufactured industrially and marketed under the trade name Sephadex. This discovery led very rapidly to widespread application of the chromatographic separation technique that is based on molecular size and became known as "gel filtration". The early gels were of low porosity and only applicable to the separation of substances of low molecular weight (*30*, *52*) or the purification and isolation of peptide hormones (*52*). However, there were soon reports that described dextran gels of a smaller degree of cross-linking with which, for instance, the relatively low molecular lecitinase A was separated from the other snake venom enzymes (*53*). No effort was spared to extend the discovery to Sephadex gels of better swelling properties (*54*). Subsequent experiments with agar were aiming in the same direction. Polson (*55*) described in 1961 for the first time the application of granulated agar. With particles of 7% cross-linked agar he succeeded in separating proteins of very high molecular weight. Agar gels with a low content of carbohydrate were applied to the fractionation of viruses (*56*) and cell particles (*57*).

The results with hydrophobic polymers were initially less encouraging than those obtained with water soluble natural products. Experiments with the copolymer of styrene and divinylbenzene held little promise (*58*, *59*). Brewer (*60*), however, succeeded in separating hydrocarbons by gel chromatography on granulated rubber that had been allowed to swell in hexane or toluene. Cross-linked polymethylmethacrylate (*61*) was useful for the separation of oligostyrenes of molecular weights of up to 2500. Technical difficulties were encountered when this gel was to be applied to the separation of macromolecules.

During the development of the so-called macroreticular ion exchangers on polystyrene basis by KUNIN et al. *(62)* at Rohm & Haas in the USA, as well as at Permutit *(63)* in Great Britain, one had, however, learned to manufacture rigid networks with large pores (cf. *44*). MOORE *(34)* followed these principles and prepared uncharged polystyrene gels and demonstrated their outstanding properties for the gel chromatography of high molecular weight synthetic polymers in organic solvents.

References

1. SVEDBERG, T., and K. O. PEDERSEN: The Ultrazentrifuge, Oxford, 1940. — SCHACHMANN, H. K.: Ultracentrifugation in Biochemistry, New York 1955.
2. HERMANS, J. J., and H. A. ENDE in B. KE (Ed.): Newer Methods of Polymer Characterisation, 525. New York 1964. — R. TRAUTMANN in D.W. NEWMAN (Ed.): Instrumental Methods of Experimental Biology, 211. New York 1964.
3. BARRER, R. M.: Ber. Bunsenges. Physik. Chem. **69**, 787 (1965).
4. — Endeavour **23**, 122 (1964).
5. — British Chem. Engng. **7**, 267 (1959).
6. SCHEUERMANN, E. A.: Chemiker-Ztg. **20**, 767 (1961).
7. GRAHAM, TH.: Phil. Trans. Roy. Soc., London, **151**, 183 (1861).
8. CRAIG, L. C., and W. KONIGSBERG: J. phys. Chem. **65**, 166 (1961).
9. PIERCE, J. G., and C. A. FREE: Biochim. biophys. Acta **48**, 436 (1961).
10. ROSENFELD, M.: ibid. **75**, 241 (1963).
11. ACKERS, G. K., and R. L. STEERE: ibid. **59**, 137 (1962).
12. RUSSELL, B., J. LEVITT and A. POLSON: ibid. **79**, 622 (1964).
13. CRAIG, L. C., and A. O. PULLEY: Biochemistry **1**, 89 (1962).
14. —, and A. ANSEVIN: ibid. **2**, 1268 (1963).
15. —, E. J. HARFENIST, and A. C. PALADINI: ibid. **3**, 764, (1964).
16. — Adv. anal. Chem. Instr. **4**, 35 (1965)
17. SYNGE, R. L. M., and M. A. YOUNGSON: Biochem. J. **78**, 31 P (1961).
18. SIGNER, R., H. HÄNNI, W. KOESTLER, W. ROTTENBURG und P. v. TAVEL: Helv. chim. Acta **29**, 1894 (1946).
19. CRAIG, L. C., and T. P. KING: J. Amer. chem. Soc. **77**, 6620 (1955); **78**, 4171 (1956).
20. WIELAND, TH., H. DETERMANN und E. ALBRECHT: Liebigs Ann. Chem. **633**, 185 (1960).
21. MOULD, D. L., and R. L. M. SYNGE: Biochem. J. **58**, 571 (1954).
22. ALLISON, A. C., and J. H. HUMPHREY: Nature, **183**, 1590 (1959).
23. SMITHIES, O.: Biochem. J. **61**, 629 (1955).
24. — Arch. Biochem. Biophys. Suppl. **1**, 125 (1962).
25. TOMBS, M. P.: Anal. Biochem. **13**, 121 (1965).
26. ORNSTEIN, L.: Ann. N.Y. Acad. Sci. **121**, 321 (1964); B. J. DAVIS: ibid. **121**, 404 (1964).
27. STAUFF, J.: Kolloidchemie, 665 ff. Berlin, Göttingen, Heidelberg 1960.
28. HERMANS, P. H.: Gels, in KRUYT: (Ed.) Colloid Science, **2**, 483. Amsterdam 1949.
29. STAUFF, J.: Kolloidchemie, 669 ff. Berlin, Göttingen, Heidelberg 1960.
30. PORATH, J., and P. FLODIN: Nature **183**, 1657 (1959).
31. FASOLD, H., G. GUNDLACH, and F. TURBA in HEFTMANN (Ed.): Chromatography, 406. New York 1961.

32. PEDERSEN, K. O.: Arch. Biochem. Biophys., Suppl. **1**, 157 (1962).

33. HJERTÉN, S., and R. MOSBACH: Anal. Biochem. **3**, 109 (1962).

34. MOORE, J. C.: J. Polym. Sci. A **2**, 835 (1964).

35. DETERMANN, H.: Angew. Chem. **76**, 635 (1964); Internat. Ed. **3**, 608 (1964).

36. SAMUELSON, O., Ref. in W. LAUTSCH: Angew. Chem. **57**, 149 (1944).

37. RAUEN, H. M., und K. FELIX: Z. Physiol. Chem. **283**, 139 (1948).

38. KUNIN, R., and R. J. MEYERS: Discuss. Faraday Soc. **7**, 114 (1949).

39. RICHARDSON, R.W.: Nature **164**, 916 (1949).

40. — J. Chem. Soc. **1951**, 910.

41. THOMPSON, A. R.: Nature **169**, 495 (1952).

42. PARTRIDGE, S. M.: Nature **169**, 496 (1952).

43. DEUEL, H., J. SOLMS und L. ANYAS-WEISZ: Helv. chim. Acta **33**, 2171 (1950).

44. MIKES, J. A.: J. polym. Sci. **30**, 615 (1958)

45. WHEATON, R. M., and W. C. BAUMANN: Ann. New York Acad. Sci. **57**, 159 (1953).

46. CLARK, R.T.: Analytic. Chem. **30**, 1676 (1958).

47. TISELIUS, A.: Naturwiss. **37**, 25 (1950); Adv. Prot. Chem. **3**, 67 (1947).

48. DEUEL, H., and H. NEUKOM: Adv. in Chemistry Series **11**, 51 (1954).

49. LINDQVIST, B., and T. STORGÅRDS: Nature **175**, 511 (1955).

50. LATHE, G. H., and C. R. J. RUTHVEN: Biochem. J. **62**, 665 (1956).

51. POLSON, A.: Biochim. biophys. Acta **19**, 53 (1956).

52. PORATH, J.: Clin. chim. Acta **4**, 776 (1959).

53. BJÖRK, W., and J. PORATH: Acta chem. Scand. **13**, 1256 (1959).

54. FLODIN, P.: Dissertation Uppsala 1962.

55. POLSON, A.: Biochim. biophys. Acta **50**, 565 (1961).

56. STEERE, R. L., and G. K. ACKERS: Nature **196**, 475, (1962); **194**, 114 (1962).

57. HJERTÉN, S.: Arch. Biochem. Biophys. **99**, 466 (1962).

58. VAUGHAN, M. F.: Nature **188**, 55 (1960).

59. CORTIS-JONES, B.: Nature **191**, 272 (1961).

60. BREWER, P. J.: Nature **188**, 934 (1960); **190**, 625 (1961).

61. DETERMANN, H., G. LÜBEN und TH. WIELAND: Makromol. Chem. **73**, 168 (1964).

62. KUNIN, R., E. MEITZNER, and N. BORTNICK: J. Amer. chem. Soc. **84**, 305 (1962). KUNIN, R., E. F. MEITZNER, J. A. OLINE, S. A. FISHER, and V. FRISCH: I & EC Prod. Res. Develop. **1**, 140 (1962). — B. P. 932 125 and 932 126.

63. MILLAR, J. R., D. G. SMITH, W. E. MARR, and T. R. E. KRESSMAN, J. chem. Soc. **1963**, 219. — B. P. 849 122.

Chapter 2

Materials and Methods

The Gels

A number of definitions have been given in Chapter I. Several of them will have to be amplified for a better understanding of the properties of gels. Certain gels can not be used as column packing material for gel chromatography.

The pore size of a gel must be carefully controlled in order to be able to apply the gel to a given separation problem. Other desirable properties of the gel forming agent are the absence of ionizing groups and, in a given solvent, low affinity to the substances to be separated. The latter is important for the unimpaired movement of a solute depending on its molecular size. Considerable affinity of the solute to the gel is frequently observed in organic solvents. (However, the proper choice of eluent will easily overcome this difficulty, cf. page. 83) The gel particles ought to be as small as possible in order to quickly establish diffusion equilibrium. The concurrent demand of relatively low flow resistance is only met by bead-shaped particles. The gel particles must not be too soft, otherwise they will suffer from deformation in the column and interfere with reasonable flow rates.

The requirements are not fulfilled equally well by the various materials which have been proposed for gel chromatography. There are in essence two approaches to the preparation of these materials: a macromolecular substance is brought into solution and allowed to react with a bifunctional reagent in order to render it insoluble, or the solution of a mixture of suitable monofunctional and bifunctional monomers is allowed to copolymerize. In either case a gel is obtained the porosity of which is a function of the concentration of the bifunctional reagent. This concentration effect on the degree of cross-linking is easily explained by the assumption that more cross-linkages *between* the polymer chains are formed in concentrated solutions. At the same concentration of cross-linking reagent, fewer cross-linkages are formed in dilute solutions because the bifunctional reagent reacts with *one and the same* molecule. With the two techniques described, bead-shaped gel particles of different porosities may be produced. Gels of high porosity, however, which are applicable to the separation of very large molecules, are relatively soft and it is difficult to handle them, particularly in organic solvents.

The application of the copolymerization technique will lead to the formation of a *new type of gel* if the cross-linking reagent is available in high

concentration and certain conditions are maintained during the polymerization in the presence of a solvent. Solvents for the monomers which do not
dissolve the polymer are most desirable (1–4). In the presence of the
precipitating agent the polymer chains are evidently added to each other as
they are formed from the dissolved monomer. Extremely porous particles
are obtained. Due to their particular structure they are very resistant to
deformation. This type of phase separation may also take place during
polymerization in solvents which dissolve polymers (5). The difference
between conventional gels (a) and the so-called macroreticular polymers
(b) is shown (schematically) in Figure 4. Under the electron microscope,
texture is clearly visible for the polymer beads of large pore-size while the
conventional gel structure appears to be completely homogenous.

In starch and particularly in agar the polymer chains are only held
together by hydrogen bonds. These rather large areas of association seem
to result in the formation of the discontinous structure that is pictured in
Fig. 4. Indeed, agar particles are highly porous and at the same time very

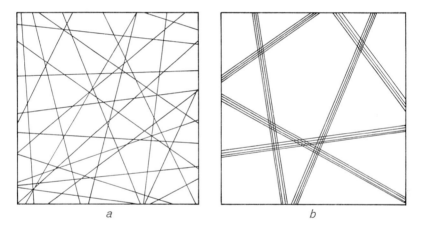

a   b

Fig. 4. Schematic representation of the cross-linked structure of gels (a) and of macroporous polymers (b) which have been formed by copolymerization in the presence of a
precipitating agent. The concentration (number of polymer threads in that picture) is
thought to be the same in both cases. The difference in average pore size is evident.

resistant to deformation. The faster migration of macromolecules in agar-
gel is an indication for its particular structure. The same macromolecules
are not as fast in solutions of identical concentration of other polysaccharides,
cf. (6). This can be demonstrated in a simple experiment:

A glass tube (1.5 mm I.D.; 10 cm long) is filled by suction to one half of its height
with a warm 7% solution of "Reinagar Behringwerke". As the solution cools down, a gel
is being formed in the glass tube. Using a fine pipette, an identical glass tube with a sealed

bottom will also be filled to one half of its height with a 7% Dextran solution ($\bar{M}_w \sim 110\,000$, Pharmacia, To 5404). Both glass tubes are mounted in the field of view of a magnifying glass in front of a piece of graph paper. Both tubes are carefully filled up with a 5% solution of Dextran-Blue (colored dextran; $\bar{M}_w \sim 2 \times 10^6$, Pharmacia). A sharp dividing line is visible in both tubes. The macromolecular dye penetrates the agar gel by 1.5 mm within 24 hours at 22°C. There is no penetration at all in the dextran-solution.

The porosity of a gel – as long as it is a genuine xerogel – may be determined from the swelling properties. PEPPER et al. (7) have defined for ionexchange resins the solvent regain S_r, i.e. grams of solvent taken up by 1 gram of xerogel during swelling (8). The solvent regain can easily be determined for a granulated gel by allowing a known amount of gel to swell in an excess of solvent. The solvent between gel particles will be removed on a sieve by careful and slow centrifugation and the weight of the gel determined again. Experimental details are to be found on page 56.

The Preparation of Hydrophilic Gels

Dextran Gels

The highpolymer carbohydrate which is produced during the growth of *Leuconostoc mesenteroides* on sucrose is known as dextran. This soluble poly-saccharide consists exclusively of glucose and contains more than 90% α-1.6-glycosidic linkages. Dextran contains 3 hydroxyl groups per glucose unit and is therefore water soluble. The high molecular weight of dextran may be reduced by partial hydrolysis in dilute mineral acid. The molecular weight distribution has been improved by solvent fractionation. Dextran fractions thus obtained are known in medicine as plasma expanders (e.g. Macrodex).

The reaction mixture of an alkaline dextran solution and epichlorohydrin solidifies exothermally. The soluble polymer chains are cross-linked by glycerin ether bonds. Epichlorohydrin reacts with two hydroxyl groups of two different chains. Under ideal circumstances the polymerization proceeds via the following reactions (8):

$$Dex\text{-}OH + CH_2\text{-}CH\text{-}CH_2\text{-}Cl \longrightarrow Dex\text{-}O\text{-}CH_2\text{-}CH(OH)\text{-}CH_2\text{-}Cl$$
$$\phantom{Dex\text{-}OH + CH_2\text{-}}{}^{\smallsmile}O^{\smallsmile}$$

$$Dex\text{-}O\text{-}CH_2\text{-}CH(OH)\text{-}CH_2\text{-}Cl + NaOH \longrightarrow Dex\text{-}O\text{-}CH_2\text{-}CH\text{-}CH_2 + NaCl + H_2O$$
$$\phantom{Dex\text{-}O\text{-}CH_2\text{-}CH(OH)\text{-}CH_2\text{-}Cl + NaOH \longrightarrow Dex\text{-}O\text{-}CH_2\text{-}CH\text{-}}{}^{\smallsmile}O^{\smallsmile}$$

$$Dex\text{-}O\text{-}CH_2\text{-}CH\text{-}CH_2 + HO\text{-}Dex \longrightarrow Dex\text{-}O\text{-}CH_2\text{-}CH(OH)\text{-}CH_2\text{-}O\text{-}Dex$$
$$\phantom{Dex\text{-}O\text{-}CH_2\text{-}CH\text{-}}{}^{\smallsmile}O^{\smallsmile}$$

However, a number of side reactions are to be expected: e.g. epichloro-hydrin may be hydrolyzed in aqueous alkaline solution and the chlorine removed. The monofunctional epoxide etherifies only one hydroxyl group.

This hydrolysis may also take place after the epoxide has reacted with a polymer. This results also in only one substitution by glycerin and no cross-linkage is formed. Chemical analysis so far has not been very revealing about the structure of dextran gels (8, 9); Fig. 5 represents a portion of a cross-linked gel showing the expected structural features. The commercially available dextran gels (Sephadex) are produced as beads of defined size. The

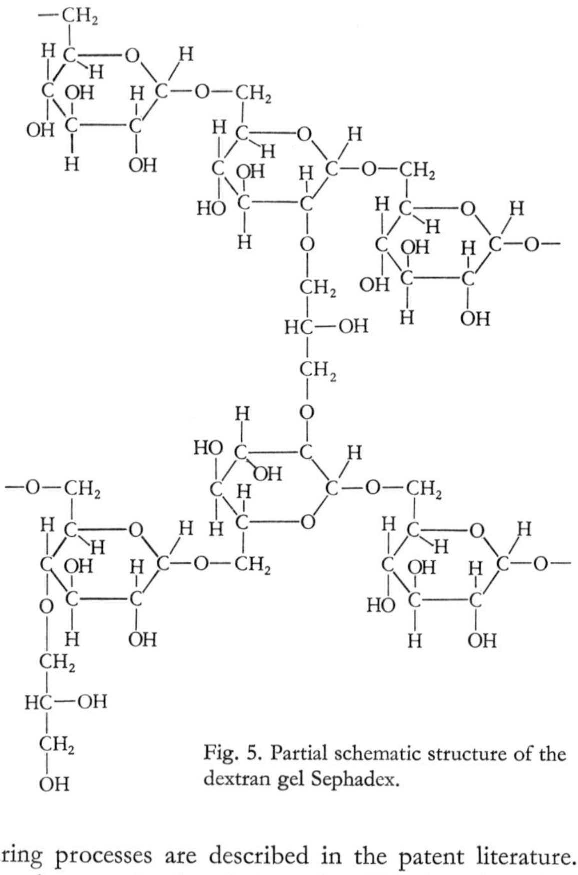

Fig. 5. Partial schematic structure of the dextran gel Sephadex.

manufacturing processes are described in the patent literature. We shall confine ourselves to the description of a "Block Polymerization" after FLODIN (8). This will be sufficient to demonstrate how the swelling properties of the dextran gel are influenced by the dextran concentration, its molecular weight, and its ratio to epichlorohydrin (Table 3):

The reaction flask was equipped with a thermometer and an efficient stirrer. Crystalline dextran (500 g) of a limiting viscosity of 0.19 (corresponding to a weight average molecular weight of 40 000) was wetted with 200 ml of water. This eliminated lump formation upon the addition of 300 ml of 5 N NaOH. Epichlorohydrin (135 g) was stirred into the clear solution. The reaction flask was placed on a waterbath of 40°C and the mixture stirred (approximately 1 hour) until it solidified to a gel block. The gel was kept at 40°C for 24 hours and an additional 12 hours at 70°C. The brittle gel was transferred to a blender and disintegrated under water. Hydrochloric acid was used to neutralize the crushed gel. The fines were removed by three decantations (water). Soluble reaction products were removed by washing on a filter. The gel was dehydrated by careful treatment with ethanol on the same filter and dried overnight in a vacuum drying oven at 70°C. The yield of xerogel was 576 g. The gel showed a water regain of 2.5 g per g dry weight.

Table 3. *The influence of manufacturing conditions on the water regain of synthetic dextran gels (8)**

Dextran concentration (%)	Molecular weight ($\bar{M}_w$)	Epichlorohydrin (% of dextran)	Water regain (g/g)
56	40 000	19	1.8
32	40 000	19	4.1
28	40 000	19	4.9
20	40 000	19	14.0
56	40 000	35.5	2.1
56	40 000	30	2.6
56	40 000	18	3.0
56	40 000	6	10.0
20	1 800 000	16	8
20	400 000	20	7.5
20	40 000	20	14

*) Sodium hydroxide was always present in equimolar amounts (10% excess).

It is evident from Table 3 that the swelling properties of the gel increase with decreasing concentrations and molecular weight of the dextran and with lower quantities of epichlorohydrin. – It is possible that dextran gels of the same swelling properties are not of the same continuous structure, if they have been synthesized by a different combination of variables. Several observations on the separatory power of these gels point in this direction (10).

Polyacrylamide Gels

Acrylamide ($CH_2=CH-CO-NH_2$) is a water soluble substance with a reactive double bond. Polymerization may be induced under mild conditions leading to the formation of soluble polyacrylamide. Polymerization in aqueous solution in the presence of a bifunctional acrylamide, such as N, N'-methylenebisacrylamide

$$H_2C=CH-\underset{\underset{O}{\|}}{C}-NH-CH_2-NH-\underset{\underset{O}{\|}}{C}-CH=CH_2$$

produces a water insoluble gel. The presence of the bifunctional reagent results in the formation of cross-linkages between two different chains of the polymer. A threedimensional network of carbon chains is obtained. The carboxylic acid amide group on every other carbon atom introduces polarity and thus the ability to swell in water.

Homogeneous gels of polyacrylamide are frequently applied to the separation of proteins. Once granulated, these gels are also applicable to gel chromatography in aqueous media (11, 12). The preparation of the gels is very simple. Ammonium persulfate is used as redox-catalyst for the radical polymerization and β-dimethylaminopropionitrile as regulator. The polymerization may also be started by light in the presence of riboflavin as long as the layer of the reaction mixture is not excessively thick (13). The gel may be isolated by lyophilization after disintegration in a mortar or by pressing the swollen material through a sieve of suitable mesh size (0.1 to 0.2 mm). Special equipment for this purpose has been developed by HJERTÉN (14). Satisfactory granulation will also result from pressing the gel with a heavy glassrod through a steel sieve (e.g. 160 μ mesh size) of the commonly available sets of sieves. The pore size of the gel is again predominantly determined by the monomer concentration in the polymerization mixture and secondly by the content of bifunctional monomer. HJERTÉN (14) was able to prepare a series of gels of different swelling properties by varying the concentration of monomer between 4 and 16%. The relative concentration of cross-linking reagent was kept constant (5%). The porosity was tested with a series of proteins. The preparation of one such gel will be described in the following in some detail (14):

Acrylamide (57 g) and N,N'-methylen-bis-acrylamide (3 g) were dissolved in 500 ml of water. The monomers may also be dissolved in the buffer which is to be used subsequently for the elution. The pH of the buffer should be above 6 in order to obtain reasonable polymerization rates. The filtered solution will be degased on an asperator for 2 to 3 minutes before 1 ml of dimethylaminopropionitrile and 1 g of ammoniumpersulfate are added. The solution has to be stirred carefully to keep it free of air since oxygen inhibits the polymerization. The induction period in well degased water is anywhere from 1–10 minutes before gelation occurs. Low monomer concentrations require longer induction periods. The gel may be granulated 10 minutes after gelation though waiting periods of several hours have been recommended.

Following a proposal of SUN and SEHON (15) the resulting gel would be designated "Polyacrylamide 12-5". The first figure refers to total concentration of monomers. The second figure gives the relative concentration of the bifunctional reagent (both values are expressed in percent).The authors have prepared quite similar polyacrylamide gels. In addition to the total concentration, the relative concentration of the cross-linking agent was also changed (from 5-5 to 20-20). Figure 6 shows that the concentration of bifunctional reagent exerts a significant influence on the swelling properties only in the case of gels of low concentrations. This is in line with the observations made earlier with dextran gels. FAWCETT and MORRIS (*16*)

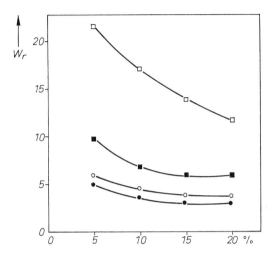

Fig. 6. The effect of total monomer concentration (□ 5%; ■ 10%; ○ 15%; ● 20%) and concentration of cross-linking reagent on the swelling properties of polyacrylamide gels (after SUN and SEHON (*15*)). Abscissa: % bisacrylamide; ordinate: water regain.

have recently shown that polyacrylamide gels of relatively high concentrations of cross-linking reagents (e.g. 6.5-15 or 8-25) are different in their structure from normal gels. These gels are considerably more porous than comparable gels of a lower degree of cross-linking. The authors were able to demonstrate with the Ogston-Laurent gel-model (cf. Chapter III) that a structure corresponding to that of Fig. 4b results from high concentrations of cross-linking reagents. Acrylamide may also be copolymerized in bead form. Such gels (Bio-Gel) of defined particle size are produced commercially (cf. Table 8).

Agar Gels, Agarose Gels

Agar is a polysaccharide which is extracted from red seaweed. Agar of more or less purified state has long been known in bacteriology. More recently the substance has also been introduced to immunology. Agar is soluble in hot water. Upon cooling, a remarkably rigid (relative to the concentration of agar) gel is formed. ARAKI (*17*) has found that agar consists of two components: a neutral main component, agarose, and of agaropectin which is supposed to contain all carboxyl- and sulfate groups. These acidic groups are the cause for the pronounced electroendoosmosis during electrophoresis in agar gels. Considerable adsorption is frequently observed for the same reason during gel chromatography (particularly at low ionic strength). Specific affects on certain types of virus have also been described. On the other hand, these gels – due to their porosity – are capable of separating virus particles by size.

ARAKI (17) has described agarose as a linear polysaccharide of D-galactose and 3.6-anhydro-L-galactose which is free of ionizable groups. Agarose suspensions appeared therefore to be very promising for gel chromatography (18). However, the process of isolating agarose from agar is very cumbersome (17) and has until recently prevented its broad-scale application. Two new approaches to prepare agarose have been reported. HJERTÉN (19) uses cetyl pyridinium chloride to precipitate the acidic components of agar solutions. The difficulty encountered here is the removal of the excess of precipitating agent. RUSSELL, MEAD and POLSON (20) have isolated agarose from agar by repeated fractional precipitation with a concentrated solution of polyethylene glycol. The products of both procedures contain still some sulfur, but they are free of charged groups. Suspensions of granulated agarose are now commercially available (cf. Table 9).

The diffusion equilibria of substances of low diffusion rates should be reached most readily by fractionation in a gel of fine particles. The uniform spherical shape of the gel particles is therefore of particular significance. Two procedures have been reported for the preparation of agar and agarose beads: 1) Agar solutions may be suspended at 50°C in the form of spheres in a mixture of benzene and toluene by the addition of stabilizing agents and the proper choice of a stirring device. The spheres gelatinate upon cooling and are isolated in the swollen state. Depending on the concentration of carbohydrate (1–15%) a suitable column packing material is obtained (21). 2) The procedure of BENGTSSON and PHILIPSON (22) will be given in detail:

Agar Noble Special (Difco) of the desired concentration was heated for 20 min. to 120°C in the autoclave. The solution was allowed to cool to 65°C and was poured into a Seitz-Filter (Fig. 7) of the same temperature. The filter was equipped with a glass jet (I.D. approximately 0.5 mm) which was attached to the outlet tube of the filter with vacuum hose which was fastened with a steel wire. A hole was cut into the asbestos layer to permit easy flow. The agar solution was sprayed into ice cold ether by applying a pressure of 2–3 atmospheres (N_2-tank). The ether was layered above ice water. The mixture was constantly agitated by magnetic stirring. The droplets of agar formed a gel as soon as they came in contact with the cold ether; the beads were collected in the water phase and withdrawn periodically. The ice water was renewed each time to prevent clogging of the beads. During one operation 1 to 1.5 l of agar solution were handled. The gel was allowed to stand overnight and then washed. Fractions from 60–100 and 100–140 mesh/inch (US-Standard) were isolated after passage of the gel through a set of copper sieves.

Agarose beads may be obtained by the same procedure. Whether agarose is required or agar is sufficient, depends upon the type of molecules or particles to be separated. Agarose beads have recently become available commercially (cf. Table 9).

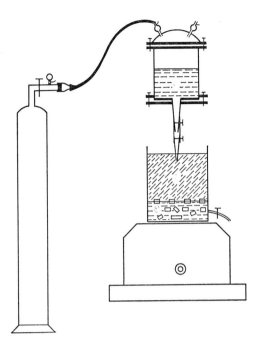

Fig. 7. Apparatus for the preparation of agarose beads according to BENGTSSON and PHILIPSON (22).

By their very nature, the range of applications of these thermally reversible gels is limited. The gel "melts" at higher temperature or upon application of eluents which are capable of breaking hydrogen bonds (e. g. urea solutions) and can no longer be used. The growth of bacteria which would cause clogging of the column has to be controlled carefully.

The Preparation of Organophilic Gels

Sephadex Derivatives

The swelling properties of hydrophilic Sephadex types in polar organic solvents improve with increasing substitution. Acylation or alkylation of the free hydroxyl groups of the dextran gel results in the formation of derivatives which display excellent swelling properties in many organic solvents and possess the corresponding resolving power. One half of the hydroxyl groups of the dextran are esterified by the action of acetic anhydride on Sephadex G-50 in benzene (23). Despite the fact that the product did not swell very well in methylene chloride, it was possible to fractionate polystyrenes of molecular weights of up to 10000. Alkylation in aqueous medium leads to the substitution of a greater number of hydroxyl groups since the dextran is swollen and more groups are accessible. Furthermore, the ether bonds are more stable to hydrolysis and are already present in Sephadex as cross-linkages. Sephadex G-25 may be methylated very effectively by treatment with dimethylsulfate and sodium hydroxide. The product is suitable for chromatography in organic solvents (24). However, depending on the substances to be separated, more or less pronounced interactions with the gel have been observed. The net result is retardation on the column, i.e. differences in the structure of the solute play an important role, not the molecular weight. The same applies to the hydroxyalkyl ethers of Sephadex (25). These products are obtained by the action of aliphatic epoxides on Sephadex G-25. Due to the particular substitution, the same swelling properties are observed in water and in many polar organic solvents. The commercial product is known as "Sephadex LH-20". The affinity of the solute to the gel depends largely upon the solvent and may therefore be suppressed by the proper choice of conditions or utilized to advantage in separations without differences in molecular weight (cf. p. 129). Sephadex G-25 was allowed to react with aliphatic isocyanates in dimethylsulfoxide. The resulting gel was swellable in organic solvents (26).

Acrylic Gels

The copolymerization of the water soluble acrylamide leads to the formation of hydrophilic gels. Other derivatives of acrylic acid are easily polymerized to lipophilic gels (27):

> The stabilizer (hydroquinone) was removed from 10 g of methylmethacrylate by extraction with 5% sodium hydroxide and the monomer dissolved in 7.6 ml of toluene. Ethyleneglycoldimethacrylate (0.1 g) and 20 mg of azodiisobutyronitrile (initiator) were added and the solution was kept under nitrogen at 90°C for 5 hrs. The water-clear, highly viscous gel which had formed after less than 30 min. was allowed to swell for several hours in methylene chloride. The resulting material was elastic to brittle and could be forced through a steel sieve with meshes of 0.20 mm. Treatment with methanol caused the gel to shrink. The dry gel was passed through a set of standard sieves to obtain fractions of more uniform particle size.

The resulting xerogel swells moderately in chloroform and benzene and is suitable for the fractionation of, for example, oligomers of polystyrene. This polymerization may also be carried out in suspension and beads will be obtained. Difficulties in the operation of the columns were observed when less than 0.25 mol% of the bifunctional monomer had been used. It is therefore not possible to obtain very porous gels following the above procedure. It appears, however, to be possible to overcome this difficulty by the sole polymerization of ethyleneglycoldimethacrylate in high concentration in isoamylalcohol (28). These cross-linked polymers showed relatively poor swelling properties (90 to 150%) in benzene but were, nevertheless, highly porous. The flow rates in very long columns (up to 5 m) were remarkable – although the gels tested did not come from bead polymerizations. It is entirely possible that these gels are also of heterogeneous structure (cf. Fig. 4b). The other approach to gel formation – cross-linking of preformed polymers – has also been applied to derivatives of acrylic acid in a limited number of preliminary experiments (29). Linear polyacrylnitrile can be cross-linked with formaldehyde and sulfuric acid under mild conditions in 60% aqueous $ZnCl_2$-solution. The same cross-linkages (methylen-bisacrylamide) are formed as in the acrylamide gels. The polyacrylonitrile gel was used in studies concerned with the fractionation of polyacrylonitrile in dimethylformamide. The bead polymerization of vinylacetate with 0.2 to 2% (weight) butane diol divinyl ether leads to the formation of a material which can be made hydrophilic by the subsequent saponification of the ester groups (26).

Polystyrene Gels

Gels of polystyrene – cross-linked with divinylbenzene – have for decades formed the basis for most ion-exchange resins. Early attempts by VAUGHAN (30) and CORTIS-JONES (31), aiming at the application of these gels to gel chromatography, were not very promising. The fractionation of polystyrene and of solutes of low molecular weight and different structure (30) on gels with good swelling properties indicated low porosity and demonstrated the predominance of adsorptive and partition effects (31). Nevertheless, polystyrene with 2% divinylbenzene (Dow Chemical Company) was found to be suitable for the perfect separation of lipids on the basis of molecular weight differences (32). It was superior to all materials in the separation of oligophenylenes (26).

The system styrene-divinylbenzene forms the basis for the polystyrene ion exchange resins and has been studied very extensively (1-4). Relatively small pores are sufficient for the purpose of ion exchange chromatography. Gel chromatography, however, requires the controlled variation of the sizes of pores over a wide range.

MOORE (33) has studied systematically the system styrene/divinylbenzene and how the properties of the resulting gel depend upon the solvent which was used in the polymerization. The observations made with the dextrans were confirmed. The porosity increases with the dilution of the polymerization mixture while the relative concentration of the bifunctional reagent remains constant or goes even up. Well defined differences in porosity in polystyrene beads were obtained by choosing polymer precipitating conditions. A series of bead polymerized gels with superior properties was isolated. The gels were very rigid despite their high porosity. Several of the preparations are recorded in Table 4. The molecular weight ($\overline{M}_{lim}$) of the (linear) polystyrene fraction which barely penetrated the pores is a measure for the porosity. The values for divinylbenzene represent the actual content of bifunctional monomer in technical products. A certain

Table 4. *Composition (weight-%) of polystyrene gels according to* MOORE *(33)*

Styrene	Divinyl benzene	Solvent toluene	Polymer precipitant	Porosity $(\bar{M}_{\text{lim}})$
92	8	—	—	1 000
79,1	4,2	16,7	—	2 500
30	10	60	—	7 000
30	10	30	30 diethylbenzene	15 000
30	10	30	30 n-dodecane	300 000
30	10	15	45 n-dodecane	2 000 000
30	10	—	{ 20 diethylbenzene 40 isoamylalcohol	8 000 000

amount of ethylvinylbenzene is contained in the values for styrene. ALTGELT (*34*) has reported the procedures for two gels of relatively low pore size of this type. It can be assumed that they apply also to the preparations of Table 4.

Styrene and divinylbenzene were copolymerized in a ratio of 3:1. The technical "divinylbenzene" used contained 53.5% divinylbenzene, 41.9% vinylethylbenzene and 3.5% diethylbenzene. It was necessary to use more of this mixture in order to compensate for the added solvents. Vinylethylbenzene was assumed to be equivalent to styrene for the calculation of the 3:1 ratio.

A) 50 ml "divinylbenzene", 53 ml styrene, 145 ml toluene, 5 ml dodecane, and 1 g azoisobutyronitrile.

B) 50 ml "divinylbenzene", 53 ml styrene, 100 ml toluene, 50 ml dodecane, and 1 g azoisobutyronitrile.

The polymerization procedure was the same in both cases. Rhodiovol HS 100 (Société Rhône-Poulenc, Paris) served as stabilizer of polyvinylalcohol type. Eleven grams of the stabilizer were dissolved in 500 ml of hot water by stirring for several hours. The Rhodiovol solution was transferred to a 2 ltr. three-neck flask equipped with stirrer, reflux condenser and thermometer. The solution was heated to 80°C and to it was added in a fine stream the freshly prepared mixture A or B. For this purpose, the thermometer was temporarily replaced by a dropping funnel. The polymerization began after two hours of vigorous stirring at 80°C and was indicated by the formation of a heavy white emulsion. Heating and stirring were continued for 24 hours. The polymer was then filtered and washed ten times with hot water, two times with cold water and five times each with acetone and benzene. Agglomerations were broken up by the addition of benzene and forcing the gel through a sieve of mesh size 0.8 mm. Fines were removed by repeated decantation. The resulting gel suspension was kept under benzene in order to prevent agglomerations. Water has to be excluded carefully if the gel is to be stored in the dry state or, the gel has to be washed with acetone and benzene prior to its use.

The polystyrene gels just described are based on gel forming products of rigid structures and show the same porosity in rather different solvents.

The eluent may therefore be changed in the column without difficulty. The gels do not shrink very much upon drying, i. e. they are hybrids of xerogels and aerogels.

Aerogels

Chromatographic separations of macromolecular substances on products void of all swelling properties have been reported repeatedly.

A large protein in aqueous solution passed more rapidly through a packing of small glass beads (20 to 35 μ) than a small one (35). Evidently the mobile phase becomes stationary in packings of spheres, provided the diameter of the spheres is small enough. Small molecules are then able to diffuse into the angular spaces of the spheres, while the larger ones are prohibited from doing so.

It is not firmly established, whether a similar effect or the porosity of the silica gel (Santocel A) of VAUGHAN (36) brought about the separation of polystyrene in benzene. In any event, the author was able to accomplish a fractionation that was in line with conventional methods while many polymer powder turned out to be ineffective. Silica gel appears to be well suited for the gel chromatography of inert polymers in organic solvents: the controlled variation of pore volume is most advantageous. So long as the separations depend upon the specific pore volume (37), it appears that genuine permeation chromatography takes place. The recent introduction of silica gel beads (38) is very promising. It appears to be possible to adjust porosity and particle size to any desire. The product should be almost ideal for the purpose of gel chromatography as long as no interactions take place with the active inner "surface". Columns can be packed in the dry state and the air will be displaced subsequently by solvent. Since the structure is totally rigid, the pore volume of the porous types may be measured by mercury intrusion. This has shown that the size distribution of pores is very narrow.

HALLER (39) has described a glass powder of regular pore size. The glass powder is prepared by heat treatment of sintered alkali borosilicate glass. Microheterogeneities are formed and extend with time. The two phases of the glass are coherent and one of them may be isolated by a leaching process. A continuous system of channels of uniform diameter is obtained. The diameter can be controlled very closely by the time of tempering (170-17000 Å). The glass pieces in the chromatography column distinguish only between those molecules or particles, which enter the system of channels and those which pass by. The glass powder is not only capable of distinguishing large and small molecules, but it allows also the absolute determination of their effective radii. HALLER (39) demonstrated these relations very impressively with viruses of different geometry in aqueous solvents. MOORE (40) has recently used this material in chromatographic processes in organic solvents to answer theoretical questions in macromolecular chemistry.

Porous glass powders may be obtained commercially from Bio-Rad Laboratories (Richmond, California, USA). However, reports on their evaluation are as yet not available.

Other materials for gel chromatography will undoubtedly be developed. Efforts will always aim at the preparation of broadly applicable structures of the defined pore size which are inert and rigid if possible. Commercially available products are to be discussed in the following section.

Commercial Gels

Sephadex

This dextran gel is the most widely used material in gel chromatography. Sephadex is available in eight different types of varying swelling properties (cf. Table 5). The range of fractionation is determined by the corresponding

Table 5. *Properties of commercial dextran gels Sephadex*)*

Type	Particle size**) (dry; in μ)	Water regain (ml/g)	Gel bed (ml/g)	Approximate separation range	
				Peptides and glob. proteins	Dextran fractions
G-10	40—120	1.0±0.1	2—3	up to 700	up to 700
G-15	40—120	1.5±0.1	2.5—3.5	up to 1 500	up to 1 500
G-25, coarse	100—300				
G-25, medium	50—150	2.5±0.2	4—6	1 000— 5 000	100— 5 000
G-25, fine	20—80				
G-50, coarse	100—300				
G-50, medium	50—150	5.0±0.3	9—11	1 000— 30 000	500— 10 000
G-50, fine	20—80				
G-75	40—120	7.5±0.5	12—15	3 000— 70 000	1 000— 50 000
G-100	40—120	10.0±1.0	15—20	4 000—150 000	1 000—100 000
G-150	40—120	15.0±1.5	20—30	5 000—400 000	1 000—150 000
G-200	40—120	20.0±2.0	30—40	5 000—800 000	1 000—200 000

*) according to statements by the manufacturer: Pharmacia Fine Chemicals, Uppsala (Sweden).

**) All types are also available in the particle size »Superfine« (10—40 μ).

porosity. These are overlapping to a considerable degree. The Sephadex grades which are available in the form of small beads are subdivided into several sieve fractions. The grade "superfine" is mainly intended for use in thin layer chromatography (cf. page 51). However, in applications to column chromatography, excellent separations have been obtained. The particle sizes of the medium and fine grades are preferred for preparative applications where better flow rates are desirable. The Sephadex grades G-25 and G-50 are also available in coarse fractions. These fractions are used in the centrifuge technique (cf. page 56) and in applications where high flow rates are required.

It is a prerequisite for all applications of Sephadex that the gel is completely swollen. It is shown in Table 6, how long the individual types should

Table 6. *Swelling time for Sephadex gels*

Sephadex-type	At room temperature	On water bath at 100°C
G-10, G-15, G-25, G-50	3 hrs.	1 hr.
G-75	24 hrs.	3 hrs.
G-100, G-150, G-200	3 days	5 hrs.

be kept in excess of solvent before they can be filled into a column. The degree of swelling is practically independent of ionic strength. Sephadex is stable to alkali and weak acids. Strong mineral acids are required to cause hydrolysis of the glycosidic linkages. One to two hours exposure to 0.1 N HCl will, however, be tolerated without damage. It was found that 0.02 N HCl did not produce any changes over a period of 6 months. Formic Acid (88%) was successfully applied to chromatography on Sephadex G-25 (*41*). Strong oxydizing agents should not be applied since they will severely affect the dextran. Carboxylic groups may be introduced and the gel aquires ionexchange properties. A very low content of carboxylic groups (0.1 to 0.2 meq./g dry Sephadex) is indeed noticable in totally ion-free eluents. Traces of cations are bound. However, if the ionic strength of the eluent is 0.01 or higher, the carboxyl groups have no effect. – During continuous elution, 0.002 to 0.003% of carbohydrate is liberated from column packings of G-25 through G-75. This value increases to 0.005% for G-200 (*9*).

The growth of microorganisms may be observed if Sephadex columns are kept for a longer period of time. The growth will depend on the buffer applied. Usually the gel packing has to be discarded. The growth of microorganisms may be prevented by the addition of 0.02% of sodium azide to the eluent or by its saturation with chloroform. The addition of the solvent may, however, cause shrinkage of the very strongly swollen gels Sephadex G-100 to G-200.

Sephadex gels may be stored in the swollen state or they may be dried again. In order to accomplish the latter the swollen gel has to be washed with water first to remove all salts. This is followed by treatment with 50% ethanol which causes the gel to shrink to one half of its original volume. To remove the remaining water, the gel will be allowed to stand for half an hour in 99% ethanol. During this time the gel should be shaken several times. The same process will have to be repeated several times.

After drying at 60-80°C Sephadex will be obtained as a freely flowing powder. The beads will agglomerate during the drying process if the water was not completely removed by ethanol. However, these agglomerates will disintegrate upon renewed swelling. Sephadex assumes a brownish color upon dry heating at 120°C. Sephadex may be sterilized in the swollen state in an autoclave at 110°C for 40 minutes without damage to its properties. In addition to water, the G-types of Sephadex are also capable of swelling in dimethyl sulfoxide, formamide, and glycol. The degree of swelling is, however, different from that in water. It has been claimed that the swelling properties of all G-types in dimethyl sulfoxide exceed those in water by 50 to 100% (42). The addition of alcohols to the gels in water causes increasing shrinkage. Sephadex G-10 and G-15 are also capable of swelling in dimethylformamide.

Sephadex LH-20

This type is prepared by alkylation of Sephadex G-25. The swelling properties for conventional solvents are shown in Table 7. The relatively uni-

Table 7. *Swelling properties of Sephadex LH-20*)*

Solvent	Solvent regain (ml/g)	Gel bed volume (ml/g)
Dimethylformamide	2.2	4.0—4.5
Water	2.1	4.0—4.5
Methanol	1.9	4.0—4.5
Ethanol	1.8	3.5—4.5
Chloroform (1% ethanol)	1.8	3.5—4.5
Chloroform	1.6	3.0—3.5
n-Butanol	1.6	3.0—3.5
Tetrahydrofuran	1.4	3.0—3.5
Acetone	0.8	—
Ethyl acetate	0.4	—
Toluene	0.2	—

*) According to statements by the manufacturers; particle size 25—100 μ.

form swelling properties in water, ethanol, and chloroform are remarkable. What has been said earlier about the other Sephadex grades applies equally well to Sephadex LH-20. The particle size (dry material) ranges from 25 to 100 μ.

Bio-Gel

This cross-linked polyacrylamide is also available in the form of bead-shaped dry particles. Nevertheless the particle sizes in the swollen state are

Table 8. *Properties of commercially available polyacrylamide gels Bio-Gel* *) **)

Type**)	Water regain (w_r, ml/g)	Gel bed volume (ml/g)	Approximate fractionation range (M) peptides, globular proteins
P-2	1.6	3.8	200— 2 000
P-4	2.6	6.1	500— 4 000
P-6	3.2	7.4	1 000— 5 000
P-10	5.1	12	5 000— 17 000
P-30	6.2	14	20 000— 50 000
P-60	6.8	18	30 000— 70 000
P-100	7.5	22	40 000—100 000
P-150	9.0	27	50 000—150 000
P-200	13.5	47	80 000—300 000
P-300	22.0	70	100 000—400 000

*) According to the manufacturer, Bio-Rad Laboratories, 32nd and Griffin Avenue, Richmond, California (USA).

**) All types are available in 3 different particle sizes (Mesh, US-Standard): 50—100, 100—200, minus 400. The grades P-2 through P-10 are also available in fractions 200 through 400.

listed. The beads show a tendency to form agglomerates upon drying. There are eleven types available which differ in the water regain. As observed on other gels, the range of application is determined by the degree of swelling. The swelling properties are very little affected by changes in ionic strength. Suggested times for the swelling of the dry powder range from half an hour (P-2) to 24 hours (P-300). Bio-Gel is claimed to be stable in the pH-range from 2 to 11. At higher hydroxyl ion concentration there exists the danger of hydrolysis of the carbonamide linkages. This results in the formation of carboxyl groups and the gel will then display ion exchange properties. From own experiences it is not advisable to apply Bio-Gel to separations in the pH-range above 9. New gel preparations also contain a number of carboxyl groups which, however, are not noticable as long as salt containing eluents are used. Being a plastic, Bio-Gel is not subject to attack by microorganisms.

Agarose

Agarose gel for gel chromatography has recently been made available commercially. Contrary to the gels discussed earlier, these gels are delivered in the swollen state (they should never be dried). So far only a limited amount of practical experience has been gained. The properties, as stated by the manufacturers, may be seen in Table 9. The fractionation ranges are somewhat vague, simply because there are not available enough high molecular weight model substances the molecular weights of which are sufficiently well ascertained. The advantages of the agarose gels rest un-

Table 9. *Properties of commercial agarose gels according to the manufacturer.*

Type	Supplier	Average particle size (ca. μ)	Approximate fractionation range for proteins
Sag 2	Seravac*)	70—140 (crushed)	$50 \times 10^4 - 1.5 \times 10^8$
Sag 4			$20 \times 10^4 - 15 \times 10^6$
Sag 6			$5 \times 10^4 - 2 \times 10^6$
Sag 8			$2.5 \times 10^4 - 70 \times 10^4$
Sag 10			$1 \times 10^4 - 25 \times 10^4$
Sepharose 2B	Pharmacia	60—300 (beads)	$8 \times 10^4 - 20 \times 10^6$**)
Sepharose 4B		30—200 (beads)	$1 \times 10^4 - 3 \times 10^6$**)
Bio-Gel A-150 m	Bio-Rad	50—100 (beads)	$1 \times 10^6 - 1.5 \times 10^8$
Bio-Gel A-50 m		100—200 (beads)	$10 \times 10^4 - 50 \times 10^4$
Bio-Gel A-15 m			$4 \times 10^4 - 15 \times 10^6$
Bio-Gel A-5 m			$1 \times 10^4 - 5 \times 10^6$
Bio-Gel A-1.5 m			$1 \times 10^4 - 1.5 \times 10^6$
Bio-Gel A-0.5 m			$1 \times 10^4 - 50 \times 10^4$

*) Seravac Laboratories (PTY). Ltd., Holyport Maidenhead, Berkshire, England. The same product apparently is available in the USA through Mann Research Laboratories, Inc. New York, 10006 (USA) as 'Ago-Gel'.

**) determined for dextran fractions.

doubtedly with the possibility to separate viruses, phages, cell particles, and bacteria. However, several restrictions have to be made: the Sagarose-product is not available in bead-form. The attainable flow rates are therefore relatively low and the gel packing cannot be very long. These difficulties are not found with the Sepharose and Bio-Gel A beads which are so elastic that the length of the gel packing is reduced at high flow rates. All products must not be brought into contact with organic solvents or other hydrogen bond breaking solutions (e. g. urea), because such contact would destroy irreversibly the gel structure. The application of strong salt solution ought to be tested first with a small quantity of the valuable product in order to ascertain compatibility. The eluent should always contain 0.02% of sodium azide in order to prevent the growth of bacteria.

Styragel

The special reaction conditions which are applied to the synthesis of this polymer of styrene and divinylbenzene (cf. page 23) produce very special physical properties in the gel. The beads are barely swollen. The material is commercially delivered in diethylbenzene and should not be dried. Eluents recommended by the manufacturer are: tetrahydrofuran, trichlorobenzene, o-dichlorobenzene, toluene, m-cresol, methylene chloride and dimethylformamide. Polar solvents, such as water, methanol, acetone, and formic acid will cause some shrinkage and may damage a prepacked column. The commercially available bead-shaped polymer consists of particle sizes between 40 and 80 μ. In Table 10 are schown the commercially available types.

Table 10. *Fractionation range of different styragel-types* *)

Type Å	Approximate fractionation range for vinyl polymers ($\bar{M}_w$)	Approximate exclusion range ($M_{\lim}$)
60	800	1 600
100	2 000	4 000
400	8 000	16 000
1×10^3	20 000	40 000
5×10^3	100 000	200 000
10×10^3	200 000	400 000
30×10^3	600 000	1 200 000
1×10^5	2 000 000	4 000 000
3×10^5	6 000 000	12 000 000
5×10^5	10 000 000	20 000 000
10×10^5	20 000 000	40 000 000

*) According to statements by the manufacturer: Waters Associates, Inc., Framingham, Massachusetts (USA).

The gel types are identified by their respective average porosity in Å. These designations are somewhat empirical. It has been recommended to mix different gels or – better – to switch several columns of different porosity in series in order to fractionate polydisperse polymers. The following has been established as a rule of thumb for the selection of types: one divides by 20 the average molecular weight to obtain the value in Å. Naturally polymers of different structure show different space filling properties in solution. Therefore, this rule (and thus the values in Table 10) is only approximate.

Equipment

Gel chromatography is conducted almost exclusively in chromatography columns. The experimental design is not much different from other techniques of liquid chromatography. (This does not take into consideration the difficulties encountered in handling several of the easily compressible gels.) Nevertheless, it appears to be appropriate at this juncture to recommend several pieces of equipment that may be used in the experimental design of Fig. 8. The separation of a component mixture takes place in a column (c) while the eluent is passing through the gel bed. The constant supply of the column with new eluent is either brought about by a pump

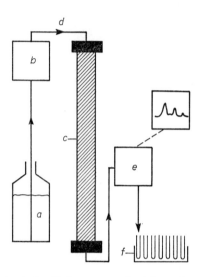

Fig. 8. The flow direction in liquid chromatography (cf. text for explanations).

(b) or simply by a solvent reservoir (a) which is placed at appropriate height. Hose connections (d) are required for this as well as for the purpose of directing the eluent to the fraction collector (f). Individual fractions are collected in the fraction collector. The availability of a detector (e) makes the fractionation convenient and accurate. In the detector a typical property of the eluent (e.g. the adsorption of ultra violet light) is measured and registered automatically. The subsequent mixing of zones has, of course, to be prevented. – The items discussed in the following are selected on the basis of subjective experience.

Columns

The design of chromatographic columns is of great importance for the reproducibility of separations. Most commonly a column will consist of a glass tube. The lower end of the glass tube is of such design that the gel will be retarted. The eluent should be flowing freely out of the column. The "dead volume" of the column must be small. On the other hand the lower end must not be clogged by gel particles. The upper end of the column should allow the convenient application of the solvent. A design which meets these requirements more or less satisfactorily does not necessarily have to be expensive. The commercially available items shown in

Table 11 do possess certain advantages over the simple
design that is shown in Fig. 9. The design principle for
the "Sephadex Chromatography Tube" has been described in detail in the literature (43). Fig. 3 shows such
columns (K 15/30) during an experiment. Simple column
designs, such as the one shown in Fig. 9, have been
used in the laboratory for many years and have been of
different dimensions (length: 20 to 250 cm, diameter: 5
to 50 mm). The dropping funnel as solvent reservoir
should be replaced in the case of larger cross sections
and when working under reduced hydrostatic pressure
(cf. page 46) by a ground joint with hose connection.
The application of glass columns of low diameter (up to
20 mm) has at times been questioned, because in aqueous
systems the so-called "wall effect" has been observed
and adversely affected the separations. We have as yet
not observed such a phenomenon.

It was natural that in many laboratories special
designs should be devised which would meet the requirement stated above. It would be too much to refer to
all minor modifications that have been introduced in the
past. There seems to be, however, common agreement
that discs of sintered glass are not very suitable at the
lower end of the chromatographic tube. In a more ele-
gant version than that shown in Fig. 9 plates made of
porous polyethylene or very fine screen are utilized (43).

It has been found advisable to apply the upward flow
technique in the chromatography on easily compressible
gels and to recycling chromatography (cf. page 49). The
latter technique requires a special design feature. The
column packing material has to be retained between
adjustable plungers. PORATH and BENNICH (44) have
described the first applicable column for this purpose
(a modification of this type of column is commercially
available from LKB; cf. Table 11). Most commercially
available columns are made of precision bore glass
tubing with adjustable plungers which provide tight
seals. Other designs have been reported in the literature
(e. g. 45). FAWCETT and MORRIS (16) have described a
very simple approach to home-made devices. The resistance to solvents
of the plastic material used has to be clearly established for columns which
are to be operated with organic solvents.

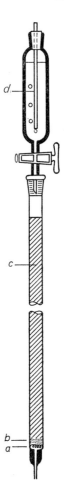

Fig. 9. Design of a
simple column for
gel chromatography
(a) glass wool;
(b) glass beads
    or sand;
(c) gel packing;
(d) eluent.

Table 11. *Commercially available chromatography columns*

Manu-facturer	Type	Inner diameter (mm)	Length (cm)	Upward flow	Solvent resistant	Cooling jacket
Pharmacia	K	15—50	30—100	optional	no	optional
Pharmacia	SR	25	45; 100	yes	yes	no
LKB	4200	6—26	15—100	yes	yes	yes
LKB	4900	32	65; 100	yes	no	optional
Serva		6—140	20—100	no	no	optional
Lab-Crest	274	5—50	15—120	no	yes	optional
Lab-Crest	275	15	25—120	yes	yes	optional
CCA		5—50	20—160	no	yes	optional
Beckman		9—38	23—160	no	no	yes
Phoenix		6—19	10—150	no	no	yes
Wright	FC	8—16	30—90	no	no	optional
Wright	AC	8—16	85	yes	no	optional

Pumps

A large number of different types of pumps is available for liquid chromatography. Frequently the application of a pump does not seem to be an absolute necessity. In principle there are two types of pumps for the

Table 12. *List of pumps for the delivery of eluents*

Manu-facturer	Designa-tion	Mode of action	Chan-nel	Delivery of pump (ml/hr.)	Remarks
Milton-Roy	—	1 piston	1	many types of different capacity	stainless steel piston and cylinder
LKB	4912 A	peristaltic	2	0—390/channel	synchronic motor gear
LKB	Miniflow	twin piston	1	3—50; 15—150	all glass
Stålprodukter	SP 1	peristaltic	3	0—60/channel	like LKB 4912 A
Desaga	—	peristaltic	5	20—2300	simple design, no synchronic motor
Holter	Roller	peristaltic	2	10—105/channel	small and simple
Bühler	mp	peristaltic	2	5—260 and 50—4500	peristaltic, 5 fingers
Sigmamotor	—	peristaltic	2	0.05—2000	many different types
Buchler	Micro-pump	piston	2	25—450; 60—950	acid and solvent resistant
Buchler	Polystaltic	peristaltic	4	3—1000	small and handy
Beckman	Accu-Flow	piston	1	3—160; 12—625	stainless steel resistant from pH 3—14
Quickfit	—	peristaltic	6	3—1000/channel	

uniform delivery of relatively small liquid volumes: piston or peristaltic pumps. The first type is applicable to the delivery of organic and aqueous eluents. The second type can only be recommended for aqueous systems since a flexible hose has to be used. The tubing is either placed over circularly arranged rollers or it is pressed against a support by the rollers. In contrast to the piston pumps, the peristaltic pumps are operating free of irregularities and mixing of the liquid to be delivered is eliminated. The feed rate of peristaltic pumps may be altered by the proper choice of tubing and by the speed of the drive mechanism. It may not always be easy to reproduce the same adjustment. Frequently several tubings are pumped simultaneously. The delivery of piston pumps may be adjusted by changing the stroke or by altering the speed of the drive mechanism. A list of re-commendable pumps is given in Table 12. The media of gel chromatography are generally compressible. It is therefore not recommended to try to force the solvent through the gel bed at the rate above its free flow. The rather rigid polystyrene gels are an exception. A piston pump will always be ap-plied for the delivery of the pure eluent, i.e. placed before or after the gel bed since there is no danger of mixing. This arrangement has made possible recycling chromatography (cf. page 49).

Hose Connections

Substances which have been separated should only be passed through capillary hose connections in order to prevent subsequent mixing. Low diameter tubing made of polyethylene and Teflon is commercially available. These types of tubing are more or less resistant to solvent and may also be sterilized. The connection of these tubings among themselves, as well as to column flow-through cells and other pieces of equipment, may create par-ticular problems. Several possibilities deserve consideration (cf. fig. 10), depending upon the requirements that have to be put forward for these connections with regard to pressure resistance or solvent stability: a simple and inexpensive way of connecting two polyethylene or Teflon tubings is to place over both of them a short piece of elastic capillary silicon rubber tubing (1 mm I.D.). In Fig. 10 A is shown the connection on a column of the type presented in Fig. 9. This type of connection, however, is not pressure-tight. It is, however, resistant to solvent as long as the pieces of tubing to be connected are closely contacted. The other two types of connecting are considerably more expensive (B and C); neither of them is sensitive to pressure or solvent. The LKB system (B) has proved its usefulness over the years in the LKB-Uvicord. – The components as well as the columns of the Beckman Spinco Chromatography System are separately obtainable. Hose connectors are also available for the heavy wall Teflon tubing which is used in this system. Chromatronix Inc. has recently brought on the mar-ket a series of connectors and valves with outstanding properties.

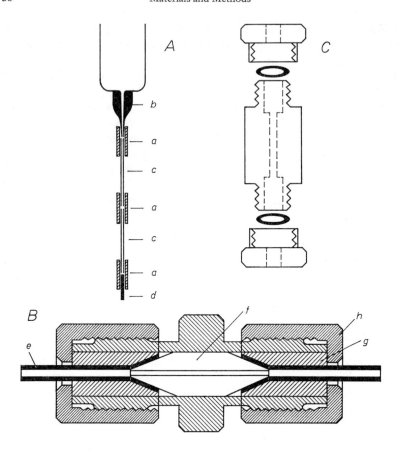

Fig. 10. Suggestions for hose connections
A: (a) Silicon rubber tubing (I.D. 1 mm); (b) capillary column terminal; (c) polyethylene
    tubing (O.D. ca. 1.6 mm); (d) glass rod seal.
B: LKB high pressure hose connection; (e) Teflon tubing (widened by warming the
    end); (f) glass body with cone; (g) counter cone; (h) cap screw.
C: CCA-universal joint for capillary glass tubing, available in different diameters (0.16
    to 6.8 mm O.D.). Teflon body, Viton O-ring.

Detectors

Great convenience is offered for routine operation if it is possible to exam-
ine continuously and automatically the column effluent for the presence
of solutes. The alternative consists in the collection of fractions of the
effluent as it is discharged from the column and in the analysis of these
fractions. Automatic analysers should preferably – while offering high sensitivity – not change the substance to be analyzed. The physical property
measured should be proportional to the concentration. The analytical data

should be plotted on a recorder. On the recorder it should also be possible to mark automatically each advance of the fraction collector.

In line with the original term "Chromatography", difference between the transmission of the eluting solvent and that of the solute serves directly for the purpose of analysis. Many of the substances to be studied do not absorb in the visible range of the spectrum. While in this sense they are not colored, frequently they show to some extent absorbance in the ultra violet range of the spectrum. This property may be recorded with high sensitivity in flow-through spectrophotometers. Any type of recording spectrophotometer is in principle applicable to this purpose, as long as it can be adjusted to the maximum of absorbance of the solute. All that is required is a flow-through cell. Many manufacturers offer parts and components to adapt photometers to the application of flow-through recording. These compromises, however, are frequently associated with considerable disadvantages: Flow-through cells are frequently much too large and mixing of the separated zones often happens; recorders are in general designed for the fast registration of extinction in dependence on wave length and do not provide an accordingly slow chart speed for the recording of extinction in dependence on elution time which frequently takes place over a period of several hours. An added disadvantage is the size of these instruments. The location of the photometer determines frequently the location of the columns and the overall purpose is not always served to the best.

Table 13. *UV-detectors for liquid chromatography*

Manu-facturer	Type	Light source	Wave length (mμ)	Light path cell (mm)	Com-pen-sation	Signal*
LKB	Uvicord I	low pressure Hg	254	0.5—5	no	T %
LKB	Uvicord II	low pressure Hg	254; 280	0.5—5	no	T %
ISCO**	UA	low pressure Hg	254	2—10	no	E
GME	UV-254	low pressure Hg	254	?	no	T %
GME	UV-262 IF UV-280 IF	high pressure Hg	{254; 280 {(filter)	?	no	T %
Buchler	Uviscan I	ozone	{230—300	1.5—5 }	no	E
Buchler	Uviscan II	ozone	{continuous	adjustable }	double beam	E
CCA	7300	hydrogen	210—340, filter	10 mm	double beam	T %, E
Vanguard	1056	hydrogen	200—400 monochromator	0.6	double beam	T %

* T % = percent transmission; E = extinction.

** directs collector in such a way that each UV-positive fraction is collected separately.

For these reasons simple and small flow-through photometers have been developed for the particular application to liquid chromatography. The housing for the lamp, the cell and the photocell are frequently connected by a cable with the amplifier, and power supply portion of the equipment can easily be mounted at the lower end of a column. The flow-through cells are of low volume but offer at the same time the longest possible light path. This is particularly true for the model from CCA. In Table 13 is given a list of commercially available instruments. Several of them are forgoing the choice of different wave length on purpose. For that reason it is not possible to determine the concentration of the eluted substance from the elution diagram directly. This, however, is not so important – though the sensitivity is poorer – for accuracy as long as the light applied is truly monochromatic. The latter can, however, be achieved easily by the application of spectral lamps. The line of highest energy of low pressure mercury vapor lamp (254 mμ) corresponds exactly to the absorption maximum of nucleic acids and of aromatic compounds, e.g. benzene. Proteins have an absorption maximum near 280 mμ and a minimum near 254 mμ. However, proteins may be analyzed almost as easily at the minimum. The LKB-Uvicord I together with "gel filtration on Sephadex" has proven its usefulness the world over. The absorption in the infrared region of the spectrum may also be utilized as a sensitive indication for the presence of certain polymers in the column effluent (46).

Another very sensitive device records automatically the difference in refractive index between the pure and the solute containing eluate (R 4 Differential Refractometer, Waters Associates). The application of this type of recording device will be essential whenever the substances to be chromatographed do not show any light absorption. The operation of this differential refractometer, despite its high sensitivity, is very simple and reproducible. A series of refractometers for the different requirements of continuous operation are now available from Phoenix. A very simple device (Nester-Faust, Newark, Delaware 19711, USA) is less sensitive, but also less expensive. The same holds for a very compact instrument (EC Apparatus Column Monitor, Philadelphia, USA). The proposal has also been made to utilize the differences in dielectric properties between solvents with or without substances (47). Accordingly a column is filled with glass beads at its lower end and one sheet of aluminium foil each act as transmitter and receiver. Salt solutions are producing very high deflections. – Ions in aqueous solution may also be detected by the continuous measurement of conductivity, e.g. in the LKB-conductolyzer. It is very important for this type of measurement to control closely the temperature in the measuring cells.

A universal type of detector for liquid chromatography has been described very recently (48). This detector takes advantage of the minimum temperature effect that is produced when the solute interacts with the column packing material. The measurements are made in a special detector column which is placed after the column on which the separation takes place. It is not clear whether this ingenious principle will be applicable to gel chromatography. The views generally held on the mechanism responsible for the separation on gel packings (cf. chapter 3) do not assume such interactions. It has, however, been demonstrated unequivocally that oligomeric saccharides and propylene glycols could be indicated in a detector column which was placed after a Sephadex G-10 column. For this application a commercially available instrument had been used (49). Another instrument of such kind will be obtainable from Bio-Cal (Munich, Germany).

Very high sensitivity and universal applicability may be expected from a device which makes possible the utilization of the flame ionization detection technique of gas chromatography in liquid chromatography (50-54). The device operates in the following way: The eluent or part of the eluent is collected on an endless moving hot chain or on a wire, evaporated and the residues transferred to the detector. The latest instrument operates without separate pyrolysis and is capable of exactly determining the amount of 30 μg of protein as separated on a 1×190 mm Sephadex G-25 column (24). Such instrument has recently become available commercially, the Liquid Chromatograph 7101 (Packard Instr. Comp., Inc., Downersgrove, Illinois 60515). A wire-type flame ionisation detector has been realized by W. G. Pye Ltd. (Cambridge, England).

Provided the substances to be separated emit energy-rich radiation, radioactivity measurements may be applied to their detection. There are also continuously operating devices for this purpose. These instruments, however, shall not be discussed here.

Fraction Collectors

We shall forgo the presentation of commercially available instruments. A large number of commercial units is available and cannot be evaluated easily. Furthermore there are a great number of new developments presently being made. Fraction collectors of the past had arranged in a circular turn table a set of test tubes which served to receive the eluent. The turn table is advanced tube by tube by rotation which is guided by electrical impulses. The electrical impuls may be derived from a clock, a photoelectric drop counter or from a siphon. The three different devices for advancing the turn table (time control, drop counting, or volume control) will also be used in the future. It appears, however, that the arrangement of the test tubes in rectangular, exchangable racks will be more favored. Greatly differing systems are in use. In some of them the tubes are moved under a permanently mounted outlet. Less advantageously, the outlet moves from tube to tube and consists of a hose connection. Collectors in which the different types have been incorporated have also been developed. Equipment of the recent past can be operated more easily. It is also smaller, and in some instances, the space occupation is so little that the units may be accommodated in a household refrigerator (LKB-UltraRac 7000). A list of manufacturers for equipment used in liquid chromatography can be found at the end of this section. Almost all of them offer different types of fraction collectors at greatly differing prices.

Integrated Units

Like other types of liquid chromatography, gel chromatography may also be conducted with very simple equipment. The various pieces of equipment that have been described in the preceding section serve only the purpose of increasing accuracy, sensitivity, and convenience. The development of instruments for gas chromatography evidently has had some bearing in that some companies manufacture complete chromatography units in which pumps, columns with thermostats, detectors, and collectors are combined to one functional unit. Beckman, for instance, offers in its "Spectrochrom" a complete laboratory for liquid chromatography in the aqueous phase. The recording detector system consists of a dual beam spectrophotometer,

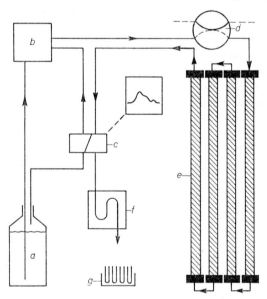

Fig. 11. Schematic representation of the gel permeation chromatograph from waters. Solvent is pumped (b) from a reservoir (a) through a pressure reducer (not shown) to the reference cell of the differential refractomer (c). A second stream of solvent passes through a valve (d) – where an exactly determined volume of solution is picked up – and on through 4 chromatographic columns (e) (each 0.95×120 cm) into the other cell of the detector. The eluent is passed through the siphon (f) into the fraction collector (g). All connectors and the columns are pressure tight and manufactured from stainless steel.

pH-meter, and conductivity cell and is also separately available as "Model 135 Spectromonitor". "ILC-2A" is a Japanese development which incorporates as detector system the highly sensitive temperature monitor which has been described; the unit also records light absorption. Other essential components are incorporated. – For the gel chromatography of polymers in organic solvents, Waters Associates have constructed the "Gel Permeation Chromatograph" (55) (GPC, Model 200). This device makes possible the automatic determination of the molecular weight distribution of a polymer within a few hours. In view of the high linear velocity one would expect a rather moderate resolution, however, the gel bed is extremely long. 4 columns of 120 cm each are put in series. The "Styragels" which are used in this system are very rigid so it is possible to apply high pressure and increase the flow rate. This in turn requires a rather elaborate set of equipment. The detector system consists of a differential refractometer. The volume of individual fractions is measured exactly into a siphon and then directed to the fraction collector. The entire system – from the application of the sample to the siphon – is temperature adjustable up to 140°C which makes possible the analysis of poorly soluble plastics. This excellent analytical tool is shown in Fig. 11.

A larger version ("Ana-Prep") has been developed recently for preparative separation based on the same principle. – ROUBAL and TAPPEL (45 a) have described a complete automatic apparatus, out of individual parts put together for the chromatography of proteins on Sephadex.

Manufacturers of equipment for gel chromatography:

Beckman Instruments, Inc., Spinco Division, Palo Alto, California (USA).
Buchler Instruments, Inc., Fort Lee, New Jersey (USA).
Bühler, Laboratoriumsgeräte, 74 Tübingen, Germany
CCA, Chromatography Corporation of America, Carpentersville, Illinois (USA).
C. Desaga G.m.b.H., 69 Heidelberg 1, Germany
Chromatronix Inc., Berkeley, California (USA).
GME, Gilson Medical Electronics, Middleton, Wisconsin (USA).
Holter, The Holter Company, Bridgeport, Pennsylvania (USA).
ISCO, Instrumentation Specialities Company, Lincoln, Nebrasca (USA).
Lab-Crest, Fischer and Porter Company, Scientific Division, Warminster, Pennsylvania (USA).
LKB Produkter AB, Stockholm-Bromma, Sweden.
Milton Roy, St. Petersburg, Florida (USA).
Pharmacia Fine Chemicals, Uppsala, Sweden.
Phoenix Precision Instrument Company, Philadelphia, Pennsylvania (USA);
Serva Entwicklungslabor, 69 Heidelberg, Germany
Sigmamotor, Inc., Middleport, New York (USA).
Stålprodukter, Uppsala 11, Sweden.
Vanguard Instrument Company, La Grange, Illinois (USA).
Waters Associates Inc., Framingham, Massachusetts (USA).
Wright Scientific Ltd., London, NW 6, England.

Experimental Techniques with Columns

Packing of the Gel Bed

The provisions that have to be made in order to obtain a reproducible packing of the gel bed and good flow rates depend largely on the properties of the applied gel particles. The more uniform the grain size and the shape of the particles are, and the more rigid, the structure of the beads, the easier it is to obtain an effective gel packing. It is naturally more difficult to pack reproducibly long columns of low diameter than to do the same with short ones of larger diameter. Details for the volume and dimensions of columns will be given in Chapter 4 for different separation problems on gel packing. A number of devices have been described in the literature which claim to guarantee uniform sedimentation of the gel particles. This was of great significance, as long as one knew only of irregular gel particles. FLODIN (56) in his methodical investigations on gel filtration described a very simple device. It operates in the following way: The column to be packed is extended by a tube. The tube has a funnel and a mechanical stirring device at its upper end. The device is mounted vertically, filled with solvent, and the swollen gel is gradually stirred into the column. The outlet of the column will be opened gradually with the growing layer of settled gel particles. The extension tube and the funnel are removed for actual chromatography. A somewhat simpler method is in use in the laboratory of the author for the packing of bead-shaped gel particles in aqueous and organic solvents. This technique is known in many other laboratories and is applicable at least to columns of 20 to 200 cm length and of 5 to 50 mm diameter:

The vertically mounted chromatographic tube (cf. Fig. 9) is closed at its lower end. Glass wool and a layer of several mm of sand or glass beads are placed into the bottom of the tube, before it is filled to one third of its height with solvent observing that no air bubbles are trapped. The gel to be packed has been allowed to swell properly before it is applied in the form of a suspension that allows the easy escape of air bubbles. The entire tube is filled in one pouring. As soon as a layer of several centimeters height of the gel particles has settled the valve of the column is gradually opened. As the solvent flows out of the tube, new gel suspension can be added to the top. It must be carefully observed during the filling operation that three zones have at all times to be in the column: The growing layer of gel particles, the gel suspension above it, and the clear solvent at the top. If the sedimentation is relatively fast with regard to flow rate, the clear supernatant of solvent may be removed from time to time from the column in order to be replaced by new gel suspension. This prevents the formation of density layers along the gel packing. The gel and the solvent ought to be allowed to acquire the environmental temperature before the operation is started. Frequently it is advisable to counteract the subsequent formation of air bubbles by evacuation or boiling of the solvent.

The filling operation may be facilitated in many instances by the extension of the column by a glass tube of the same diameter. In doing so, the entire amount of gel suspension required for packing can be applied in one pouring. Columns which are to be packed with the easily compressible gel beads (e. g. Sephadex G-200 or Bio-Gel P-300) require special attention during the filling operation. High hydrostatic pressures on the gel bed have to be prevented. For this purpose a piece of tubing is attached to the outlet of the chromatographic tube the other end of which is positioned only 10 to 20 cm below the liquid level in the column.

These techniques, which are very common in liquid chromatography, and which are described here in some detail, have been modified in many ways: It is possible to stir the gel suspension in the chromatographic tube (45b) or the gel suspension may be led through tubing from a reservoir which is equipped with a stirring device (57). The velocity of the packing operation can be adjusted by changing the level between reservoir and column outlet. Several columns may be packed "automatically" and simultaneously (57). ALTGELT (34) has described a device with which the column to be packed may be constantly rotated during the sedimentation of the gel particles. Very homogeneous packings are thus obtained. The rigid polystyrene gel allows the application of high pressure during the packing operation, if, as is the case with the GPC-apparatus, columns of stainless steel are used.

The surface of gels in glass columns is usually stabilized by a cover of an exactly fitting piece of filter paper. It has been suggested to apply to the top of easily compressible, highly swollen gels a layer of somewhat more rigid gel particles. Many of the commercially available columns (cf. table 11) are equipped with plungers that guarantee tight seals. These plungers can be adjusted to the upper layer of the gel packing. The supernatant solvent has to replace the air during this operation.

Organophilic gels do not settle in solvents of higher density. The swollen gel is floating on top of the solvent. This can be prevented by packing at high flow rates and by the immediate application of the upper plunger. Other types of columns are not applicable in such instances. Alternatively, the swelling and the filling may be carried out in a lighter solvent. The solvent must then be replaced in the column by a heavier one. The two solvents must have the same swelling properties and they must be miscible.

Chromatography

Sample Application

There are three reliable approaches to the application of a sharp zone of the mixture of substances to be separated to the gel packing. The invasion of the gel bed by air has to be prevented. The column must not run dry. The first procedure to be described has been used very widely and is usually also applied in liquid chromatography:

The eluent above the gel packing is removed almost completely. The remainder is allowed to just penetrate the gel packing. The solution of the substances to be separated is applied at once and carefully to the gel packing. (Details on the size of the sample volume are given in Chapter 4). As soon as the sample has completely entered the column packing, the top of the column is rinsed twice with an identical volume of eluent. Thereafter the solvent on top of the column packing is connected with the continuous supply of solvent. The starting and rinsing operation may be conducted while the steady flow of the column is maintained. Alternatively, it is advisable to close the lower outlet between individual steps.

The time required for the starting of a column by this procedure is a function of the flow rate. CURTAIN and NAYLER (58) have made an interesting suggestion for the automation of the operation of columns with aqueous eluents: The column contains two contacts. One of them is positioned inside the gel packing, the other one just slightly above the gel bed. As long as the two are connected by a conducting buffer, the buffer is forced continuously by air pressure into the gel bed. Before the column has a chance to run dry the circuit is disrupted and the pressure released. Next the sample is automatically applied. The circuit is closed again only to be opened as

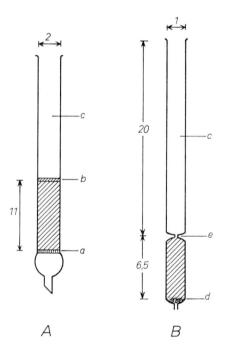

A   B

Fig. 12. Suggestions for small columns to be used for desalting and other applications (measurements in cm). At A the gel is supported by a rigid disc (a) and covered with a piece of sponge (b). In B the glass tube has a constriction (e). The column is packed with gel up to the constriction. The gel is supported by glass wool and a layer of sand (d).

soon as the sample has been applied. The washing operations are carried out just as rapidly and also automatically. – Chromatonix, Inc. offers a liquid level control which can be used for the same purpose.

The same complicated automated control is not required for small columns. This effect can be produced in a simpler way, either by placing a circular piece of sponge (59) on top of the gel packing or by constricting the glass tube at the upper end of the future gel packing (60) (cf. Fig. 12). In both cases the eluent can only flow from (c) until it has reached the gel surface. The capillary forces prevent also air from entering into the gel packing. This applies also when no eluent is left above the gel packing and the column is open at its lower end. These small (automatic) columns proved to be very useful during routine separations of highmolecular weight substances from low molecular weight contaminants (cf. Chapter IV).

Another approach is applicable to very viscose sample solutions, i.e. especially to macromolecular substances. This approach is simpler than the one described above.

The supernatant is not removed from the gel packing. Rather, the sample solution is placed underneath the eluent with the help of a syringe the needle of which has been replaced by thin tubing. Should the solution be too dilute, its density may be raised by the addition of a low molecular weight substance. (Sucrose has been used succesfully for the separation of proteins on Sephadex in aqueous buffers.) The rinsing operations are eliminated and the elution may be started directly. In order to prevent contamination of the supernatant by traces of the substances to be separated, a small volume of air is sucked into the syringe and the tubing on the syringe is wiped clean. After the application of the sample solution, a small volume of solvent may be withdrawn above the zone of the sample solution and the tubing carefully removed.

Sample solutions are applied most conveniently and accurately to a column in which the gel bed is positioned between two porous plates. Commercial columns (Table 11) which are adaptable to flow in either direction are equipped at top and bottom with devices to which capillary tubing may be attached at very low dead volumes. It is then possible to pass the eluent either from top to bottom or from bottom to top through the gel packing. At any given moment the eluent may be replaced by the sample solution without any additional changes. This is accomplished either by the use of a T-piece or by a three-way stop cock which allows the switching of the liquid flow or – more primitively – by placing the end of the tubing that normally is in the eluent for a short period of time into the sample solution. During this manipulation air must not be allowed to enter the closed system. In the GPC-apparatus (cf. Fig. 11) the starting of a column is quickly and reproducibly accomplished in the following way: A measured volume of the sample solution is accommodated in a loop and simply applied by turning a stop cock. This device can also be kept at controlled temperature and may be automated.

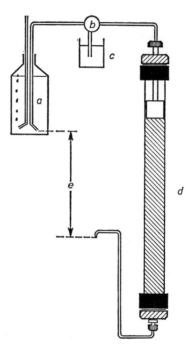

Fig. 13. Gel chromatography on compressible gels; (a) solvent reservoir; (b) three-way stop cock; (c) sample solution; (d) column with a plunger at the top; (e) effective pressure difference.

Elution

The flow rate of xerogels should be adjusted in such a way that it is smaller than that of a freely flowing column. While describing pumps, it was already indicated that simple devices are available for maintaining constant flow rates. In the device of Fig. 9, for instance, the flow rate is controlled by a dropping funnel with a tightly inserted vent pipe. Mariotte's principle is also valid for the design shown in Fig. 13. Here the flow rate may be readily changed by appropriately positioning the reservoirs. The maximally attainable flow rate depends on the size and shape of the gel particles as well as on their compressibility. Fig. 14 shows for various Sephadex gels that the flow rate of bead-shaped xerogels of minor swelling properties increases linearly at moderate pressures with the pressure applied (61). The rigid aerogels show the same behavior. It is shown in Fig. 14 for Sephadex G-200 that strongly swollen porous gel beads are easily deformed. The flow rate decreases considerably with increasing hydrostatic pressure. The deformation of the gel particles is irreversible. These gels should always – the packing operation included – be operated under moderate hydrostatic pressure

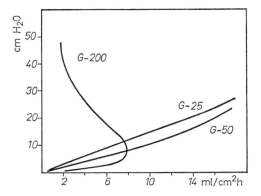

Fig. 14. Dependence of the flow rate on the hydrostatic pressure for different Sephadex gels (61); abscissa: flow rate in ml/cm²h; ordinate: hydrostatic pressure (cm H_2O).

(10-30 cm). This may be accomplished easily by either positioning the solvent reservoir relatively low or by positioning the end of the hose at the outlet relatively high. The optional difference in pressure between the air entrance of the bottle of Mariotte and the outlet of the column depends – just like the maximally attainable flow rate – also on the height of the gel packing. An initial increase in the flow rate is observed with increasing hydrostatic pressure. However, this is soon followed by a very rapid decrease. Attempts have been made repeatedly to stabilize the gel packing by inert additives. Cellulose powder (15-20%) was, for instance, added to Sephadex G-200 (62).

Analysis

The effluents of gel chromatography columns may be analyzed by any of the conventionally applied methods. Apart from automatically recording devices which have been discussed in the preceding section, substances with aromatic systems (e.g. polystyrenes, proteins, nucleic acids) may be analyzed quantitatively by reading the individual fractions in a spectrophotometer. For all solid substances a procedure proposed by CRAIG is suitable. The samples are evaporated and weighed in semispherical small dishes (63). Many other components may be analyzed by sensitive specific reactions. For proteins, for instance, the Folin-Lowry-color reaction is more sensitive than the direct analysis in UV-light. This reaction may be carried out continuously in an autoanalyzer (45a). A considerably more sensitive method (up to 0.45 μg protein per ml) operates as follows: In a continuous process the Biuret-complex is formed with an excess of radioactive copper. The excess of copper is removed on Sephadex G-25 and the sample analyzed in a counter (64). The elution diagram of 10 μg of a serum fraction from Sephadex G-100 (1.2×30 cm) was still easily detectable by the addition of acetic acid/ferricyanide to aliquots of the eluate and by measuring the turbidity in a fluorometer (*65*). Whenever enzymes are present the responsible protein may be analyzed by its activity (optical or other tests). These analyses are highly sensitive. For many of these tests autoanalytic methods have been devised (e.g. *66*). Minute quantities of an easily detectable enzyme may be used to label certain elution volumes in order to be able to compare the results of quite different experiments. Alkaline phosphatase (*67*) and lactate dehydrogenase (*68*) are, for instance, suitable for this purpose.

Extension of the Gel Bed

If substances to be separated have only minor molecular weight differences, one can only expect small differences in their elution volumes. A longer gel packing will then result in better resolution than a shorter one. Any extension of a gel packing faces an upper limit since it results in an increase in flow resistance. This is true in particular for soft, compressible gels. During the operation of columns that are longer than 1 m considerable difficulties are observed frequently. However, several reports from the literature in which particularly long columns were applied successfully (*69-75*) are compiled in Table 14. The gel bed may also be extended effectively by

Table 14. *The application of very long Sephadex gel columns*

Type	Remarks	Gel bed (cm)	Separated substances	References
G-25*	in 30—50% AcOH	4.0 × 500	cyclic oligamides from Nylon	(*69*)
G-25	dry sieving	0.9 × 310	tryptic peptides from RNase	(*70*)
G-75	dry sieving	2.5 × 200	pollen proteins	(*71*)
G-100		1.1 × 192	molecular weight determination of proteins	(*72*)
G-100 G-200		3.0 × 235	proteins from liver	(*73*)
G-200		3.0 × 210	proteins from soyabeans	(*74*)
G-200		0.9 × 280 7.0 × 150	soluble ribonucleic acid	(*75*)

* Similar results were obtained in analogous experiments with Bio-Gel P-10.

connecting the outlet of the first column to the inlet of a second column (e.g. *71, 76*). The head of the second column, however, has to consist of a plunger with a minimal dead volume in order to prevent excessive dilution or mixing of the zones. KING and NORMAN (*71*) have applied in this fashion a gel bed of 2.5 × 600 consisting of three sections of 200 cm each to the separation of allergenes on Sephadex G-75.

Recycling Chromatography

Another approach to improve the resolving power of a gel bed of relatively moderate length does not require several columns. PORATH and BENNICH (44) have described an arrangement in which the effluent of a Sephadex column is subsequently pumped again on to the same column. Prior to the second application the eluent passes a flow-through photometer (Fig. 15). This requires that the dead volume in the column (d), the hose connections, the detector (f), and that of the pump (a) are kept as small as possible.

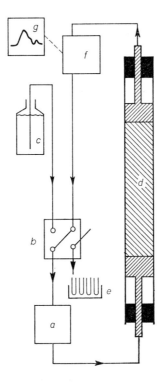

Fig. 15. Schematic representation of the recycling chromatography according to PORATH and BENNICH (44). (a) pump; (b) 4-way valve; (c) solvent system reservoir; (d) gel column; (e) fraction collector; (f) detector; (g) recorder.

The gel packing of a recycling column is also held between two adjustable plungers and the flow of solvent is directed from bottom to top. During each passage, the zones are naturally broadening to some extent which poses the danger of mixing eventually the first zone with the last one. In order to prevent this, a 4-way valve (b) is inserted in the closed system. With its help new solvent from the reservoir (c) can be pumped into the column while, simultaneously, the eluent is directed to a fraction collector. In this way undesired fractions are removed from the cycles during actual separation. The sample solution is also applied through the 4-way valve.

The mode of action of recycling chromatography is exemplified in Fig. 16 by the isolation of the hemoglobin/haptoglobin-complex from a serum fraction on Sephadex G-200 (77).

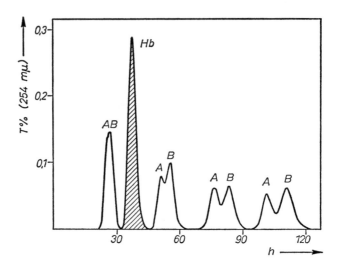

Fig. 16. Recycling chromatography on Sephadex G-200 of the haptoglobin fraction from 25 ml of serum after the addition of an excess of hemoglobin (Hb); gel bed volume 1340 ml (4.2×96.5 cm); 0.1 M Tris-HCl (pH 8.0) + 0.5 M NaCl; 25 ml/h. (A) hemoglobin-haptoglobin-complex; (B) other serum-proteins; according to KILLANDER (77).

In the first cycle the excess of hemoglobin (shaded) was eluted. In the fourth cycle the complex (A) could be collected separately from the remaining serum proteins (B). KILLANDER succeeded also by recycling chromatography with the separation of the macroglobulins of serum on Agargel (78). The technique has so far been applied predominantly to the isolation of plasma proteins (e.g. 79, 80). In a new approach to the rapid and convenient isolation of lactate dehydrogenase from beef heart, recycling chromatography on Sephadex G-200 represents an important step in the isolation (81). The essential components of recycling chromatography (column, 4-way valve, pump) are available commercially from LKB as an integrated unit under the name "ReCyChrom".

It can be expected that the recycling chromatography technique may be automated (e.g. 80) and will undergo further improvements. It has, for instance, been demonstrated that the eluent, as long as it contains macromolecular substances, may be concentrated by continuous withdrawal of part of the water through a dialysis membrane. The partially separated zones are then placed again onto the gel bed as sharp bands. POLSON and RUSSELL (82) utilized as concentrator a rod of perspex into which a spiral-like groove had been cut. Over the rod is placed a dialysis tubing around which in a spiral-like fashion a thread is wound. In this way a spiral-like tubing is formed, one wall of which is permeable for water. The rod is then placed into a tube of larger diameter in which warm air from a blower is flowing over it. While flowing through the tube, the eluent is more or less strongly concentrated (approximately 30 to 75%). In the design suggested by the authors the blower is switched on automatically as soon as the pen of the detector is deflected. Naturally the buffer salts are also concentrated during this process. Another disadvantage is the existing danger of heat de-naturation of the sensitive proteins. These disadvantages are eliminated according to a suggestion of PORATH and BENNICH (83) by bringing the rod with the attached membrane into an osmotically active, concentrated polymer solution.

Thinlayer Gel Chromatography

Thinlayer chromatography was introduced at the same time when gels were developed to a standard laboratory method for the chromatographic separation of substances (84, 85). It appeared to be desirable to combine both techniques in order to apply the technique of thinlayer chromatography to proteins. All experiments with this aim in mind were conducted with various types of Sephadex. The layer of swollen Sephadex is in principle an "open" gel bed which differs from that in a column only in so far as it is easily accessible for all manipulations (application of the sample solution or the staining of separated substances). In thinlayer chromatography (84, 85) one commonly uses plates with a dry carrier material; the solvent system is transported by capillary forces while the plate is kept in a vertical position in the eluting solvent. Such experiments were also conducted with Sephadex (86). The bead-shaped Sephadex grades which are now available are, how-ever, not applicable to this technique. All subsequently described techniques (cf. Table 15) use the open gel bed that was first described by JOHANSSON and RYMO (87).

Preparation

Dry Sephadex superfine must first be allowed to swell in a buffer as indicated in Table 6. Several authors (88, 90) use just enough liquid to obtain a heavy suspension which may be applied immediately to the plate. The danger of lump formation will be eliminated by allowing the gel to swell in an excess of buffer and by the removal of this excess of buffer by decantation before the

application to the plate. As soon as the swollen material has settled completely the proper consistency has been reached. If necessary (e. g. in the case of
strongly swelling gels) sedimentation may be improved by centrifugation.
In case of doubt the slurry ought to be prepared preferably too heavy
rather than too light. It can always be diluted subsequently. A layer of a

Table 15. *Techniques of thinlayer gel chromatography*

Authors	JOHANSSON and RYMO (*88*)	ANDREWS (*89*)	MORRIS (*90*)	DETERMANN and MICHEL (*91*)
Sephadex-types	G-25, G-50, fine; G-75 to G-200, superfine	G-100, super-fine	G-100, G-200, superfine	G-200, superfine
Plate size	20×40; 20×50	10×20	10×20	20×20; 20×40
Applicator	Desaga	Desaga	Camag	Camag
Thickness of layer (mm)	0.5	0.5	0.9	0.5
Separatory Chamber	humid chamber	10—20° inclination	humid chamber	sandwich, 20—40°
Preparation	1 hour prerun	several hours prerun	18 hours hori-zontal storage	24 hours hori-zontal storage
Separation time	1—2 cm/h.	8—10 hours	4—5 hours	2—6 hours
Development	on the plate with Amido Black 10B	on the plate with iodine vapor	print	print with Pauly reagent
Application	serum proteins	molecular weight determination of proteins	molecular weight determination of proteins	test proteins

thickness of 0.9 mm requires 6 g of Sephadex G-100 and 4 g of Sephadex
G-200 for six plates of a size 10×20 cm (*90*). With 15 g of Sephadex G-200
ten plates (20×20 cm) will be obtained at a thickness of 0.5 mm (*91*). The
plates have to be cleaned very carefully before the application of the layer.
Traces of lipids interfere seriously with the uniform application of the
layer. It is advisable to store the clean plates in concentrated sodium carbonate solution and to rinse them with distilled water shortly before they
are to be used. Scouring agents and detergents are applicable. They will,
however, have to be washed off again very carefully. Rinsing with solvents
did not prove to be very effective.

The applicator offered by CAMAG (Muttenz, Switzerland) was found
to be very suitable for the application of suspensions. The open design of
this device offers the opportunity to dilute the suspension or to stir it.
Layers of a thickness of 0.5 mm seem to be advisable. It was found to be
more difficult to reproduce the results obtained with thinner as well as with
thicker layers. After the application the plates should be stored carefully in

horizontal position in a humid chamber at least for one night (desiccator with wet paper lining or similar provisions). This seems to improve the homogeneity of the layers. Several authors have proposed this alternative: The plates are equilibrated for some time in a separatory chamber with buffer before the substances are applied (cf. Table 15). Depending on the saturation, the plates may be kept for immediate use in a humid chamber over a period of one to three weeks. Precautions must, however, be taken to prevent the growth of microorganism.

Chromatography

The chromatographic procedure must be such that the layer does not dry out during the several hours run. A certain angle of inclination has to be maintained and care must be taken of a steady supply and discharge of the buffer. Usually sufficiently large vessels are used in which the entire apparatus (plate, holding device, and the buffer vessel with transfer device) can be accomodated. In the laboratory of the author the so-called sandwich technique, which is well known from conventional thinlayer chromatography, proved to be very useful (91). Sandwich chambers of various designs are commercially available. As can be seen in Figure 17, the plate with the gel layer is covered by a second glass plate. This glass plate is supported at the long side by two cardbord strips and thus positioned at a short distance from the layer.

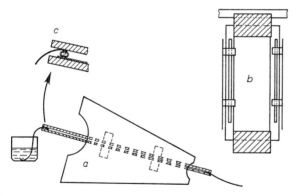

Fig. 17. Schematic representation of the equipment for thinlayer gel chromatography: (a) longitudinal cut; (b) top view; (c) details of the paper support.

The two plates are kept in the proper position by clamps which are obtainable from Camag. In order to secure proper contact with the layer of filter paper which supplies and drains the buffer (Macherey and Nagel 212) the paper is rolled as indicated in Fig. 17 c or enforced by an additional filter paper strip.

The equipment is inexpensive and the reproducibility of the results is good. Compared with other techniques the actual time required for chromatography is short, since the solvent does not evaporate. After the passage through the layer, the eluent is absorbed by a filter paper sheet which is attached to the lower end of the plate and is in contact with the gel layer. Circular spots of several mm diameter of the protein solution are applied with the help of capillaries in volumes of approximately 1 to 5 microliters. The lower limit of sensitivity is approximately 0.1 to 1 micrograms.

The progress of the chromatography may be observed by applying simultaneously an intensively colored protein. Cytochrome c (89) and to a somewhat less extent hemoglobin (90) are suitable for this purpose. Proteins which were stained by the reaction with fluorescein isothiocyanate may easily be made visible in UV-light (88). It has to be borne in mind, however, that the rate of migration may be changed considerably by the staining (91). Serum proteins which have been stained with Amido Black may also be applied (92).

The spots of separated proteins may easily be made visible by transferring them to a paper sheet after the chromatographic separation has been completed and by staining them on the paper. For layers on Sephadex G-100 the following paper grade is recommended: Schleicher and Schuell 2043b and for Sephadex G-200: Whatman 3 MM (90) and Macherey and Nagel 212 (91), respectively. The sheet of chromatography paper of proper size is applied to the wet gel layer beginning at the starting line. The inclusion of air bubbles must be prevented carefully. The dry paper absorbs instantaneously together with the buffer the larger portion of the protein. A considerable amount of the gel layer will also be transferred to the paper. The print will be dried immediately in hot air and subsequently stained with one of the conventionally employed reagents. Next to the reaction with Amido Black 10 B (approximately 10 minutes dipping in a saturated solution in methanol/glacial acetic acid, washing with methanol/glacial acetic acid 10:1) the Pauly reagent is universally applicable (spraying with a freshly prepared approximately 0.01% solution of diazotized sulfanilic acid in 10% sodium carbonate solution). For small protein quantities dipping in an 0.01% solution of nigrosin in methanol/water/glacial acetic acid (50:40:10) seems to be particularly suitable (90, 92). Enzymatic reactions may also be carried out on the paper by saturating it with substrate before the print is made (88) or by subsequent spraying. Naturally, the paper sheet must not be dried in this case.

The plates themselves may also be dried carefully and stained subsequently. A drying oven (50°C) which is lined with wet paper is suitable for this purpose. The wet paper is required for a slow and uniform drying process. Following this approach, one obtains within 1.5 hours, particularly with Sephadex G-100 and G-200, perfectly homogenous and scratch-resistant layers. Without these precautions the drying normally results in very uneven layers with many cracks. The following technique has been suggested for the staining of proteins in dry Sephadex layers:

The dry plates are allowed to swell for ten minutes in a mixture of methanol/water/ glacial acetic acid (75:20:5). Subsequently the plates are stained in a bath consisting of a saturated solution of Amido Black 10 B in the same solvent system. The staining is allowed to proceed for five hours. Excess dye is removed by bathing the plates for two hours in the same liquid before they are dried. This procedure should be followed carefully in order to obtain clearly visible blue spots against a very faint back ground for quantities of 1 to 5 micrograms of proteins.

Immediately after the completion of the chromatography the moist plates may be exposed to an atmosphere of halogen. The N-Halogen compounds are stained with KI/starch after the excess of reagent has been removed (83, 93).

Results

It has been pointed out already that the application of thinlayer gel chromatography (with the exception of a few experiments in the field of peptides (86, 87), with mucosaccharides (93) and in the prepurification of ribonucleotides (94)), so far, has been restricted to proteins in aqueous buffers. Chances are that the thinlayer technique will find wide application as a microtechnique in addition to the column technique. The equipment required as well as the sample quantities are comparatively small and the thinlayer technique makes it possible to complete a large number of experiments in a relatively short time. Thinlayer gel chromatography is thus particularly well suited for the simple determination of protein molecular weights (cf. page – 113). The accuracy is not as good as with the column technique. However, this may be compensated by the statistical interpretation of many parallel experiments. Since it is possible to show the presence of many enzymes on the plate or on the paper print by appropriate direct tests, it is possible to get an approximate molecular weight even from impure preparations. It is furthermore possible to establish quickly suitable conditions for additional steps of purification.

Another application is the study of serum and other body fluids, which frequently are available only in very small quantities. A two-dimensional technique has been proposed for this application (92, 95). Chromatography is followed in the second direction by electrophoretic separation. This technique has also been coupled with immuno-chemical tests (cf. 96). The application of thinlayer gel chromatography to the study of Bence-Jones proteins in urine indicated the medical-diagnostic potential (97).

Strips (0.6 × 3.5 cm) of Sephadex G-100 or G-200 (98) applied to slightly inclined microscope slides are occupying an intermediate position between columns and thin layers. On this micro-column a minute quantity of serum may be separated, the components of which may then be identified on this very microscope slide by immunodiffusion (before applying the gel strip a portion of the microscope slide is covered with a layer of agar). Following the gel chromatography, the strip is placed next to the agar layer and the antiserum applied to a preformed trough.

Centrifuge Technique

On the basis of theoretical considerations (cf. chapter 3) it was concluded that the gel chromatographic separation should be independent of the concentration of the sample solution. This is true up to a certain limit and in agreement with experimental findings. The limit is given by the viscosity of the sample solution. If the viscosity is high, the diffusion of the solutes is influenced considerably and the separation is rather incomplete. For all practical purposes this becomes very disturbing if large quantities of high molecular weight substances have to be separated from low molecular weight substances, for instance, in the case of a classic desalting problem. The dilution of the colloid is frequently considerable. This difficulty has been overcome by a new technique which has been developed by Pharmacia Research Laboratories, Uppsala, Sweden (99). In a basket centrifuge water is first removed from a Sephadex gel bed. Thereafter the solution to be desalted is brought into uniform contact with the gel whereby the lower molecular weight components diffuse into the gel beads until equilibrium has been reached. The solution of macromolecules will then be centrifuged. This single equilibrium formation does naturally not result in complete desalting: As a rule, however, more than 90% of the low molecular weight components are removed from solutions of high viscosity without dilution.

In connection with the swellable xerogels the basket centrifuge is also of great value for the mild concentration of dilute solutions of macromolecules. One applies the dry gel, allows it to swell, and centrifuges the remaining solution. Only the solvent and small molecules are taken up by the gel particles during the swelling process so that the macromolecules are concentrated in the supernatant.

Equipment

If one wants to remove the solvent from between the gel beads (in all cases studied, aqueous solutions were used) the gel bed in the centrifuge has to be supported by a porous layer which is positioned perpendicularly to the direction of the gravity. The porous layer thus permits the drainage of the water. This condition is fulfilled by the so-called sieve or basket centrifuges which are constructed in principle like a conventional laundry spinner (cf. Fig. 18). The sieve-like rotor of stainless steel is located in a housing with outlet for the centrifuged solvent.

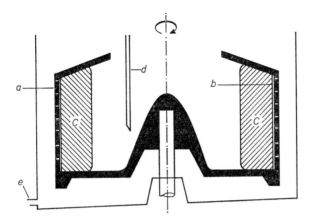

Fig. 18. Schematic drawing of a basket centrifuge: (a) rotor with holes; (b) filter insert; (c) gel bed; (d) inlet tube; (e) outlet.

In order to retain the gel particles in the rotating cage (a) the basket has to be equipped with a suitable filter insert (b) (Fig. 18). Porous polyethylene (VYON, Porous Plastics, Ltd., Dagenham Dock, Essex, England) was found to be applicable to this purpose. Suitable centrifuges are commercially available from a number of manufacturers. Well known are the types MSE Model 300 and Model 3000 for 0.3 l and 3 l of gel bed volume, respectively (Measuring and Scientific Equipment Ltd., London SW 1, England). It is frequently possible to insert sieve drums into standard centrifuges. The sample solution may slowly be sprayed into the rotating cage by an appropriate device (d).

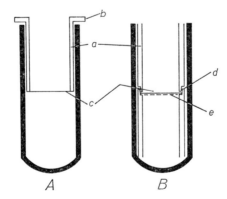

Fig. 19. Adaptation of a conventional centrifuge to a basket centrifuge: (a) perspex tube; (b) holder; (c) nylon screen; (d) connecting point; (e) support.

These centrifuges are very well suited for the handling of large volumes and thus for the concentration and desalting of larger loads. For small quantities any type of laboratory centrifuge is suitable after appropriate adapters have been placed into centrifuge tubes (cf. Fig. 19). It is important to support the gel somewhere in the center of the glass tube in such a way that the solvent may be centrifuged.

For low diameters the insert (8) shown in (A) may be suitable while the tube (B) may sooner be applicable to medium sizes. There the fine perlon screen is supported by a coarser screen of heavier wire. The sieve shown was equipped with Monodur perlon sieve (Vereinigte Seidenwebereien AG, Krefeld, Germany) of a mesh size of 0.06 and 1 mm. The tube itself (B) is manufactured from two pieces of perspex tubing (wall thickness 3 mm) between which the two sieves were held.

Illustrative Experiments

Desalting

An example (a) of technical dimensions (according to information by Pharmacia Fine Chemicals, Uppsala, Sweden) shall be first described, thereafter an example (b) in a laboratory centrifuge (according to own experiments).

(a) An MSE basket centrifuge (Model 3000) is equipped with a 1/32″ VYON filter insert and loaded with 3 l of hydrated Sephadex G-25, fine. Upon centrifuging at 1000 g the gel bed forms a uniform layer in the centrifuge cage (cf. Fig. 18) and the water between the gel beads is displaced. The rotation is now reduced to 60 g and the sample solution applied. The sample solution consisted of 123 g of dextran and 32.5 g of sodium chloride in 500 ml of water and had a relative viscosity of 220 cps. After 10 minutes – during which time this solution had penetrated completely the gel layer – the centrifuge speed was increased again to 1000 g and maintained until no liquid ran out of the centrifuge. A total of 93.5 g (86%) of dextran in 565 ml of solution was recovered. This solution was now contaminated by 100 mg of sodium chloride. At a dilution of only 13% this highly viscous dextran solution has thus been freed from sodium chloride to the extent of 99.9%. The salt may now be washed out of the gel in a continuous fashion at a speed of 60 g. Thereafter the centrifuge is ready for a new experiment. The entire cycle was completed in 3 hours. Sephadex G-25, superfine has been recommended for sample solutions of lower viscosities (1–50 cps). For particularly high viscosities (200–2000 cps) Sephadex G-25, coarse has been recommended for desalting in the centrifuge.

(b) A centrifuge tube (4×11 cm) is equipped with a sieve insert (cf. Fig. 19). The sieve is loaded with approximately 12 ml of hydrated Sephadex G-25, fine. In a laboratory centrifuge (distance between the center of the rotor and the sieve 8.3 cm) the water is removed at approximately 1300 rotations per minute over a period of 20 minutes. The liquid is removed from the centrifuge glass and 3 ml of a 10% soltuion of hemoglobin which contains also 10% of sodium chloride are pipetted on to the gel. This is followed by 20 minutes of centrifugation as described above. During this centrifugation 2.9 ml of a solution of 270 mg of hemoglobin (90% yield) are collected in the glass. The solution contains practically no sodium chloride.

Concentrating

Solutions of macromolecules may be concentrated without change of the pH-value and the ionic strength by the addition of Sephadex G-25, coarse. The swelling Sephadex beads take up only water and the low molecular weight substances (Bio-gel P-2, coarse is also recommended by the manufacturer for this purpose). It is, for instance, possible to concentrate in seawater the complex of vitamin B_{12} and a polysaccharide by the addition of dry Sephadex G-25. The concentration in the supernatant increases up to the point of microbiological sensitivity *(100)*. The supernatant solution has to be separated as quantitatively as possible from the swollen gel in order to recover the concentrated macromolecules with good yields. It is the experience of the author, however, that the macromolecules will be recovered with very poor yields, if one, for instance, centrifuges in a conventional centrifuge tube and decants the supernatant or, if one filters the swollen Sephadex on a Büchner funnel by suction or on a folded filter as is sometimes recommended *(101-103)*.

The centrifuge technique was first described by FLODIN, GELOTTE, and PORATH *(104)* for the concentration of a culture filtrate of *Polyporus versicolor*. The authors succeeded in concentrating 7.5 l (in several portions) by adding Sephadex G-25, coarse (300 g per l culture filtrate) to 410 ml. The cellulase activity increased in the course of the operation from 0.532 units/ml to 8.48 units/ml and the loss of total activity during the entire operation amounted to only 13%. This impressive experiment was subsequently repeated on a larger scale *(105)*, whereby 85 l were concentrated to 315 ml.

It is surprising that this technique has so far been applied relatively seldom, though the experiments described are very promising. Several experiments of concentrating are therefore described in somewhat greater detail in Table 16. These experiments were carried out with the help of the sieve tube and the centrifuge described in the experiment on page 58 (cf. Fig. 19).

Table 16. *Concentrating experiments with Sephadex G-25, coarse*

Starting solution					Resulting solution			
Vol. (ml)	Conc. (mg/ml)	Polymer	Spec. activ. (units)	Dry gel (g)	Vol. (ml)	Conc. (mg/ml)	Yield (%)	Spec. activ. (units)
50	2.0	Dextran	—	10	25.5	3.92	100	—
99	0.5	Hemoglobin	—	25	41.0	1.16	95	—
40	1.16	Hemoglobin	—	10	16.5	2.25	80	—
15.5	2.25	Hemoglobin	—	4	7.0	5.50	86	—
12.5	0.68	Lactate dehydrogenase	20550*	3	6.0	1.30	91	20050*
25	0.205	Pepsin	0.095**	5	14.8	0.28	81	0.095**

* Bücher units   ** Kunitz test

The solution of the polymer is mixed with the quantity of Sephadex G-25, coarse that is given in Table 16 and allowed to stand for 10 minutes. The slurry is then transferred to one (or several) sieve tube(s) and centrifuged at 3000 rotations per minute for 20 minutes. The solution may subsequently be analyzed or used in other ways. The experiments with hemoglobin and lactate dehydrogenase (from pig heart) were carried out in phosphate buffer (pH 7.2, $I = 0.1$) and those with pepsin in acetate buffer (pH 4.0, $I = 0.1$). The pH-value and the ionic strength were found to be unaltered in all cases. In the case of hemoglobin the concentrated solution was twice applied and thus an elevenfold concentration with a total yield of 65% accomplished.

References

1. KUNIN, R., E. MEITZNER, and N. BORTNICK: J. Amer. chem. Soc. **84**, 305 (1962).
2. —, —, J. A. OLINE, S. A. FISHER, and N. FRISCH: I & EC Prod. Res. Develop. **1**, 140 (1962).
3. LLOYD, W. G., and T. ALFREY, jr.: J. polym. Sci. **62**, 301 (1962).
4. MILLAR, J. R., D. G. SMITH, W. E. MARR, and T. R. E. KRESSMAN: J. chem. Soc. **1963**, 218; **1963**, 2779; **1964**, 2740; **1965**, 304.
5. DUŠEK, K.: Polymer Letters **3**, 209 (1965).
6. OGSTON, A. G.: British Medical Bulletin **22**, 105 (1966).
7. PEPPER, K.W., D. REICHENBERG, and D. K. HALE: J. Chem. Soc. **1952**, 3129.
8. FLODIN, P.: Dissertation, Uppsala 1962.
9. GRANATH, K., in A. T. JAMES, and L. J. MORRIS (Ed.): New Biochemical Separations, 111. London 1964.
10. GABERT, A., H. SEIDE und G. LANGHAMMER: IUPAC Symposion on Macromolecular Chemistry, Preprint 475. Prag 1965.
11. LEA, D. J., and A. H. SEHON: Canad. J. Chem. **40**, 159 (1962).
12. HJERTÉN, S., and R. MOSBACH: Anal. Biochem. **3**, 109 (1962).
13. CURTAIN, C. C., and W. G. NAYLER: Biochem. J. **89**, 69 (1963).
14. HJERTÉN, S.: Arch. Biochem. Biophys., Suppl. **1**, 147 (1962).
15. SUN, K., and A. H. SEHON: Canad. J. Chem. **43**, 969 (1965).
16. FAWCETT, J. S., and C. J. O. R. MORRIS, Separation Science **1**, 9 (1966).
17. ARAKI, C.: Bull. Chem. Soc. Japan **29**, 543 (1956).
18. HJERTÉN, S.: Arch. Biochem. Biophys. **99**, 466 (1962).
19. — Biochim. biophys. Acta **62**, 445 (1962).
20. RUSSELL, B., T. H. MEAD, and A. POLSON: ibid. **86**, 169 (1964).
21. HJERTÉN, S.: ibid. **79**, 393 (1964).
22. BENGTSSON, S., and L. PHILIPSON: ibid. **79**, 399 (1964).
23. DETERMANN, H.: Angew. Chem. **76**, 635 (1964); Internat. Ed. **3**, 608 (1964).
24. NYSTRÖM, E., and J. SJÖVALL: J. Chromatog. **17**, 574 (1965); Anal. Biochem. **12**, 235 (1965).
25. Brochure Sephadex LH-20 for gel filtration in organic solvents, Uppsala: Pharmacia 1965.
26. HEITZ, W., H. ULLNER und H. HÖCKER: Makromol. Chem. **98**, 42 (1966).
27. DETERMANN, H., G. LÜBEN und TH. WIELAND: Makromol. Chem. **73**, 168 (1964).
28. HEUFER, G., and D. BRAUN: Polymer Letters **3**, 495 (1965).

29. FRITZSCHE, P., und V. GRÖBE: IUPAC Symposion on Macromolecular Chemistry, Preprint 422. Prag 1965.
30. VAUGHAN, M. F.: Nature **188**, 55 (1960).
31. CORTIS-JONES, B.: Nature **191**, 272 (1961).
32. TIPTON, C. L., J.W. PAULIS, and M. D. PIERSON: J. Chromatog. **14**, 486 (1964).
33. MOORE, J. C.: J. Polymer. Sci., Part A **2**, 835 (1964).
34. ALTGELT, K. H.: Makromol. Chem. **88.**, 75 (1965).
35. PEDERSEN, K. O.: Arch. Biochem. Biophys., Suppl. **1**, 157 (1962).
36. VAUGHAN, M. F.: Nature **195**, 801 (1962).
37. KOHLSCHÜTTER, H.W., K. UNGER und K. VOGEL, Makromol. Chem., **93**, 1 (1966).
38. le PAGE, M., and A. J. DE VRIES: Third Intern. Seminar on Gel Permeation Chromatog., Genf 1966.
39. HALLER, W.: Nature **206**, 693 (1965).
40. MOORE, J. C.: Third Intern. Seminar on Gel Permeation Chromatog., Genf 1966.
41. KONIGSBERG, W., K. WEBER, G. NOTANI, and N. ZINDER: J. biol. Chem. **241**, 2579 (1966).
42. LINDBERG, J. J., K. PENTTINEN, and C. MAJANI: Suomen Kuuistilekti Sect. B **38**, 95 (1965).
43. GELOTTE, B., and J. PORATH: Gel Filtration in HEFTMANN (Ed.), Chromatography, New York 1966
44. PORATH, J., and H. BENNICH: Arch. Biochem. Biophys., Suppl. **1**, 152 (1962).
45. a) ROUBAL, W.T., and A. L. TAPPEL: Analyt. Biochem. **9**, 211 (1964); b) ROTHSTEIN, F.: J. Chromatog. **18**, 36 (1965).
46. RODRIGUEZ, F., R. A. KULAKOWSKI, and O. K. CLARK: I & EC Prod. Res. Develop. **5**, 121 (1966).
47. JACKSON, A.: J. chem. Educ. **42**, 447 (1965).
48. NAONO, T., und K. PRCHAL: Ber. d. Bunsenges. Phys. Chem. **69**, 900 (1965).
49. Brochure: Universal Type Automatic Recording Liquid Chromatograph, Japan Electron Optics Laboratory Co., Ltd.
50. HAAHTI, E., and T. NIKKARI: Acta chem. Scand. **17**, 2565 (1963).
51. JAMES, A.T., J. R. RAVENHILL, and R.P.W. SCOTT: Chem. Ind. **1964**, 746.
52. STOUFFER, J. E., T. E. KERSTEN, and P. M. KRÜGER: Biochim. biophys. Acta, **93**, 191 (1964).
53. JAMES, A. T., R. P. W. SCOTT, and J. R. RAVENHILL: J. Assoc. Offic. Agr. Chem. **48**, 78 (1965).
54. HAAHTI, E., T. NIKKARI, and J. KÄRKKÄINEN: J. Gas. Chromatog. **4**, 12 (1966).
55. MALEY, L. E.: J. Polymer. Sci. Part C **8**, 253 (1965).
56. FLODIN, P.: J. Chromatog. **5**, 103 (1961).
57. WIDÉN, R., and K. E. ERIKSSON: ibid. **15**, 429 (1964).
58. CURTAIN, C. C., and W. G. NAYLER: Biochem. J. **89**, 69 (1963).
59. HICKS, G. P., and S. J. UPDIKE: Anal. Biochem. **10**, 290 (1965).
60. PATRICK, R. L., and R. E. THIERS: Clin. Chem. **9**, 283 (1963).
61. JOUSTRA, M. K.: Protides of the Biological Fluids **14**, 533 (1967).
62. CRAVEN, G. R., E. STEERS, jr., and C. B. ANFINSEN: J. biol. Chem. **240**, 2468 (1965).
63. CRAIG, L. C., W. HAUSMANN, E. H. AHRENS, jr., and E. J. HARFENIST: Analyt. Chem. **23**, 1326 (1951).
64. GRÄSBECK, R., and R. KARLSSON: Acta chem. scand. **16**, 782 (1962).
65. TAPPAN, D. V.: Anal. Biochem. **14**, 171 (1966).
66. WILDING, P.: Clin. Chim. Acta **8**, 918 (1963).
67. FOUGEREAU, M., and G. M. EDELMAN: Biochemistry **3**, 1120 (1964).
68. WIRTH, K., U. ULLMANN, K. BRAND, K. HUTH und B. HESS: Klin. Wochenschr. **43**, 528 (1965).

69. Kusch, P., und H. Zahn: Angew. Chem. **77**, 720 (1965).
70. Plummer, T. H., jr., and C. H. W. Hirs: J. Biol. Chem. **239**, 2530 (1964).
71. King, T. P., and P. S. Norman: Biochemistry **1**, 709 (1962).
72. Whitaker, J. R.: Anal. Chem. **35**, 1950 (1963).
73. Sorof, S., E. M. Young, R. A. McBride, and C. B. Coffey: Arch. Biochem. Biophys. **113**, 83 (1966).
74. Hasegawa, K., T. Kusano, and H. Mitsuda: Agr. Biol. Chem. **27**, 878 (1963).
75. Delikas, N., and M. Staehelin: Biochim. biophys. Acta **119**, 385 (1966).
76. François, C., and M. J. Glimcher: Biochim. biophys. Acta **97**, 366 (1965).
77. Killander, J.: Biochim. biophys. Acta **93**, 1 (1964).
78. —, S. Bengtsson, and L. Philipson: Proc. Soc. exp. Biol. Med. **115**, 861 (1964).
79. Porath, J., and N. Ui: Biochim. biophys. Acta **90**, 324 (1964).
80. Kickhöfen, B., R. Warth und D. Scheel: Science Tools **12**, 1 (1965).
81. Chersi, A.: Science Tools **11**, 1 (1964).
82. Polson, A., and B.W. Russell: Biochim. biophys. Acta **117**, 477 (1966).
83. Porath, J., and H. Bennich: Metabolism, **13**, 1004 (1964).
84. Stahl, E.: (Hrsg.): Thinlayer Chromatography, Heidelberg 1965.
85. Randerath, K.: Thinlayer Chromatography, Weinheim 1965.
86. Determann, H.: Experientia **18**, 430 (1962).
87. Johansson, B. G., and L. Rymo: Acta chem. scand. **16**, 2067 (1962).
88. —, —, Acta chem. scand. **18**, 217 (1964).
89. Andrews, P.: Biochem. J. **91**, 222 (1964).
90. Morris, C. J. O. R.: J. Chromatog. **16**, 167 (1964).
91. Determann, H., und W. Michel: Z. Anal. Chem. **212**, 211 (1965).
92. Hanson, L. Å., B. G. Johansson, and L. Rymo: Clin. chim. Acta **14**, 391 (1966).
93. Roberts, G. P.: J. Chromatog. **22**, 90 (1966).
94. Stickland, R. G.: Anal. Biochem. **10**, 108 (1965).
95. Hanson, L. Å., B. G. Johansson, and L. Rymo: Protides Biol. Fluids **14**, 579 (1967).
96. Grant, G. H., and P. H. Everall: J. clin. Path. **18**, 654 (1965).
97. Agostini, A., C. Vergani, and E. Cirla: Protides Biol. Fluids **14**, 625 (1967).
98. Carnegie, P. R., and G. Pacheco: Proc. Soc. exp. Biol. Med. **117**, 137 (1964).
99. Gelotte, B., und A. Emnéus: Chem. Ing. Techn. **38**, 445 (1966).
100. Daisley, K.W.: Nature **191**, 868 (1961).
101. Wagner, M.: Zbl. Bakt. **185**, 124 (1962).
102. Deutsch, B., R. D. Levere, and J. Levine: J. clin. Path. **16**, 183 (1963).
103. Painter, R. H., and A. G. McVicar: Canad. J. Biochem. Physiol. **41**, 2269 (1963).
104. Flodin, P., B. Gelotte, and J. Porath: Nature **188**, 493 (1960).
105. Petterson, G., E. B. Cowling, and J. Porath: Biochim. biophys. Acta **67**, 1 (1963).

Chapter 3

Theory

The experiment of Chapter 1 (page 6, cf. also Fig. 3) and a large number of experimental data which will be discussed in the following chapters demonstrate that solutes leave the bed of a granulated gel in the order of decreasing molecular weight as long as they have been applied jointly as a zone and have been washed through the column by the eluent. What happens in the gel bed is more easily understood if one assumes the following for diffusion equilibrium: The solvent in the swollen gel particles is not equally well accessible for molecules of different size (cf. Fig. 1). Only the solvent *between* the gel particles is flowing, and only its solutes will be advanced more rapidly than the smaller molecules which are in diffusion equilibrium with the resting gel phase (cf. Fig. 2).

This model had already been presented in Chapter 1 and is sufficient for the interpretation of most separations. For all practical purposes the conclusion may be drawn that during chromatography on porous gels *large molecules* will normally be eluted *sooner than small molecules*. Thus, gel chromatography is a process in which (largely independent of the charged state and solubility) separation takes place on the ground of differences in molecular weight. By contrast to all other chromatographic techniques, the elution behavior is also independent of other substances on the column.

It will undoubtedly be advantageous to know as much as possible about the events in the gel bed in order to be able to interpret difficult separation problems. The understanding of the peculiarities of this chromatographic process facilitates the choice of experimental conditions. The potential and the limits of gel chromatography will be recognized more readily. In this connection it is important to consider the different *volumes of a gel bed* which in turn makes possible the *numerical interpretation* of the *results* of gel chromatography. Data obtained in different laboratories may then be compared. This book is intended for the laboratory and in this respect the consideration of models on the *mechanism of separation* is only of secondary interest. These aspects will therefore be discussed only briefly. The consequences for practical applications will be stressed. The knowledge about the *interaction of solutes and gel phases* frequently helps to overcome difficulties in gel chromatography and – sometimes – results in unexpected separations.

Numerical Evaluation of Experimental Data

Volumes in the Gel Bed

The particles of a gel are suspended in a solvent, filled into a vertically mounted glass tube and allowed to settle. That portion of the tube which is filled by the gel (gel bed) consists of two phases: solvent within the gel particles and outer free solvent between the particles. Three components contribute to the total volume of the gel bed (V_t = total volume): the volume between the gel grains (V_o = outer volume), the solvent volume inside the gel particles (V_i), and the volume of the gel matrix (V_m) (1).

$$V_t = V_o + V_i + V_m \qquad \text{(Eq. 1)}$$

The *total volume* of the gel bed (V_t) can easily be determined by measuring the volume of the column from the support of the gel bed to the upper end. The *outer volume* may be established by chromatographing on the gel packing a high molecular weight substance which cannot enter the gel grains. The solvent volume which leaves the column between the start and the appearance of this substance in the effluent corresponds exactly to the liquid volume between the gel particles. A high molecular weight colored polysaccharide (Blue Dextran, Pharmacia, Uppsala) is suitable for the characterization of aqueous gels. Other soluble substances the molecular weights of which are known to be above the *exclusion limit* (M_{lim}) are also applicable to this purpose. This limit is found in the molecular weight of that substance which during the chromatography of homologous polymers is not at all penetrating the gel phase. Like all substances of higher molecular weight it has the elution volume corresponding to the outer volume (V_o). The exclusion limit for commercial gels may be determined approximately from the separation ranges which are tabulated in the second chapter.

It is more difficult to determine the other two volumes (V_i and V_m). The *inner volume* (V_i) is naturally related to the porosity of the gel. Porous gels and those gels which swell very strongly hold relatively large volumes of solvent and consist of very little matrix. The particles of gels which do not swell very strongly consist of more solid material and retain smaller volumes of liquid. The inner volume (V_i) of *xerogels* may be calculated relatively easily, once the solvent regain (S_r) is known. The solvent regain (S_r) has been defined on page 15. The weight of dry gel has to be multiplied with S_r and to be divided by the density (ϱ) of the solvent.

$$V_i = \frac{a \cdot S_r}{\varrho} \qquad \text{(Eq. 2)}$$

The weight of the dry gel is frequently not known. The inner volume V_i may then be calculated with the help of eq. 1 by substituting the volume of the gel matrix V_m by the density in the swollen state (d):

$$V_i = \frac{S_r \cdot d}{\varrho\,(S_r/\varrho + 1)}\,(V_t - V_o) \qquad\qquad \text{(Eq. 3)}$$

The density in the wet state (d) is easily determined in the pycnometer and (like S_r) represents a constant for each gel in a given solvent. The partial specific volume of the polymer which forms the gel has to be known for the exact calculation of the matrix volume (V_m).

In the case of *Sephadex gels*, the partial specific volume of dissolved dextran molecules (2) may be used for this value. GRANATH (3) has determined the partial specific volume of dextran molecules to be 0.61. – The density in the swollen state (d) is also known for each type. In Table 17 the numerical values and the approximate values for the volume are compiled for 1 g of dry gel. The inner volume increases rather slowly with increasing porosity since the more strongly swollen particles can no longer be packed so densely. As a result of that the outer volume (V_o) is also increased. The remaining matrix volume (V_m) may be neglected for the strongly swollen types.

Table 17. *Approximate volumes of 1 g of Sephadex after swelling in water**

Gel type	Gel bed volume** (V_t, ml)	Outer volume (V_o, ml)	Inner volume (V_i, ml)	Density (swollen) (d, g/ml)
G-10	2	0.8	1	1.24
G-15	3	1.1	1.5	1.19
G-25	5	2	2.5	1.13
G-50	10	4	5	1.07
G-75	13	5	7	1.05
G-100	17	6	10	1.04
G-150	24	8	15	1.03
G-200	30	9	20	1.02

 * According to statements by the manufacturer, Pharmacia, Uppsala, Sweden.

** With regard to the variation, cf. Table 5; correspondingly, the values for the other volumes are also subject to more or less pronounced variations.

It is more difficult to determine the volumes of gels the porosity of which is not brought about by swelling (aerogels and other structures such as the polystyrene gels of MOORE, cf. page 23). Only the sum of inner volume and matrix volume ($V_i + V_m$) may be obtained with some certainty with the help of equation 1. There are great differences in density within individual gel grains and it is difficult to distinguish between V_i and V_m.

Elution Parameters

In our experiment of Chapter 1 we had used 17 g of dry Sephadex G-25 to obtain a gel volume (V_t) of 87 ml. We had applied to the gel packing a mixture of starch and glucose in 2 ml of solution and eluted with a salt solution. We had placed a graduate under the column to collect the effluent. The presence of starch and glucose in the effluent of the gel had been determined by suitable analytical tests. The presence of starch could be seen from 32 to 44 ml and that of glucose from 66 to 80 ml. In both cases the zones had been broadened considerably during chromatography. The concentration in the starch zone initially increased strongly before it gradually decreased again. Based on experience, an unsymmetrical distribution has to be assumed for the excluded substance (starch), while for glucose a reasonably symmetrical distribution may be expected (cf. Fig. 22), i.e. we may subsequently draw the elution pattern that is represented by Fig. 20. For this purpose we plot on the ordinate the concentration and on the abscissa the volume of the effluent. The effluent as measured from the application of the substance to the elution of the component in maximum concentration is known as *elution volume* (V_e).

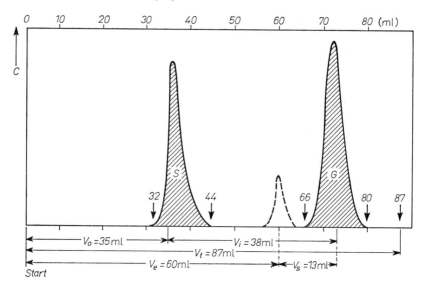

Fig. 20. Construction of an elution pattern from the analytical data of the experiment on page 15; separation of starch (S) and glucose (G) on 87 ml of Sephadex G-25. Between the peaks corresponding to glucose and starch the elution peak of an additional (fictive) substance has been plotted. This substance is only capable of partial penetration of the gel particles. Ordinate: concentration (arbitrary). Abscissa: elution volume in ml. V_o = outer volume; V_i = inner volume; V_t = total volume; V_e = elution volume; V_s = separation volume.

On a given gel bed the same substance will always be eluted at the same elution volume. In our example (Fig. 20) we find for starch $V_e = 35$ ml and for glucose $V_e = 73$ ml. The starch molecules are not capable of penetrating the gel grains, i.e. they ought to be eluted in the outer volume ($V_e = V_o$). One may expect that glucose is capable of entering into all regions of the gel phase and as a result of that the sum of outer and inner volume ($V_e = V_o + V_i$) is required for its elution.

The comparison of the data of Figure 20 with the values calculated for Sephadex G-25 from Table 17 showed the following: The theoretical value of $17 \times 5 = 85$ ml had been calculated for V_t. The experimental value is 87 ml. The volume of 35 ml for $V_o = V_e$ (starch) is in good agreement with the expected value of $17 \times 2 = 34$ ml. Only the theoretical value of 42.5 ml for V_i is significantly higher than the experimental value of 38 ml. It has been observed frequently that low molecular weight substances may also be eluted somewhat earlier (cf. 4). The following explanation has been offered repeatedly. A portion of the solvent that has been taken up during the swelling process is required for solvation of the polymer chains which form the gel. This volume is thus not available for diffusion of the solute molecules. It is of particular importance and interest to observe the behavior of substances which are neither completely excluded nor able to diffuse freely. Only a fraction (K_d) of the inner volume is available to them for diffusion. For these molecules the elution volume has to be calculated from eq. 4 (5).

$$V_e = V_o + K_d \cdot V_i \qquad \text{(Eq. 4)}$$

It is, however, the elution volume that is normally measured, and the so-called K_d-*value* may be *calculated* if V_o and V_i are known (cf. Table 18). The K_d-value is a constant for a given gel and thus independent of the column applied. Its value is only determined by the molecular dimensions of the substance under study. Despite the fact that the K_d-value was associated from the beginning with "gel filtration on Sephadex" (cf. 1), it has never been accepted in general to describe experimental results. This is due to the uncertainties in the determination of V_i with which we have become familiar already in our initial experiment.

We shall use the "theoretical" value (Table 17) for V_i (42.5 ml) to calculate the K_d-values. By definition, we obtain $K_d = 0$ for starch and $K_d = 0.89$ for glucose. A K_d-value of 0.59 was calculated for the substance of medium molecular weight ($V_e = 60$ ml) which had been accommodated arbitrarily in Fig. 20. Using the "experimentally determined" inner volume ($V_e$glucose $- V_o$), a K_d-value of 0.63 will be found. In view of these difficulties other parameters have been explored for a better description of the elution behavior of substances to which only a portion of the gel phase is accessible (cf. Table 18).

LAURENT and KILLANDER (2) have defined a constant K_{av} (av = available) which appears to be most generally applicable to this purpose. This constant differs from the K_d-value in the following way: The total volume of the gel phase ($V_g = V_t - V_o = V_i + V_m$) instead of the inner volume (V_i) is applied to its calculation. Here all variables are easily measured (cf. above). The difference between K_d and K_{av} is the smaller, the more porous (the more strongly swollen) the gel under consideration is. The difference is naturally considerable for gels of high polymer concentration. In our experiment we calculate for glucose a value for $K_{av} = 38/(87 - 35) = 0.73$ (as opposed to $K_d = 0.89$) and for the (fictive) substance of medium molecular weight we calculate a value for $K_{av} = (60 - 35)/(87 - 35) = 0.48$ (as opposed to $K_d = 0.63$ and 0.59, respectively). It is undoubtedly possible to employ any one of the parameters of Table 18 for the comparison of experimental data as long as certain standard conditions are observed; advantages and disadvantages are compared in Table 18.

Table 18. *Parameters for the description of the elution behavior in gel chromatography*

Parameter	Calculation	Remarks	Authors
V_e	direct measurement	only the results obtained on the same gel bed can be compared	—
$\dfrac{V_e}{V_t}$	division of the elution volume (V_e) by the total volume of the gel bed (V_t).	independent of the geometry of the column; sensitive to differences in packing density; greatest accuracy for small V_e (large molecules)	GRANATH, FLODIN (6)
$\dfrac{V_e}{V_o}$	division of the elution volume (V_e) by the elution volume of an excluded substance (V_o).		WHITAKER (7)
K_d	$K_d = (V_e - V_o)/V_i$ V_i (volume inside of the gel grains); dependent on the amount of dry gel and its solvent regain upon swelling (S_r).	independent of the geometry and packing density of the column; uncertainty in the determination of V_i; greatest accuracy for large V_e (small molecules).	WHEATON, BAUMANN (5)
K_{av}	$K_{av} = \dfrac{V_e - V_o}{V_t - V_o}$	independent of the geometry and packing density of the column; all colums are easily measured; greatest accuracy for large V_e (small molecules).	LAURENT, KILLANDER (2)

The parameters defined in Table 18 may be employed to decide whether it is possible to separate two substances on a given gel bed. The so-called separation volume (V_s) may be calculated from the K_{av}-values if V_t and V_o of a gel packing are known. The separation volume (V_s) is defined as the solvent volume by which the maxima of two substances (with the K_{av}-values K_{av}' and K_{av}'') are separated in the course of the elution.

$$V_s = V_e' - V_e'' = (K_{av}' - K_{av}'') \, (V_t - V_o) \qquad \text{(Eq. 5)}$$

In our example (Fig. 20) the imaginary substance ($V_e = 60$ ml) was separated from glucose ($V_e = 73$ ml) by a $V_s = 13$ ml. Since the bands are broadened the separation volume (V_s) must be at least 10 ml in order to accomplish an almost complete separation in our example. According to Eq. 5, however, V_s is directly proportional to V_t and one may therefore (for a constant difference of the K_{av}-values) obtain a larger separation volume on a larger gel bed.

Effectivity of a Gel Column

The exact analysis of Figure 20 demonstrates the limits of gel chromatography: only a rather small portion ($V_t - V_o$) of the volume of a gel bed is actually available for separation. Without interactions of the solutes with the gel phase, which delay the substances to be separated, they are all eluted after a quantity of eluent corresponding to the total volume has percolated the gel bed and not later. This is significantly different from other chromatographic processes in which the substances to be separated are retarded "reversibly" (cf. the previous section). The volume which is available for resolution and thus the separation volume is always only a fraction of the gel bed volume. It is therefore natural that rather large gel beds (cf. Table 14) are desirable for the resolution of the relatively small differences in molecular size. This, however, poses the danger of considerable dilution of the components during separation. The practical consequences which result from this particular feature of gel chromatographic separation are discussed in the second chapter.

The operation of very long gel columns is technically difficult on the one hand. On the other hand the *broadening of peaks* is frequently the limiting factor for the effectivity during gel chromatography of substances with small molecular weight differences. The broadening will be the larger, the more the equilibrium is removed from ideality. The calculation of the *equivalent height of one theoretical plate* (EHTP) of a chromatography column is an exact measure for this phenomenon. According to WICKE (8) it is better to discuss "dilution steps" instead of "theoretical plates" in chromatographic separation processes. Thus, taking into consideration the fact that separation here is normally brought about by selective dilution, the chromatographic process cannot be compared with distillation, because in the latter the "stationary phase" is also, so to say, flowing. Therefore, the separation power of each "plate" is so much smaller, that in effect only 30 to 40 chromatographic plates are corresponding to one plate in distillation.

Despite these restrictions, it is possible to get an impression of the efficiency of a gel column by calculating its EHTP. The method of GLUECK-

AUF (*9*) is usually applied to this purpose. This method has been modified slightly and been adapted to the requirements of gas chromatography (cf. *10*); a molecularly uniform substance is allowed to chromatograph on a gel column under well defined conditions. One obtains as elution diagram (Fig. 21) for instance a Gaussian distribution curve.

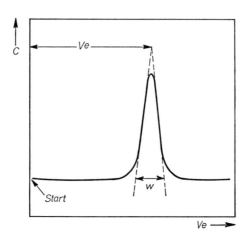

Fig. 21. Approach to the calculation of the height equivalent of one theoretical plate (EHTP) from an elution diagram of an uniform substance V_e = elution volume; w = width of the elution peak.

The tangents are applied as shown in Fig. 21 and the width of the peaks (w) and the elution volume (V_e) are thus determined, for instance, in ml. The number of plates may then be calculated from:

$$N = \left(\frac{4 \cdot V_e}{w}\right)^2 \qquad \text{(Eq. 6)}$$

By dividing the length of the gel bed into the number of plates one obtains the length of the column that corresponds to one plate (EHTP). The smaller the base of the elution curve is, the smaller will be the value for EHTP, i.e. the greater will be the effectivity of the gel bed.

Which factors, then, have an influence on EHTP? Broadening of the bands is brought about, among other things, by an incompletely established diffusion equilibrium. The diffusion equilibrium is reached more easily for small gel particles and for low flow rates in the gel packing. Several determinations of EHTP from the literature are compiled in Table 19. It can be seen that – under otherwise comparable conditions – the EHTP-value is different for each substance and that it is influenced differently by changes in the variables. The rate of diffusion for larger molecules (e.g. cytidylic acid) is smaller than that for small molecules (e.g. hydrochloric

acid). Therefore, the EHTP-values of the nucleotide are considerably higher
at high flow rates, while the value for hydrochloric acid is barely influenced.
Evidently small molecules are capable of establishing perfect diffusion
equilibria even at the highest possible flow rate. The longitudinal diffusion
is also greater, which means an increase in the EHTP-value will also be

Table 19. *EHTP-values in gel chromatography*

Gel (solvent)	Grain size (mesh, US)	Column dimensions (cm)	Flow rate (ml/h.)	Test substance	EHTP (mm)	Ref.
Sephadex G-25 (water)	50—80 (140—200)*	2×65	10	Uridylic acid	0.39 (0.102)*	(1)
			24		0.72 (0.182)*	
			51		1.49 (0.21) *	
			90		2.62	
			130		4.14	
			190		5.49	
Sephadex G-25 (water)	50—80 (270—400)*	2×67	14	Hydrochloric acid	1.05 (0.23) *	(1)
			24		0.69 (0.26) *	
			48		0.44	
			70		0.45	
			96		0.51	
Sephadex G-200 (water)	100—200	4×42	50	Serum-albumin	4.80	(11)
			25		0.80	
Styragel 40-Å and 20-Å (tetrahydrofuran)	200—270	0.775×360	4.5	Benzene (p-dibromo-benzene)*	0.168 (0.260)*	(12)
			17		0.268 (0.409)*	
			23		0.360 (0.460)*	
			45		0.505 (0.610)*	
			97		0.838 (0.960)*	

* The values in parantheses belong together in the horizontal groups.

reached for extremely low flow rates in the case of small molecules. Two
essential factors which have an effect on EHTP and thus the separation
power of a gel bed have been named: The rate of establishing diffusion
equilibrium and the longitudinal diffusion. It appears thus as if a change
in the grain size of a gel would have the greatest influence on the base width
(*w*) of the elution curve. A third factor has to be added: The EHTP increases
quite considerably in columns which are not packed uniformly. Likewise,
it is affected by technical mistakes in the experimental design. Each dead
volume in the column and in the detector system contributes to this increase.

Finally it must be said that it is entirely possible to determine the
effectivity of different gel columns by comparing the theoretical plate
height (EHTP) for one and the same test substance. For a given separation
problem (difference in K_{av}-values known) one may calculate the required
dimensions of a gel packing according to FLODIN (13), if one knows the
EHTP. LAURENT and LAURENT (14) have constructed an electrical model

(analog-computer) for gel chromatography with the help of which one can simulate the elution curve if the K_{av}-value and the time required for establishing equilibrium between the stationary and the moving phase are known. One can thus study the effect of the change in flow rate on the shape (width) of the elution curve. Recently a theory on the broadening of zones during gel chromatography was derived from a generally valid equation for the plate height (61).

Approaches of Interpretation

Gel chromatography was developed out of a few accidental observations into a widely used separation technique and was initially without any theoretical foundation. In order to understand better the series of events which take place during chromatography, as they have been outlined earlier, one can (and one must) rely on the results of literally hundreds of *experiments* which are described in detail in the literature:

FLODIN (1, 13) has already clearly distinguished in his systematic study of gel filtration between the essential factors: The *elution volume* of a substance is determined by its molecular size. It is largely *independent* of the *flow rate* and of the *concentration* of the sample. (The sharpness of the separation suffers only when the viscosity is strongly increased relative to the eluent (1)). No doubt has ever been cast on these two facts. A (minor) concentration dependence of the elution volume was only observed during frontal analysis of proteins on Sephadex G-100 (15). The independence of the elution from the flow rate in the column is of decisive importance for the discussion of the separation mechanism (cf. below). These findings have therefore been checked frequently. Only few authors were able to observe (really minor) reproducible differences (e. g. 12).

Recently experiments were conducted to study the effect of temperature on the elution volume. For the chromatography of proteins on xerogels not only the effect of the increased temperature on the space filling properties of a protein molecule (cf. 16) but also the influence on the degree of swelling of the gel has to be taken into consideration (17). The calibration curve for the elution behavior of polystyrenes on Styragels (18), which is shown in Fig. 35, contains values which were determined at three different temperatures. These values demonstrate convincingly that the elution volume is *independent of temperature*. Evidently it is only influenced by the size of the molecule. It will be explained in detail in Chapter 4 (cf. Table 26) how the elution volume is influenced by the molecular weight. Without going into details, it may, however, be stated that the elution volume is directly proportional to the *logarithm of the molecular weight*.

Each theory on the behavior of molecules of different size on a bed of granulated gel has to take these results into consideration. The nonstatistical evaluation of results is frequently not sufficiently accurate. This has to be borne in mind during the experimental examination of any new theory by testing the elution behavior in dependence on the different molecular properties of the test substances. In the following several of the approaches will be introduced briefly and discussed in the light of available experimental data.

The Exclusion Principle

The discussion of the volume ratios in a gel bed was based on the assumption that a swollen gel contains regions which the molecules of a solute cannot enter unless they are below a certain size. There is, thus, for each molecular size a volume which is accessible by diffusion. FLODIN (13) gave the following explanation. There are regions near the point of cross-linking in a swollen xerogel in which the concentration of the gel-forming polymer is so great that large molecules can no longer diffuse into these regions. The area and the number of these regions is determined by the degree of cross-linking (the swelling properties) of the gel on the one hand, and by the size of the molecule under study on the other hand. For aerogels, or at least for similarly rigid materials (e.g. Styragels), the area of unaccessible regions is determined by the particular structure of the polymer. In this case one may truly speak of "pores", which in the case of xerogels is only permissible in an oversimplification.

It is a prerequisite for reproducible chromatographic separations on gels that the molecules to be separated have enough time during elution to diffuse into the regions accessible to them. This is indeed the case for the commonly used particle sizes of today's gels (cf. Chapter 2) and also applicable to macromolecules. Calculations by FLODIN (13) and subsequently by ALTGELT and MOORE (19) have demonstrated that the diffusion is fast enough to penetrate the interior of a gel grain. Experimental support was furnished by the fact that the elution volume is independent of the (technically) realizable flow rate in the column.

Simple Geometric Models

The volume in a gel which is accessible by diffusion for the molecules of the solute may be considered to be a cone. If one assumes spherical molecules, it is clear that the spheres are capable of penetrating the cone the more deeply, the smaller their radius (r) is against the radius of the cone (R). PORATH (20) has first developed this model and concluded that the volume accessible to a given molecule may also be considered to be a cone. PORATH compared the volume of this cone (corresponds to $K_d \cdot V_i$, cf. Eq. 4) with that of the total cone (corresponds to V_i) and obtained an expression for the accessible fraction of the inner volume (K_a). Except for a proportionality constant (k) we find only the two radii in this formula:

$$K_a = k \left(1 - \frac{2r}{R}\right)^3 \qquad\qquad \text{(Eq. 7)}$$

The volume of the large cone is proportional to the swelling ($R^3 = k \cdot S_r$); for flexible macromolecules with even segments the following holds according to (21) $M = k \cdot r^2$. Equation 7 then becomes

$$K_a = k_1 \left(1 - k_2 \frac{M^{1/2}}{S_r^{1/3}}\right)^3 \qquad\qquad \text{(Eq. 8)}$$

Equation 8 is valid for a given gel in the simplified form: $K_a^{1/3} =$ const. — const. $\cdot M^{1/2}$. Porath (20) has checked the validity of the expression with the help of literature values for K_a and molecular weights of dextran fractions. The cubic root of the K_a-values was directly proportional to the square root of the molecular weight. This relation has been repeatedly applied to the determination of molecular weights (cf. Chapter 4). Squire (22) made similar assumptions and considered the inner volume to be composed of cones (radius R), cylinders (radius R), and cracks (width 2 R). On the basis of this assumption the following expression was obtained for the quotient of elution volume and outer volume (cf. Table 18),

$$\frac{V_e}{V_o} = \left[1 + g\left(1 - \frac{r}{R}\right)\right]^3 , \qquad\qquad \text{(Eq. 9)}$$

in which g is a constant which represents the geometric relations of the accessible volume. The similarly to equation 7 is evident; Squire applied equation 9 to globular proteins assuming that r^3 is proportional to M. R may also be expressed by the molecular weight (M_{lim}) of the smallest molecule that is no longer capable of penetrating the accessible volume (e. g. that of the cone).

$$\frac{V_e}{V_o} = \left[1 + g\left(1 - k \frac{M^{1/3}}{M_{lim}^{1/3}}\right)\right]^3 \qquad\qquad \text{(Eq. 10)}$$

Since, however, M_{lim} is a constant for a given gel, equation 10 may also acquire the simplified form $(V_e/V_o)^{1/3} =$ const. — const. $\cdot M^{1/3}$. The requirement is met by a number of proteins in different Sephadex gels but not by all of them equally well (22).

The two approaches cited make arbitrary assumptions on the shape of the accessible regions in the gel, yet they offer applicable explanations for the relations between elution behavior and molecular weight. In any event, the fact that the equations deduced are supported by the experiment must be considered to be a confirmation of the basic assumption (that a portion of the gel phase is not accessible).

The Ogston-Laurent Gel Model

T. C. LAURENT has advanced a consideration of the exclusion mechanism which is more closely related to the actual structure of a gel. The author compared the swollen gel with the solution of a polymer; an acidic poly-saccharide (hyaluronic acid) had an effect on the sedimentation of macro-molecules which could be explained by the assumption of a three-dimen-sional network of the polymer chains which acted like a sieve for the macro-molecules (*23*). – Upon adding a high molecular weight dextran to the solution of a protein, protein is precipitated as long as the dextran con-centration increases (*24, 25*). The assumption was made that the dextran, as it dissolves, requires part of the water for hydration and the protein is excluded. High molecular proteins are indeed precipitated more readily than low molecular ones (*24*). In another series of experiments LAURENT (*26*) compared the exclusion of proteins (during equilibrium dialysis against a solution of hyaluronic acid) with the behavior during chromatography on a hyaluronic acid gel of equal concentration (*27*). Calculations show that the results were in agreement with the hypothesis that the hyaluronic acid in water (irrespective of being cross-linked or not) represents a continuous network of long linear polysaccharide chains.

According to a model of LAURENT and KILLANDER (*2*), the neutral dextran chains in a Sephadex gel may also be considered to be a three-dimensional network of statistically distributed rigid fibers. The volume accessible for the spherical particles in such a system depends naturally on their radius (r). The accessible volume is determined by the radius (R) and the concentration (L) of the polysaccharide "rods". According to a calcu-lation by OGSTON (*28*) the following expression is valid for the fraction of the accessible volume (cf. Table 18):

$$K_{av} = e^{-\pi L \cdot (r + R)^2}. \tag{Eq. 11}$$

LAURENT and KILLANDER (*2*) have subsequently estimated the radius of a corresponding sphere (r) for a large number of substances (protein and polysaccharides) and calculated the K_{av}-values from their own and other measurements on different Sephadex types. A certain degree of flexibility and branching of the polysaccharide chains was taken into consideration. The radius of the particles was assumed to be 7 Å. With these data, values were determined for L, which corresponded best to the experimental results. The authors found for the Sephadex types G-25 through G-200 "concentrations" of 14×10^{12} to 3×10^{12} (cm/ml). These numerical values for L were again directly proportional to the corresponding gel density. This then demon-strates that the simple model of the gel structure is capable of interpreting very satisfactorily the property under consideration (exclusion of molecules in dependence on their effective radius). – Dextran which has been dissolved in the eluent (29) causes the gel grains to shrink and the effect on the exclusion properties cannot be clearly recognized.

FAWCETT and MORRIS (62) succeeded also in calculating the values of L and R for the extensive series of polyacrylamide gels which they had tested. As expected, L is linearly dependent upon the polymer concentration in the gel in the case of the types of a low degree of cross-linking, while for a high degree of cross-linking in essence only the thickness of the rods increases, when there is more monomer in the reaction mixture. This results in the formation of porous material of the type depicted schematically in Fig. 4b.

PEDERSEN (30), while considering the exclusion principle for gel chromatography, has pointed to the long established fact that, in a narrow capillary, flowing particles are moving faster than the solvent which is also exposed to turbulent flow patterns on the wall. PEDERSEN attempted (cf. page 25) to demonstrate these relations with the help of packings of very fine glass beads. It can be envisioned that, in packings of gel particles, channels or cracks may also exist in which the large molecules (in the middle of the channel) are flowing faster than the smaller ones (cf. 19). The separative effect, however, is certainly minor.

The Principle of Restricted Diffusion

Proteins and viruses of known particle radius were allowed to diffuse through membranes which were made of agar gels of different concentration. The observation was made that the particles were slowed down considerably as compared to free diffusion in solution. The gel phase was considered to consist of cylindrical pores in which free diffusion of the molecules was hindered sterically (depending on the size) and by friction. ACKERS and STEERE (31) applied the equation of RENKIN (32) to calculate the effective pore radius of the gels from diffusion inhibition and from the radius of the particle under consideration. The radii of pores which were calculated with the help of different macromolecules for gels of different density were in good agreement. This simplified model of the gel must therefore be considered to be correct.

ACKERS (33) applied the principle to gel chromatography and proposed for the very porous gels the mechanism of "restricted diffusion". (For Sephadex G-200 – in contrast to the other gel-types – the distribution coefficient between gel and solvent phase as determined in equilibrium experiments deviated considerably from the K_d-value that was determined on the column.) According to the new principle the elution volume of macromolecules (proteins) on packings of granulated agar gels or Sephadex G-200 is determined by their diffusion rate in the gel phase. Due to the lower diffusion into the resting gel phase, larger molecules are eluted from the column earlier than the smaller ones. ACKERS applied again the Renkin-equation (*32*) and has thus linked the elution behavior to the quotient of Stokes' radius of proteins (*r*) and the effective radius (*R*) of the pore:

$$K_d = \left(1 - \frac{r}{R}\right)^2 \left[1 - 2,104 \left(\frac{r}{R}\right) + 2,09 \left(\frac{r}{R}\right)^3 - 0,95 \left(\frac{r}{R}\right)^5\right] \quad \text{(Eq. 12)}$$

The effective pore radius (*R*) was calculated with the help of eq. 12; from known Stokes' radii and the elution data of a number of authors as determined by gel chromatography of proteins. The results were in rather good agreement for various agar gels and for Sephadex G-200, thus supporting the theory.

The fact that the elution volume is not sensitive to differences in flow rates speaks against its dependence on the rate of diffusion. ACKERS himself has pointed out this problem. The author attempted to explain this discrepancy by the assumption of immobile solvent which surrounds the gel grain. The thickness of the solvent layer depends upon the flow rate and exhibits an inverse effect on the elution volume.

SMITH and KOLLMANSBERGER (*12*) have studied the behavior of low molecular weight aliphatic and aromatic hydrocarbons on a Styragel of relatively low porosity at different flow rates. The authors made the observation that variations in the elution volumes (which are primarily dependent upon the molecular volume) are governed by the reciprocal value of the diffusion coefficient. This behavior differs from that observed in other separation processes (gas chromatography or ion exchange chromatography), and makes the mechanism of limited diffusion probable.

Comparison of the Various Interpretations

The only possible control of the more or less arbitrary concepts on the separation mechanism is the comparison of experimental results with the deduced equations. For the exclusion principle one of the two equations

$$K_d^{1/3} = \text{const.} - \text{const.} \cdot r \quad \text{or} \quad (-\log K_{av})^{1/2} = \text{const.} + \text{const.} \cdot r \quad \text{(Eq. 13)}$$

should be valid. The two equations are obtained from equations 7 and 9, respectively, and from equation 12. It should be possible to demonstrate the validity of the diffusion principle in the following way: The same effective pore radius will always be obtained from K_d and r with the help of the complicated function (eq. 12) of ACKERS (*33*) and the numerical values tabulated by him. SIEGEL and MONTY (*34*) have recently demonstrated with own determinations and those of others that all three requirements are fulfilled to the best. ANDERSON and STODDART (*35*) have attempted independently to combine the two principles by altering the deduced equations, but did not go into the details of the opposing concepts of the models. The authors were able to demonstrate linear dependence in a certain range of the logarithm of the quotient r/R of equations 7 and 12 from the K_d-value. It appears, however, questionable, whether in view of the assumption made for the models of PORATH (20) and ACKERS (33) respectively, it is permissible to identify the radius of the cone (R in Eq. 7) with the effective radius of the pore (R in Eq. 12). Following the authors arguments, one finds that the two model concepts have a common expression in the relation:

$$K_a = \text{const.} - \text{const.} \cdot \lg M \qquad \text{(Eq. 14)}$$

This, however, is exactly the correlation which has been found so many times empirically and has been applied frequently (cf. Chapter 4). Equation 14 may indeed be correlated with the exclusion principle as is evident from the fact that the theory requires linear dependence on the density of the gel for the second constant (36) (cf. Chapter 4).

Since most systematic studies with proteins were conducted on Sephadex gels, an investigation of TAKAGI (37) deserves particular interest. The author measured the elution volumes of linear polyethylene fractions in the GPC-Apparatus on Styragel and found that the two relations of eq. 13 are also valid for these statistically coiled polymers. Only a minor correction of the exclusion volume (V_o) was required. The elution volume (V_e) of that polyethylene fraction was chosen as V_o for which the calibration curve (log. chain length versus V_e) showed a bend. The exclusion limit of polymers without tertiary structure is evidently not as well defined as that of proteins.

The Partition Principle

Next to the exclusion and diffusion principle, a third approach to the theoretical treatment of gel chromatography may be advanced. Partition chromatography is the basis of this principle. The entire gel phase (not only the solvent contained in it) is considered as stationary phase. BRÖNSTED (38) has discussed the significance of molecular size for partition in different phase equilibria and found that λ in the Boltzmann equation

$$K_a = \frac{c_1}{c_2} = e^{-\frac{\lambda}{k \cdot T}} \qquad \text{(Eq. 15)}$$

is proportional to the molecular weight. The implication for gel chromatography is that the gel phase has a lower affinity for larger molecules (larger positive λ) than for smaller ones. The question of the type of interaction will not be considered initially.

ANDERSON and STODDART (35) have already pointed out that as a result of that a dependence of the molecular weight on the logarithm of the elution constant would have to be expected from eq. 15 instead of eq. 14. This is evidently not the case for proteins on Sephadex. HOHN and POLLMANN (39) have, however, described earlier the validity of such a relation (cf. Table 26) for oligonucleotides of thymidylic acid on Sephadex G-25. It is also known that these substances interact with the gel phase (cf. the following section). BREWER (40) has recently found in experiments dealing with the chromatography of polyisobutylene fractions ($\bar{M} < 10000$) on ground synthetic rubber in cyclohexane that a linear correlation exists between the molecular weight and the logarithm of the elution volumes. In the unpolar solvent an interaction between the dissolved hydrocarbons and the swollen network is entirely possible, thus bringing about the characteristic feature of genuine partition chromatography. TAKAGI (37) was only able to confirm the relation of BREWER (40) for the very low molecular weight portion of his polyethylene (chromatography in trichlorobenzene on polystyrene at 130°C).

It is probably not a coincident that the gel chromatographic applications of the temperature detector, which was discussed in Chapter 2, dealt exclusively with low molecular weight substances (on Sephadex G-10 in water). Due to the high polymer content of the gel phase an interaction with the small molecules (oligosaccharides and ethylene glycols) is entirely possible, thus producing the temperature effect. *Vice versa*, the validity of the partition principle, as outlined here, would require a temperature dependence of the elution volume, since temperature enters into equation 15. It is, however, well known that changes of the elution volume with temperature have not been observed experimentally (cf. above).

In summary, it can be said that the independence of the elution volume from variations in the flow rate or temperature offers a strong argument in favor of the exclusion mechanism. For normal applications, gel chromatography is thus, also from the point of view of mechanistic interpretation, an entirely new and independent chromatographic procedure. It differs from the various types of adsorption and partition chromatography in that the concentration in the stationary phase is never greater than that in the mobile phase. The stationary phase has the same composition like the mobile phase. The only difference is the immobility of stationary phase (41). This immobility is brought about by the gel structure, which also brings about the differences in accessibility for the molecules of solutes. There are naturally exceptions from this strict formulation and cross relations to other chromatographic techniques. The latter ones are the result of interactions of the solutes with the gel phase. These aspects are to be discussed in the following section.

Affinity of Solutes to the Gel Phase

The acceptance of the exclusion principle as explanation for the separation effect in gel chromatography does not interpret all phenomena. Possible interactions of solutes with the gel phase will still have to be considered.

It has been pointed out already that polymer-rich gel phases differ considerably from the mobile phase. During chromatography on gels of high density, phenomena will frequently be observed which cannot be explained by the exclusion principle. This was already indicated in the previous section, when we became acquainted with several cases in which the logarithm of the distribution coefficient was directly proportional to the molecular weight. We were then dealing with the chromatography of substances of relatively low molecular weight on gels of relatively high density.

Earlier we had developed the "partition principle" in order to be able to explain this abnormal behavior. The retardation of certain substances (42, 43), which is frequently observed during gel chromatography, is known as "reversible adsorption". PORATH (42) noticed already that certain other forces were effective during "gel filtration" when he studied systematically the behavior of amino acids, amino acid derivatives, peptides, and proteins of low molecular weight on Sephadex. The effects observed were strongly dependent upon the composition of the eluent. GELOTTE (43) determined simultaneously a large number of K_d-values for aromatic and heterocyclic compounds of low molecular weight as well as those for charged substances on Sephadex G-25 for a series of eluents. He interpreted the observed discrepancies in terms of interactions, which are to be described subsequently. In most of these cases the partition coefficient (K_d or K_{av}) is larger than 1, i.e. the partition coefficient assumes values which are incompatible with the exclusion principle.

Partition and Adsorption

A solute which remains in the gel grain for a longer period of time than that assigned to it according to the diffusion equilibrium with the flowing solvent must be under the influence of certain forces in the gel phase. Such forces may be: Firstly, Coulomb interactions between ions and charged regions in the gel (ion exchange), secondly, van der Waals interactions between the solute and the gel phase as a whole (partition), and thirdly, adsorption of the substances on to the high molecular weight structure which forms the gel. The interaction between charged groups is well understood. The presence of these forces can easily be eliminated, or it may be utilized to advantage for certain separations without differences in molecular weight (cf. page 129). It is, however, more difficult to deal with partition and adsorption. It is also not easy to clearly distinguish between the two effects in the case of gels. Therefore, the two phenomena will be treated jointly. They have in common a delay of the elution of a solute as brought about by an interaction with the column packing.

The peaks of strongly retarded solutes appear also always completely symmetrical and, independently of concentration, in the right position. Such behavior is commonly observed in partition only (linear concentration isotherm). The concept of adsorption should probably not be discarded completely since in the gel the "adsorbent" (the macromolecular network) is exceptionally easily accessible for the solutes (it has a large surface). The result are linear isotherms, even for the adsorption over a wide range of concentrations.

In any event the very general Boltzmann equation (Eq. 15) is valid and the concentration in the stationary phase may now be larger (at times and locally) than the concentration in the mobile phase. It is only significant in what way λ is dependent upon the molecular weight, i.e. whether λ_o in $\lambda = \lambda_o \cdot M$ is negative or positive. For actual adsorption λ_o must be negative, i.e. substances of higher molecular weight are adsorbed more strongly than lower molecular weight substances of similar structure. Various efforts to separate the homologous series of polymers are based upon this fact (cf. e.g. *44*). Recently a separation on Sephadex LH-20 has been described which followed exactly this scheme (*45*):

What is described is the separation of benzene, naphtalene, anthracene, and that of five other polycyclic hydrocarbons on a 1.1 × 112 cm (96 ml) gel bed in isopropanol. These substances were eluted between effluent volumes of 80 and 250 ml in the order of *increasing* molecular weights and were very well separated. The picture changed completely, when chloroform was used as eluent (V_t now 102 ml). Most of the components were then eluted between 50 and 60 ml (evidently not separated). It was possible to demonstrate with the help of the characteristic UV-spectra that separation in the sense of gel chromatography (large molecules eluted earlier than small molecules) had occurred to some extent. Chloroform is a much better solvent for polycyclic hydrocarbons, which means that the molecular sieving properties of the gel are dominating the solvating properties.

If, however, solubility does not play a role, then polarity of the three participating components (gelmatrix, swelling medium, and solvent as well as the solute) frequently decide whether the elution behavior is in accordance with the rules of gel chromatography, that means, governed by these factors, or the affinity of the gel phase will dominate. In these cases the outcome of the experiment may be the result of a combination of the two effects (exclusion and interaction) or a partition with a positive λ_o. The example of Fig. 27 (Chapter IV) is a clear demonstration of such combination. When ethanol was used as eluent, the glycerides appeared in elution volumes which corresponded to the molecular weights. The difference in polarity between hydroxyl containing and hydroxyl free glycerides was cancelled out by the polar solvent. Now only the rules of gel chromatography were applicable.

LH-Sephadex and Styragel are applied preferably in organic solvents (only there the differences in polarity are clearly demonstrated). These materials have a relatively high polymer content. In spite of that, disturbing interactions have thus far been observed only rarely. (Only water and other polar contaminants are retarded strongly in the GPC-apparatus). The particular structural features (cf. Chapter 2) of these gels establish themselves also in this respect. The rigid polystyrene structure swells hardly and offers thus rarely an opportunity for "partition" or "adsorption". The difference is clearly demonstrated by the comparison of these gels with conventional cross-linked polystyrenes which are capable of swelling (46, 47). There one could barely observe the molecular sieving action in the presence of adsorption and partition effects.

Hydrophilic Gels

Hydrophilic gels swell in water. Water also serves normally as the mobile phase. Due to the high polarity the effects described above for lipophilic gels are reduced to a minimum. Another fact, however, is even more remarkable, i.e. Aromatic and heterocyclic compounds are frequently distinguished by high *affinity to the gel phase*. MARSDEN (48) concludes from experiments with alcohols (C_2—C_5) that there is also a so-called "aliphatic adsorption" on Sephadex G-10. (With increasing molecular weight, these alcohols are eluted somewhat later). According to own experiments (49) cyclohexane and glucose, however, are eluted simultaneously from Sephadex G-25 in water, while benzene clearly appears later. In Sephadex G-15, cyclohexane maintaines its position, glucose is eluted somewhat earlier, while benzene is retarded very strongly. This demonstrated clearly that benzene has a much higher affinity to the dextran gel than cyclohexane which behaves practically according to its molecular weight.

Interaction is not restricted to dextran gels. CRAIG and ANSEVIN (50) made the following observation during the determination of the dialysis rate of amino acids through very selective membranes of *acetylated cellulose*; the amino acids with aromatic residues migrated much more rapidly than would have been expected for their size. Evidently the diffusion is enhanced by intermediary adsorption to the membrane. The swollen membrane was rapidly isolated after 50% of passage and it was shown that it contained considerably larger quantities of amino acids with aromatic residues than others. Certain aromatic compounds are also retarded by *polyacrylamide gels*. The affinity of the gels does not seem to depend exclusively on the quantity of polymer in the gel phase. SUN and SEHON (51) have observed that a polyacrylamide gel of good swelling properties (5–20, $W_r = 13$, cf. page 19) retards tryptophan more strongly than the type 15–15 of higher density $w_r = 7$. The *structure of the gel* plays evidently a decisive role for the affinity toward aromatic substances. This applies also to the dextran gels: in the series of the Sephadex types G-200, G-75, G-25, G-15, and G-10 the K_{av}-value of phenol increases very strongly, as one may expect. If one eliminates, however, by calculation the fact that the dextran content of the gel bed is also greatly increased, then a considerable increase in the affinity remains for G-15 and G-10, which can only have been brought about by the structure (49). We have not been able to observe this extraordinarily large increase for the Bio-Gels P-100, P-30, and P-2. The retardation of phenol increased only proportional to the amount of polymer in the gel packing. For the types of higher density it was clearly smaller. Thus, we succeeded on Bio-gel P-2 in the separation of sodium chloride from a tripeptide (tyrosyl-isoleucyl-glycine), which on Sephadex G-10 was not possible due to the stronger retardation of the peptide.

It is completely unknown how the interaction between the gels which have been allowed to swell in water and the aromatic compound comes about. The effect may be suppressed by various additives to the eluent. High concentrations of rhodanide or urea are claimed to normalize almost completely the elution of picric acid and tryptophan (52). Polyphenols behaved according to molecular size in alcohol/water mixtures on Sephadex G-25. The compounds were retarded rather badly in pure water (53). Possible binding sites in the gel cannot be "saturated" by the addition of aromatic substances (e. g. 0.2N sodium salicylide) to the eluent (42). In 1M pyridine, however, the dinitrophenylderivatives of amino acids are no longer eluted after the amino acids but rather before them. Upon chromatography in phenol/acidic acid/water (1/1/1) the gel does not seem to have any longer an affinity toward aromatic substances (54). CARNEGIE (55) was able to confirm in this system on Sephadex G-25 (undisturbed by side effects) with a series of peptides one of the common relations between molecular weight and elution volume (cf. Table 26). The author assumes that genuine gel chromatography takes place for molecular weights over 400, since partition should no longer be effective (cf. 63). It is, however, no longer ascertained that the solvent of the gel phase is of the same composition as that outside of the gel phase.

The situation in pure aqueous solvent systems is complicated by the fact that the affinity of different classes of substances to the gel phase is evidently quite different. While we had observed earlier that phenol is less retarded on Bio-gel P-2 than on Sephadex G-10, the situation is reversed for nucleic acid components. (The behavior of nucleic acids and their components on dextran gels will be discussed separately in Chapter 5.) Bases and nucleosides have a high affinity for Sephadex (43) and Bio-Gel (56). Only the nucleotides are eluted earlier than salt on G-10 and P-2. In own experiments practically no difference was observed between the two gels. In view of the very different chemical composition this is highly astonishing. More strongly phosphorylated nucleosides are subject to the reverse effect on Sephadex G-25 (57). These compounds are excluded from the gel phase and appear in the effluent considerably sooner than would be expected from their molecular weight. This, however, is also the case for other aromatic substances which carry still an ionizable group (however, only in strongly alkaline solution) (43, 49).

This exclusion phenomenon remains also largely unexplained. It is possibly related to the fact that all these gels contain a small amount of carboxylic groups (cf. page 27). – The negative charges are held responsible for the exclusion of low molecular weight anions from the gel phase upon application in low quantity to the gel packing and elution with ion free water (43). Like a highmolecular substance, they appear with the exclusion volume (V_o). This effect can be very disturbing, particularly in studies with radioactive anions, e. g. iodide (58). Radioactivity in the exclusion volume may be misleading due to the erroneous indication of a labeled macromolecule under certain circumstances. The presence of other electrolytes, however, normalizes the elution volume completely (43, 58). – Despite their aromatic character, humic acids in distilled water are completely excluded from dextran gel. Upon the addition of salt it is even possible to estimate their molecular weight by gel chromatography (59).

Naturally the carboxyl groups have the opposite effect on cations. In salt-free medium smaller quantities are strongly retarded by the gel (43). Here the presence of a large excess of additional ions results also in displacement and thus in a normalization of the elution behavior. – Ions of heavy metals are sometimes bound irreversible to the dextran gels (60).

References

1. FLODIN, P.: J. Chromatog. 5, 103 (1961).
2. LAURENT, T. C., and J. KILLANDER: ibid. 14, 317 (1964).
3. GRANATH, K. A.: J. colloid. Sci. 13, 308 (1958).
4. DETERMANN, H., und B. GELOTTE in RAUEN (Hrsg.): Biochemisches Taschenbuch, Band II, 906. Berlin, Görtingen, Heidelberg 1964.
5. WHEATON, R. M., and W. C. BAUMANN: Ann. N.Y. Acad. Sci. 57, 159 (1953).
6. GRANATH, K. A., and P. FLODIN: Makromol. Chem. 48, 160 (1961).
7. WHITAKER, J. R.: Anal. Chem. 35, 1950 (1963).
8. WICKE, E.: Ber. Bunsenges. Physik. Chem. 69, 761 (1965).
9. GLUECKAUF, E., in: Ion exchange and its applications, Soc. Chem. Ind., 34. London 1965.
10. PURNELL, G. G., in: Gas Chromatography, 108. New York: 1962.
11. PORATH, J., and P. FLODIN: Protides of the biol. Fluids 10, 297 (1963).
12. SMITH, W. B., and A. KOLLMANSBERGER: J. phys. Chem. 69, 4157 (1965).
13. FLODIN, P.: Dextran Gels and their Applications in Gel Filtration, Dissertation, Uppsala, 1962.
14. LAURENT, T. C., and E. P. LAURENT: J. Chromatog. 16, 89 (1964).
15. WINZOR, D. J., and L.W. NICHOL: Biochim. biophys. Acta 104, 1 (1965).
16. LEACH, A. A., and P. C. O'SHEA: J. Chromatog. 17, 245 (1965).
17. SELBY, K., and C. C. MAITLAND: Biochem. J. 94, 578 (1965).
18. MOORE, J. C., and J. G. HENDRICKSON: J. polymer. Sci., Part C, 8, 233 (1965).
19. ALTGELT, K. H., and J. C. MOORE: in CANTOW (Ed.): Polymer Fractionation, p. 123, New York, 1967.
20. PORATH, J.: Pure appl. Chem. 6, 233 (1963).

21. ZIMM, B. H., and W. H. STOCKMAYER: J. chem. Physics 17, 1301 (1949).
22. SQUIRE, P. G.: Arch. Biochem. Biophys. 107, 471 (1964).
23. LAURENT, T. C., and A. PIETRUSZKIEWICZ: Biochim. biophys. Acta 49, 258 (1961).
24. — Biochem. J. 89, 253 (1963).
25. — Acta chem. scand. 17, 2664 (1963).
26. — Biochem. J. 93, 106 (1964).
27. —, K. HELLSING und B. GELOTTE: Acta chem. scand. 18, 274 (1964).
28. OGSTON, A. G.: Trans. Faraday Soc. 54, 1754 (1958).
29. HELLSING, K.: Acta chem. scand. 19, 1791 (1965).
30. PEDERSEN, K. O.: Arch. Biochem. Biophys., Suppl. 1, 157 (1962).
31. ACKERS, G. K., and R. L. STEERE: Biochim. biophys. Acta 59, 137 (1962).
32. RENKIN, E. M.: J. gen. Physiol. 38, 225 (1955).
33. ACKERS, G. K.: Biochemistry 3, 723 (1964).
34. SIEGEL, L. M., and K. J. MONTY: Biochim. biophys. Acta 112, 346 (1966).
35. ANDERSON, D. M.W., and J. F. STODDART: Anal. chim. Acta 34, 401 (1966).
36. DETERMANN, H., und W. MICHEL: J. Chromatog. 25, 303 (1966).
37. TAKAGI, T.: 3rd International Seminar on Gel Permeation Chromatography, Genf, Mai 1966.
38. BRÖNSTED, J. N.: Z. physikal. Chem. Bodenstein Festband 1931, 257.
39. HOHN, TH., und W. POLLMANN: Z. Naturforsch. 18 b, 919 (1963).
40. BREWER, P. I.: Polymer 6, 603 (1965).
41. TISELIUS, A., J. PORATH, and P.-Å. ALBERTSSON: Science 141, 13 (1963).
42. PORATH, J.: Biochim. biophys. Acta 39, 193 (1960).
43. GELOTTE, B.: J. Chromatog. 3, 330 (1960).
44. SI JUNG YEH, and H. L. FRISCH: J. polymer Sci. 27, 149 (1958).
45. WILK, M., J. ROCHLITZ und H. BENDE: J. Chromatog. 24, 414 (1966).
46. VAUGHAN, M. F.: Nature 188, 55 (1960).
47. CORTIS-JONES, B.: Nature 191, 272 (1961).
48. MARSDEN, N. V. B.: Ann. N.Y. Acad. Sci. 125, 428 (1965).
49. DETERMANN, H., und I. WALTER: in preparation.
50. CRAIG, L. C., and A. ANSEVIN: Biochemistry 2, 1268 (1963).
51. SUN, K., and A. H. SEHON: Can. J. Chem. 43, 969 (1965).
52. GELOTTE, B., and J. PORATH: in HEFTMANN (Ed.) Chromatography, New York 1966.
53. SOMERS, T. C.: Nature 209, 368 (1966).
54. BAGDASARIAN, M., N. A. MATHESON, R. L. M. SYNGE and M. A. YOUNGSON: Biochem. J. 91, 91 (1964).
55. CARNEGIE, P. R.: Nature 206, 1128 (1965).
56. SCHWARTZ, A. N., A.W. G. YEE, and B. A. ZABIN: J. Chromatog. 20, 154 (1965).
57. HAYES, F. N., E. HANSBURY, and V. E. MITCHELL: J. Chromatog. 16, 410 (1964).
58. SPITZY, H., H. SKRUBE und K. MÜLLER: Microchim. Acta 1961, 296.
59. POSNER, A. M.: Nature 198, 1161 (1963).
60. GEORGE, W. H. S.: Nature 195, 155 (1962).
61. GIDDINGS, J. C., and K. L. MALLIK: Anal. Chem. 38, 997 (1966).
62. FAWCETT, J. S., and C. J. O. R. MORRIS: Separation Sci. 1, 9 (1966).
63. GRASSMANN, W., und G. DEFFNER: Z. physiol. Chem. 293, 89 (1953).

Chapter 4

Principles of Application

There are basically three ways of classifying the more than one thousand scientific publications which describe the application of porous gels to the separation of substances. In one approach *classes of substances* are the guiding principle. In another attempt the experimental data are organized by *areas of application*. (In Chapter 5 of this monograph an approach will be presented which takes both possibilities into consideration). Alternatively one could attempt – without consideration of classes of substances – to draw from practical experience in order to develop principles of application of gel chromatography and arrive at a classification. The latter approach has a didactic advantage. The reader does not have to carry an excessively large number of references and is in a position to obtain quickly information about possible approaches to the solution of a given separation problem. The present chapter is based on *methodical aspects* and amplified by a number of selected practical applications.

Gel chromatography is primarily a method by which very large molecules are separated from very small molecules. This implies that the molecular weight of one type of molecules is outside the exclusion range of the applied gel, while the other type of molecules is capable of penetrating the gel completely. This application is most closely related to the process of sieving or filtering. Therefore the term "*Gel Filtration*" will be chosen for it. However, as soon as mixtures of molecules of various sizes are to be separated, the resolving power of the gel must cover this range of sizes as completely as possible. Very small differences in elution volumes will have to be expected and experimental conditions must be selected very carefully. This type of separation will be called "*Gel Chromatography*". It has been demonstrated that the elution behavior of macromolecules is proportional to molecular size and that it is possible to estimate molecular weights from the elution volumes. This type of gel chromatography enjoys wide application on an analytical scale and will be treated separately under "*Molecular Weight Determination*". Finally, there are types of applications in which differences in molecular size are less significant than the interactions of the substances to be separated with the gel phase. These applications will be treated separately in the section "*Separation without Difference in Size*".

Gel Filtration

In line with the definition given above, the experimental examples to be described here are all separations of substances with considerable differences in molecular weight. In "gel filtration", the separation of substances by chromatography on porous gels competes with the long-known dialysis. Gel filtration, as opposed to dialysis, has a great advantage, namely, that of considerably shorter time requirements. The time for gel filtration is independent of the amount of material to be handled as long as experimental conditions are carefully selected. This may be of great importance in the case of sensitive natural products. The excessive dilution of the high molecular weight component – which is absent in dialysis – is frequently hold against gel filtration. This, however, is only the case when the volume of the solution is not in the right proportion to that of the gel packing. Careful observation of the volume ratios, which are discussed in Chapter 3, will decisively influence the success of the operation. (Following Fig. 22, an illustrative example will be presented.)

Substances which are to be purified or investigated by gel filtration are predominantly water-soluble natural products. The gels for these experiments are therefore swellable in water. In the majority of cases the dextran gel Sephadex G-25 was used. This gel allows the passing of all substances with molecular weights above 5000 in the outer volume. Frequently, however, the macromolecules to be studied are of higher molecular weight and the more strongly swellable Sephadex G-50 may be applied. This gel has two considerable advantages over the most frequently used one: On the one hand, one gram of dry gel upon swelling produces twice the volume of a gel bed, thus making the procedure much more economical. On the other hand, due to the fact just indicated, only half as much of the polysaccharide-matrix is present in the column. The potentially dangerous and disturbing interactions of the macromolecules with the gel are greatly reduced.

A gel filtration experiment is indeed very simple. The gels used – of relatively high degrees of cross-linking – pose no problems with regard to their handling. The gel packings do not have to be particularly long. Frequently a diameter to height – ratio of 1:5 to 1:10 was found to be applicable. The volume, however, is of great significance. The concentration of the components is also not important, unless the viscosity of the solution to be tested is too high. Gel filtration has become the method of choice for the classic problem of "desalting" colloids. No attempt will therefore be made to discuss or tabulate even the most important applications. However, the potential of the method and possible sources of error will be outlined. Examples of applications from different classes of substances will be discussed. If the low molecular weight substances which are to be separated from macromolecules are not salts the term *"group separation"* on the basis of molecular weight differences should be employed. Numerous different possibilities have to be considered here. Frequently such mixtures of substances result from attempts of *"modifications of macromolecules"*. The problem may be the removal of the excess of reagent or the separation of the products of the reaction. – If a polymer interacts with low molecular weight substances in one way or the other, then this *"complex formation"* in connection with gel filtration offers remarkable preparative and analytical possibilities.

Desalting

In view of the importance of this operation for protein chemistry, optimal conditions were studied very early and very extensively by FLODIN (*1*). From these studies are taken the experimental examples which are presented in Fig. 22. The same column was used for both separations. The sample volume was 40 times larger in (B) than in (A). Despite this unfavorable ratio, the separation of protein and salt was almost complete. While in (A) hemoglobin left the column in approximately 10-fold dilution, in the case of (B) the dilution was only 1.25-fold. The components may be isolated practically undiluted, as long as the elution curve is horizontal and one is willing to accept small losses. This will always be possible if one adjusts optimally the *volume of the gel bed* to the volume of the solution to be desalted – the latter one is almost invariably the determinant:

If the macromolecules are completely excluded by the gel particles ($K_{av} = 0$) and the salts are able to diffuse freely ($K_{av} = 1$), then the difference in elution volume is equal to the inner volume of the gel packing (according to the considerations in Chapter 3). Thus, the tolerable sample volume for complete separation should be the same. Taking into consideration the fact that completely free diffusion of the salts is rarely possible ($K_{av} < 1$) and that the zones are broadening during chromatography, one arrives at the conclusion that the sample volume may amount to approximately 75% of the inner volume. This signifies for the Sephadex gels G-25 and G-50 that a volume of *40% of the total gel-volume* may be applied and complete desalting should be possible. This was exactly the case in the illustrative example (Fig. 22 B). – Upon desalting 500 ml of serum on a 9×60 cm (3 l) gel packing of Sephadex G-25, the proteins were collected in 600 ml of buffer (*2*). The dilution was only 1.2-fold despite the fact that the test solution was only 17% of the gel bed volume.

The possibility to desalt highly viscous solutions without practically any dilution in a basket centrifuge may only be mentioned here (cf. page 56).

During the elution with distilled water, proteins may be retarded by the interaction with the few carboxyl groups in the gel (cf. page 27) and not be liberated from salt (*3*). As has been pointed out above, the gel bed of the more strongly swelling Sephadex G-50 contains a smaller amount of dextran

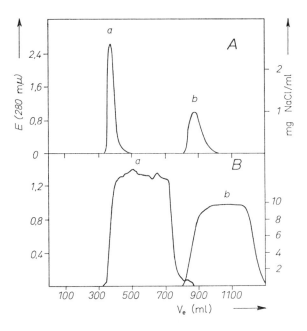

Fig. 22. Elution diagram of hemoglobin (a) and sodium chloride (b) on Sephadex G-25; gel bed 4×85 cm (1070 ml); A: sample volume 10 ml (100 mg of hemoglobin and 100 mg of sodium chloride); B: sample volume 400 ml (400 mg of protein and 4 g of sodium chloride); eluent: water (240 ml/h); according to FLODIN (*1*). Ordinate: extinction at 280 mμ and concentration in sodium chloride (mg/ml); abscissa: elution volume.

and thus even fewer carboxyl groups, whereby this risk is greatly reduced. The elution may also be carried out with volatile buffers and the protein isolated by lyophilization. This approach has been recommended for the desalting of proteins which are insoluble at low ionic strength and would lead to clogging of the columns. FLODIN (*1*) has shown that the so-called "*buffer exchange*" takes place smoothly and without excessive changes in the pH-value.

The polyacrylamide gel may also be applied to desalting. Bio-Gel P-10 (corresponding to Sephadex G-25) is applicable to proteins (cf. *4*).

Desalting by gel filtration is not restricted to *proteins*. Other water soluble molecules may also be liberated from salt. It is possible, for instance, to remove completely the salts (and phenol) from suspensions of different *viruses* (*5*). The presence of chloride ions is a disturbing factor in the quantitative determination of *humic acid* (*6*) or of mucopolysaccharide (heparin) (*7*). In these cases it was possible to remove quickly the salt with the help of Sephadex G-25. With the polysaccharide the yield of the sensitive macromolecules (*7*) was better than that after dialysis. The *separation of the soluble main components of grasses* (*8*) demonstrates that sizable quantities can be handled in a single process.

> The deproteinized grass extract (19.4 g) is almost completely separated on a gel bed of 4×70 cm (800 ml) of Sephadex G-25. The expected oligo- and polysaccharides (6.63%) are found in one fraction, in the other, saccharose and the salts (87.7%). Without deproteinization "only" 10 g of extract may be handled on this column.

Biochemists were soon convinced of the usefulness of gel filtration as a method of desalting macromolecules and began to ask for gels which would allow the desalting of fragments of macromolecules (e. g. *peptides* or *nucleotides*). This demand was met by the industry by the synthesis of strongly cross-linked gels with small pores in the swollen state (Sephadex G-15 and G-10; Bio-Gel P-2). It has already been stressed repeatedly that in gels in which the gel-forming macromolecules are packed very densely frequently other interactions are dominating the steric factors. It is therefore sometimes more difficult – due to the observed affinity to the gel phase – to desalt low molecular weight substances than macromolecules. However, in the brochures of the manufacturers promising examples have already been described in detail.

> Oligosaccharides (sample volume 2.5 ml) were separated and desalted on a gel bed of Sephadex G-15 (1.4×100 cm $= 154$ ml) in phosphate buffer (6 ml/h). – The antibiotically active peptide bacitracin (10 mg, M $= 1400$) was applied in a sample volume of 1 ml to a column of Bio-Gel P-2 (1.3×36 cm $= 48$ ml) and separated completely from 10 mg of sodium chloride.

The interaction with the gel phase was particularly strong during the purification of nucleic acid components. On Bio-Gel P-2 nucleotides can only be desalted if the sample volume is less than 10% of the gel bed volume and the pH-value higher than 7. If this is not the case, overlapping with the salt has to be expected. Nucleosides and particularly the bases are as strongly retarded as on Sephadex (*9*).

Group Separation

During the isolation of macromolecules from mixtures of natural products one uses not only salt in high concentrations but, occassionally, also other chemicals. At a later stage of the isolation process, it is highly desirable to remove the chemicals again. As a representative example, the separation of *phenol* from a solution of *deoxyribonucleic acid* is shown in Fig. 23 (*10*). It is commonplace to use phenol for the liberation of nucleic acids from proteins; earlier, the phenol was removed by ether extraction. This poses the danger of denaturation of the sensitive polymers due to solvent effects and of depolymerization due to shearing forces.

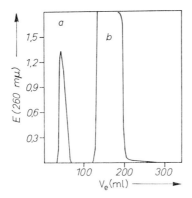

Fig. 23. Gel filtration of a mixture of deoxyribonucleic acid (a) and phenol (b) on Sephadex
G-25; gel bed 2.0×30 cm (94 ml); sample volume 5 ml (approximately 20 mg of nucleic
acid in phenol-saturated water); eluent water (48 ml/h); according to SHEPHERD and
PETERSEN (10). Ordinate extinction at 260 mμ; abscissa: elution volume. (This applies
to all of the following elution diagrams unless otherwise stated.)

These risks are greatly reduced in the separation of the phenol under the
mild conditions of gel chromatography (10). – It is frequently possible to
concentrate protein solutions by imbedding them in dialysis tubing in
crystal sugar which absorbs part of the water. The dissolved *sugar* penetrates
the tubing and thus contaminates the *protein*. The sugar can, however, be
removed easily by gel filtration on Sephadex G-25 (11). – *Proteins* which
have been isolated by starch-gel electrophoreses may be contaminated by
starch. The substances to be separated do not show great differences in
molecular weight and a suitable gel has to be selected very carefully. It was
demonstrated successfully that such eluates (5 ml in each case) may be
separated simultaneously from starch and salt on a Bio-Gel P-100 column
(0.9×150 cm) (12). – *Enzymatic reactions* which are triggered by the de-
struction of the cell membrane *prohibit* frequently the isolation of the
original natural products from plants. STEGEMANN and LOESCHKE (13)
succeeded in the rapid removal of the phenol oxydases from the juice of
frozen potatoes (which had been obtained by pressing), using a large Sephadex
G-25 column (10×100 cm, flow rate 1.2 l/h).

Dilution of the components during group separation by gel filtration
can be *prevented* to a great extent by observing the volume ratios which have
been discussed in detail in the section on "desalting". The dilution of a
suspension of *viruses* from red beats was only 20 to 30% when the separation
from the accompanying *pigments* was carried out by gel filtration on the
6- to 4-fold volume of Sephadex G-75 (14). – On a small gel bed of Sephadex
G-25 (2×25 cm = 78 ml) the *catecholamines* adrenaline and noradrenaline
were isolated undiluted and free of *proteins* from 20 ml of serum (27% of

the gel bed volume) (15). Gel filtration on Sephadex G-50 proved to be far superior to dialysis when KISLIUK (16) attempted the separation of an *enzyme* from its cofactors. It is thus possible to obtain the cofactors in a relatively small volume and to study the effect of their renewed addition to the enzyme. Upon gel filtration a completely inactive protein was isolated; the activity was increased to 86% of that of the initial activity by the addition of the low molecular weight fraction. Dialysis lowered the activity of the enzyme only to 38% (16). Group separation by gel filtration makes possible the convenient separation of low molecular weight *antigens* from *antibodies*. Frequently one accomplishes the dissociation of an antigen-antibody complex by the addition of an excess of hapten which may then be removed again from the protein by gel filtration (17). In bacteriology, gel filtration may be applied to the convenient isolation of *extracellular* toxins on Sephadex G-75 or Bio-Gel P-100. Before inoculation the *cultur medium* will be liberated from high molecular weight components by gel filtration. On the same gel packing – after removal of the bacteria – the macromolecular toxins may again be separated from the culture medium (18).

The *lipophilic gels* for separations in organic solvents are only available commercially for a brief period of time and very few reports on their application have been published. However, it seems to be certain that group separation in organic solvents will also become a very important area of application of gel chromatography. In many syntheses of organic chemistry high molecular weight substances are frequently expected in the resin like byproducts. As long as affinity effects (cf. page 82) do not strongly interfere, it appears to be promising to attempt purification of the desired – usually low molecular – synthetic product by gel filtration (e.g. on Sephadex LH-20). Naturally, the relatively poorly swelling lipophilic gel is very wel suited for the removal of a *product of polymerization* from the remaining *monomer* and also the possibly present *oligomers*. Thus, one obtains upon chromatography of several mg of commercial polystyrene (DOW resin PS-3) on Sephadex LH-20 (3×20 cm) in chloroform in essence three fractions: the polymer, the softener, and the monomeric styrene (19).

Modification of Macromolecules

Chemical reactions on high molecular weight substances require a considerable excess of reagents, because of the relatively low rate of reaction. These excesses, just like the possible conversion products of the reagents, have to be removed again. This may also be accomplished by gel filtration under particularly mild conditions. Here also, the new technique of group separation proved very soon its superiority over the conventional dialysis. This is clearly demonstrated by the detailed experiments of antibody *labeling* with *fluorescein isothiocyanate* (cf. Table 20). While 5 to 6 days of dialysis are required in order to obtain the stained protein completely free of low mo-

Table 20. *Literature on the fluorescent labeling of proteins.*

KILLANDER, J., J. PONTÉN, and L. RODÉN: Nature **192**, 182 (1961). Rapid preparation of fluorescent antibodies using gel filtration.

FOTHERGILL, J. E., and R. C. NAIRN: Nature **192**, 1073 (1961). Purification of fluorescent protein conjugates: comparison of charcoal and Sephadex.

GEORGE, W., and K.W. WALTON: Nature **192**, 1188 (1961). Purification and concentration of dye-protein conjugates by gel filtration.

ZWAAN, J., and A. F. VAN DAM: Acta Histochemica **11**, 306 (1961). Rapid separation of fluorescent antisera and unconjugated dye.

WAGNER, M.: Zbl. Bakt. **185**, 124 (1962). Die Verwendung von Sephadex zur raschen Reinigung von fluoreszenz-markierten Antikörperlösungen.

GORDON, M. A., M. R. EDWARDS, and V. N. TOMPKINS: Proc. Soc. exptl. Biol. Med. **109**, 96 (1962). Refinement of fluorescent antibody by gel filtration.

RINDERKNECHT, H.: Nature **193**, 167 (1962). Ultra-rapid fluorescent labelling of proteins.

TOKUMARU, T.: J. Immunol. **89**, 195 (1962). A kinetic study on the labelling of serum globulin with fluorescein isothiocyanate by means of the gel filtration technique.

---

lecular weight dye stuff, such purification can be accomplished on Sephadex G-25 or G-50 in less than 1 hour. It is possible to work with very small gel bed volumes since the separation is enhanced, due to the fact that the low molecular weight dye stuff is strongly retarded by the gel phase. Because of that, the recommandation has been made to use a new column for each experiment. – Dextrans may also be stained by the reaction with 1-dimethyl-aminonaphthalene sulfochloride-5 and then be purified in the same fashion (20).

Proteins are also *labeled* in a very sensitive way and under mild conditions by the reaction with $^{131}J_2$. Halogen which did not react to completion is generally reduced to iodide and will then have to be removed from the reaction solution. This is frequently done by gel filtration on Sephadex G-25 and G-50 (cf. Table 21). (The principally identical application of radioactive iodine to test the function of the thyroid gland will not be considered at this time; this important analytical method of clinical chemistry will be discussed in Chapter 5.) The minor *ion exchange effect* of Sephadex tends to be rather *disturbing* during studies with radioactive anions. It is, therefore, of particular importance to work in dilute salt solution whenever possible.

ANFINSEN and HABER (21) have made frequent use of gel filtration on Sephadex G-25 in their classical experiments on the *reduction* and *recombination* of the four *disulfide bridges* in ribonuclease. Initially urea, salts and mercaptoethanol were removed from the reduced protein. Subsequently the excess of reagents from the substitution of the SH-groups were also removed by gel filtration. A similar approach was followed during the reversible substitution of the amino groups of the same protein by the trifluoroacetyl

Table 21. *Literature on the labeling of proteins with radioactive iodine.*

SPITZY, H., H. SKRUBE und K. MÜLLER: Microchim. Acta **1961**, 296. Radiochemische Untersuchung über das Verhalten von anorganischen Ionen während der Gelfiltration an Sephadex.

LISSITZKY, S., J. BISMUTH and M. ROLLAND: Clin. Chim. Acta **7**, 183 (1962). Separation of iodo-compounds of serum and thyroid by filtration through gel (Sephadex).

JACOBSSON, L., and G. WIDSTRÖM: Scand. J. clin. Lab. Invest. **14**, 285 (1962). Separation of iodine compounds in serum by gel filtration.

HUNTER, W. M., and F. C. GREENWOOD: Nature **194**, 495 (1962). Preparation of iodine-131 labelled human growth hormone of high specific activity.

ABDEL-WAHAB, M. F., and S. A. EL-KINAWY: Intern. J. appl. Radiation Isotopes **16**, 267 (1965). Preparation of radioiodinated serum albumin and radioiodinated egg albumin by gel filtration.

— — Intern. J. appl. Radiation Isotopes **16**, 668 (1965). Preparation of iodine-131 labelled insulin and isolation by gel filtration.

HÖYE, Å.: Nature **211**, 746 (1966). Purification of insulin labelled with iodine-131.

HOCMAN, G., M. KUTKA, and V. LICKO: Clin. chim. Acta **13**, 775 (1966). Comparison of three methods for the estimation of the conversion factor (ratio protein bound I-131 to total I-131) in biological material.

group (*154*). – The disulfide bonds of ribonuclease may also be split by the action of radioactively labeled trisodium thiophosphate. The liberated mercapto groups are thiophosphorylated simultaneously (*22*). Two elution curves from this publication are shown in Fig. 24. It can be seen how fast and effective the separation of the labeled protein from the excess of thiophosphate (A) is.

That the acid residue is indeed located at the sulfur can easily be detected with certainty (*155*) by the fact that reduced and subsequently alkylated ribonuclease does not react with thiophosphate (B). STEINER (*23*) was able – while using Sephadex G-25 – to repeat the experiment of Anfinsen with the trypsin inhibitor from soybeans. In the latter case, higher aggregates of inactive and contaminating substances had to be removed (after recombination) by gel chromatography on Sephadex G-100.

Gel filtration on Sephadex G-25 was also applied after the various reaction steps of the removal of the amino terminus from an otherwise intact protein by treatment with glyoxalate, o-phenylene diamine, and ferricyanide (*24*).

Gel filtration is the method of choice whenever large molecules have to be *separated very quickly* from small ones. ENGLANDER (*25*) succeeded in separating tritium labeled water from ribonuclease within two minutes on a specially packed column (3×6 cm) of Sephadex G-25. With this rapid analytical technique it was possible to establish the *kinetics* of the *tritium uptake* and *release*, and thus to draw conclusions on the helix content of the dissolved protein. The same experimental technique was subsequently ap-

plied to the elucidation of the superstructure of "soluble" ribonucleic acids
(26) and of desoxyribonucleic acids (27). – Nucleic acids may also be
modified chemically, e.g. by the action of diazotized sulfanilic acid (28).
The excess of reagent and low molecular weight conversion products were
removed on Sephadex G-50.

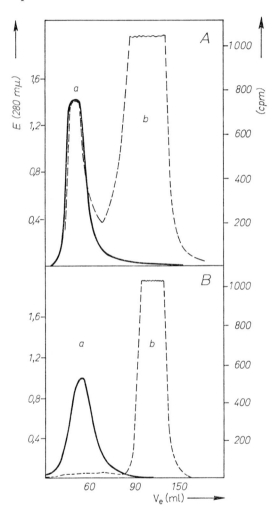

Fig. 24. Separation of the reaction product of trisodium thiophosphate (160 Mol) and
ribonuclease (2 μMol) in 2 ml of tris-HCl pH 9.0 with 8 M urea on Sephadex G-25;
gel bed 1.4×70 cm (108 ml); A: native and B: reduced and alkylated RNase (a). The
trisodium thiophosphate (b) was labeled with ^{32}P and ^{35}S, respectively. According to
NEUMANN, GOLDBERGER, and SELA (22). Ordinate: extinction at 280 mμ (solid line) and
radioactivity in counts per minute (dashed).

Complex Formation

The reversible binding of the low molecular weight reagents (tritium ion) to macromolecules has already been pointed out in the experiments describing the tritiation of proteins and nucleic acids. Gel filtration was used with advantage in the study of such reversible interactions.

In several instances complex formation was utilized in the *preparative separation of low molecular weight substances*. PORATH et al. (*29*) took advantage of the fact that under the conditions of the extraction from the dry acetone powder the physiologically active peptides of the posterior lobe of the pituitary gland (oxytocin and vasopressin) are associated with the accompanying proteins (cf. Fig. 25). The hormones together with the proteins are first eluted on Sephadex G-75 (A) and separated from the low molecular weight components. In a different solvent they can be separated from the

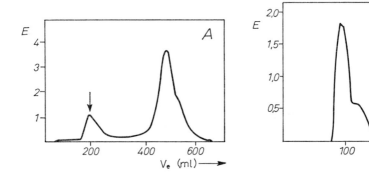

Fig. 25. A: Elution diagram of a 10 ml extract from 2.88 g of the posterior lobe of the pituitary gland on Sephadex G-25; gel bed 4×60 cm (750 ml); eluent 0.05 M acetic acid in 0.2 M pyridine (pH 5.9) (190 ml/h); B: gel filtration of the lyophilized active fraction 480 mg from A (after 10 minutes of heating to 70°C in 5 ml of 1 N formic acid on Sephadex G-25; gel bed 2.5×50 cm(236 ml); eluent 1 N formic acid (30 ml/h) the arrows indicate the location were hormone activity was found; according to LINDNER, ELMQVIST, and PORATH (*29*). Ordinate: (A) extinction of the ninhydrin reaction; (B) extinction of the Folin-Lowry reaction.

protein carriers and appear (increased by a factor of 50) in the low molecular weight fraction of a new gel filtration (B). This is a particularly favorable case, the macromolecular complex forming agent was present in the native environment; the complex forming agent may also be added. Such technique was applied to the concentration of vitamin B_{12} in sea water (*30*). Since sodium chloride interferes with the microbiological test, a vitamin B_{12}-binding mucopolysaccharide was added and the complex separated by gel filtration on Sephadex G-25.

Gel filtration frequently makes possible the *quantitative* determination of the composition (*31*) and the degree of binding (*32*) of such complexes, provided the experiments are carried out carefully.

HUMMEL and DREYER (*31*) equilibrated a gel bed of Sephadex G-25 (0.4×100 cm) with 9×10^{-5} M 2'-cytidylic acid in 0.1 M acetate buffer (pH 5.3) and started the elution with 2 mg of ribonuclease in the same buffer. In the elution diagram ($K_{av} = 0$) the protein peak was followed by a valley with a K_{av}-value of approximately 1. Cytidylic acid which had formed a complex with ribonuclease was absent in the effluent. Upon the addition of increasing amounts of cytidylic acid to the 2 mg-solution of ribonuclease the valley became smaller and smaller and a peak appeared finally. The concentration of cytidylic acid at which the area of the peak went through a minimum was the point of equivalence for the enzyme inhibitor complex.

MUDD and MANN (*32*) have extended this technique, initially on the same system and demonstrated that the dissociation constant of the complex can be calculated from the results of these experiments. The authors applied

Table 22. *Literature on the binding of pharmaceuticals and metals on serum proteins.*

HARDY, T. L., and K. R. L. MANSFORD: Biochem. J. **83**, 34 P (1962). Gel filtration as a method of studying drug-protein binding.

BARLOW, C. F., H. FIREMARK, and L. J. ROTH: J. Pharm. Pharmacol. **14**, 550 (1962). Drug-plasma binding measurement by Sephadex.

SARIS, N. E.: Acta chem. scand. **17**, 872 (1963). Differentiation of free and protein bound sulfonamide with the aid of Sephadex G-25.

ACRED, P., D. M. BROWN, T. L. HARDY, and K. R. L. MANSFORD: Nature **199**, 758 (1963). A new approach to studying the protein-binding properties of penicillins.

POTTER, G. D., and J. L. GUY: Proc. Soc. exp. Biol. Med. **116**, 658 (1964). A micro method for analysis of plasma salicylate.

SCHOLTAN, W.: Arzneimittel-Forschung **14**, 146 (1964). Vergleichende quantitative Bestimmung der Eiweißbindung von Chemotherapeutika mittels Sephadex und Dialyse.

WILCOX, P. E., and J. LISOWSKI: Federat. Proc. **19**, 333 (1960). Applications of gel filtration in studies of protein-metal complexes.

EKMAN, L., E. VALMET, and B. ÅBERG: Int. J. appl. Rad. Isotopes **12**, 32 (1961). Behavior of yttrium-91 and some lanthanons towards serum proteins in paper electrophoresis, density gradient electrophoresis and gel filtration.

BARBER, A. A., C. DEMPSTER, and N. G. ANDERSON: Clin. chim. Acta **8**, 143 (1963). A gel filtration method for studies on protein-iron binding.

HOLEYSOVSKA, H.: Collect. Czechoslov. chem. Commun. **31**, 130 (1966). Examination of interaction of manganous ions with human serum albumin by means of gel filtration.

BOOCOCK, G., and D. S. POPPLEWELL: Nature **210**, 1283 (1966). In vitro distribution of americium in human blood serum proteins.

VAN TONGEREN, J. H. M., and C. L. H. MAJOOR: Clin. chim. Acta **14**, 31 (1966). Demonstration of protein-losing gastroenteropathy. The disappearance rate of Cr-51 from Plasma and the binding of Cr-51 to different serum proteins.

the method to the quantitative description of the interactions between the methionine activating enzyme and different substrates or coenzymes (cf. also *156*).

The reversible reactions with low molecular weight substances are not restricted to enzymes. *Serum proteins* show the same type of *interaction*. Investigations concerned with the binding of *pharmaceuticals* and *metals* (cf. Table 22) are of particular interest. The qualitative and quantitative tests which are described there (frequently compared with dialysis experiments) demonstrate, also for this application, the great value of the gel filtration technique. Several experiments were carried out by adding dry Sephadex to the solution of those components. The application of the centrifuge technique which has been described in Chapter 2 would undoubtedly result in greater accuracy. The interactions of tryptophan and several of its derivatives with serum albumin were studied in column experiments and the advantages over the dialysis technique clearly demonstrated (*157*).

Phenol red in serum is bound almost exclusively by serum albumin. The binding is particularly strong at pH 4.5 but reversible at pH 8.5 (*33*). Gel filtration may be employed to utilize this fact for the *determination of the albumin content* in serum. – It was shown in gel filtration experiments that progesterone is bound in plasma by two independent systems of greatly different capacity and affinity (*34*).

The investigation of soluble *antigen-antibody complexes* which are generally formed with low molecular weight antigens, causes frequently great difficulties. Gel filtration offers also in this case great advantages (*35*):

An antiserum may be prepared against the decapeptide angiotensin, provided the hormone is applied while attached to polylysine. Upon incubation of the serum with radioactively labeled angiotensin and chromatography on Sephadex G-25, one can observe its migration with the serum proteins in the exclusion volume ($K_{av} = 0$). As increasing amounts of inactive angiotensin are added, larger amounts of the radioactively labeled compound appears in the low molecular weight fraction ($K_{av} = 1$). This behavior indicates clearly that a specific antibody is present in the serum applied.

Complexes of *nucleic acids* with low molecular weight substances have also been studied. The complex of desoxyribonucleic acid and actinomycin C_1 may easily be separated on Sephadex G-50 from an excess of the antibiotic (*36*). The binding is specific for DNA and related to the biological mechanism of action of the actinomycins. This observation was subsequently studied in greater detail by HARTMANN and his coworkers and extended to other systems (*37*).

A system consisting of, so to say, three phases is formed when an eluent (first phase) percolates a gel packing (second phase) which contains a *micelle-forming substance* (third phase). The distribution of different solutes between gel, eluent, and micelle was studied, as well as the influence of the

micelles on the reaction between dinitrofluorobenzene and glycine amide
(38). Prior to that, the surprising observation had been made that during
chromatography of gall bladder bile on Sephadex G-75 in distilled water
the entire amount of cholesterin and the phospholipids migrated in the
exclusion volume (39). Evidently the two compounds are capable of
forming micelles. The radii of the micelles were determined by BORGSTRÖM
(40) in a series of outstanding experiments. It was found that the micelle of
Na-dodecylsulfate in 0.15 molar solution of sodium ions (assuming spherical
structure) has a radius of 16–20 Å, while the sodium salt of the taurine ester
of desoxycholic acid has a radius of 35–50 Å. Both compounds are still
excluded by Sephadex G-50 ($K_{av} = 0$). The high molecular, cholesterin-
binding fraction from gall bladder bile has been studied on Sephadex more
frequently (158, 159).

Gel Chromatography

If the differences in size between the components of a substance mixture are
only minor, then the differences to be expected in the elution volume are
also not great. Since the separation volume (cf. page 68, 69) is always a certain
fraction of the total volume of the gel bed, it becomes clear that the separation – under otherwise identical conditions – is the better, the longer the
column is. The porosity of the gel used must also be adapted optimally to
the given separation problem. The fractionation ranges of the commercially
available gels are recorded in the Tables of Chapter 2. It is advisable to
select the gel in such a way that only one of the expected components is so
large that it does not at all enter into the gel grains. Preliminary separations
on a gel of medium porosity are recommended if the molecular weights are
spread over a very wide range. The low molecular weight fraction is again
chromatographed on a gel with small pores and the high molecular fraction
on a gel with large pores. Several gels will have to be used for a given
separation problem if the pore size distribution of a gel is rather narrow
and the sample is heterogeneous.

Contrary to the preceding section, the experimental data to be presented
here cannot be organized systematically. Most of the applications discussed
in Chapter 5 would then also have to be presented here. A *representative
selection* of detailed experiments has been compiled in the following figures.
Only the separation of well defined substances is described in these experiments. While this approach offers the advantage of better understanding, it
has the disadvantage that the chromatography of artificial mixtures is described on the more common examples (Fig. 26, 27, 32, 33). The experiments are organized by increasing molecular weight of the substances investigated and thus also according to increasing porosity of the gels applied.

An attempt has been made to present the individual classes of substances in accordance with the frequency of their occurrence in the literature.

Fig. 26 shows the elution diagram of the *fractionation of a mixture of polyethylene glycols* on a gel bed of 1.3×102 cm (136 ml) on Sephadex G-10. The solution was applied in a volume of 1 ml and a concentration of 2%; phosphate buffer (0.05 M; pH 7.0) was used as eluent at a flow rate of 6 ml/h. The polyethylene glycol with the average molecular weight 600 (a)

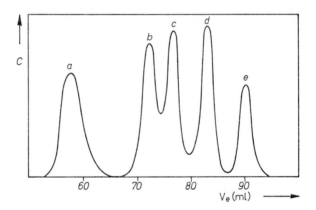

Fig. 26. Fractionation of polyethylene glycols on Sephadex G-10 according to GELOTTE and PORATH (*41*); ordinate: concentration.

has its maximum at an elution volume of 40% of the total volume (cf. Table 17). It is thus excluded. The other components: (b) tetraethylene glycol ($M = 194$); (c) triethylene glycol ($M = 150$); (d) diethylene glycol ($M = 106$) and (e) ethylene glycol ($M = 62$) show elution volumes which are directly proportional to the logarithm of the molecular weight.

A separation strictly on the basis of molecular weight differences is also possible in organic solvents. This applies also to the low molecular weight substances of a homologous series of molecules. The behavior of the triglycerides of the higher fatty acids was in agreement with the rules of gel chromatography (Fig. 27) when these substances were chromatographed in chloroform on a gel bed of 2.5×35 cm (170 ml) of Sephadex LH-20. The following pattern was obtained when a total of 2 ml of a 0.2% solution was applied: (a) tristearin ($M = 891$); (b) tricaprin ($M = 555$); (d) tributyrin ($M = 302$), and (e) triacetin ($M = 218$). The glycerides with free hydroxyl groups are evidently entering into an interaction with the gel, which causes a stronger retardation. This is the reason for the fact that (c) dipalmitin ($M = 569$) and primarily (f) monostearin ($M = 359$) are eluted much too late with regard to their molecular weights.

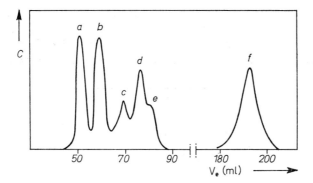

Fig. 27. Gel chromatography of glycerides on Sephadex LH 20 according to JOUSTRA (42); ordinate: concentration.

Certain pentapeptides may be polymerized by condensation in concentrated aqueous solution under the influence of the catalytic action of pepsin (plastein reaction). The *mixture of oligomeric pentapeptides* from tyrosyl-leucyl-prolyl-glutamyl-phenylalanine was separated on a long gel bed of Sephadex G-25 (4.2×200 cm $= 2.8$ l) (Fig. 28).

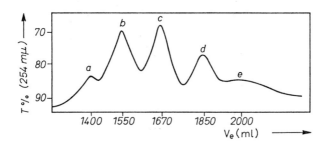

Fig. 28. Separation of the polycondensation products of a pentapeptide ("plastein") on Sephadex G-25 according to DETERMANN and KÖHLER (43). Ordinate: percent transmission at 254 mμ.

The column was started with 81 mg in 20 ml of dilute ammonium hydroxide; the eluent was 0.2% NH_4HCO_3 (50 ml/h). The individual fractions were rechromatographed on the same column and subjected to chemical structural analysis. As expected, they were from (a) through (d) the pentamer to the dimer of the pentapeptide used initially. A small amount (e) of the original pentapeptide was found in the reaction mixture.

It can be seen from Fig. 29 that Sephadex G-75 is best suited for the separation of the *enzymatic activities of the pancreas extract*. The experiments were carried out with three different types of Sephadex on gel beds of identical size (2×42 cm; 130 ml). The extract was obtained by treating defatted pancreas powder of the dog with 0.05 M sodium acetate buffer (pH 5.3) in 0.005 M calcium acetate (5 ml/g of powder) for 30 minutes. Three milliliters each of this solution were applied to the appropriate column

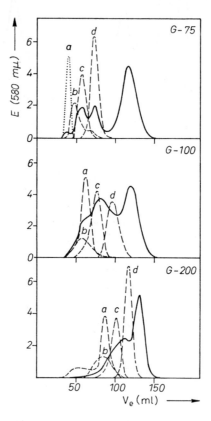

Fig. 29. Separation of the enzymes of the pancreas extract on the three different types of Sephadex according to GELOTTE (44).

and eluted with the same buffer. The following enzymes were found in this order: (a) lipase, (b) ribonuclease, (c) trypsinogen and chymotrypsinogen, and (d) amylase.

The *isolation of pure hemoglobin from erythrocytes* requires few steps: the washed cells are allowed to disintegrate in distilled water. The stromata are removed by filtration. Enzyme activities (primarily that of catalase) are, however, also liberated in the course of this operation. These enzymes will contaminate hemoglobin. The hemoglobin (d) from 3 ml of lysate may be obtained in the pure state on a gel bed of Sephadex G-100 (20×52 cm;

163 ml) in 0.1 M NaCl (40 ml/h) (Fig. 30). The accompanying enzyme activities: aldolase (a), catalase (b), and lactate dehydrogenase (c) were eluted earlier.

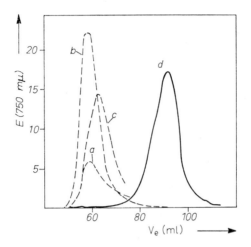

Fig. 30. Elution diagram of the proteins from erythrocytes on Sephadex G-100 according to AEBI, SCHNEIDER, GANG, and WIESMANN (45). Ordinate: extinction of the Folin-Lowry reaction.

Sephadex G-200 is the gel of choice for the separation of serum proteins. One obtains in essence three fractions the first of which contains in addition to the lipoproteins the α- and β-(19S) globulins. The center fraction consists primarily of γ-(7S) globulins and the last peak represents the serum albumin.

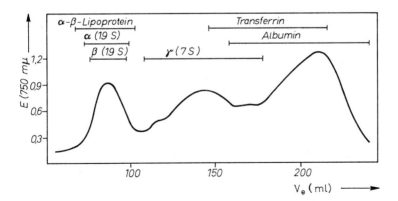

Fig. 31. Gel chromatography of human serum on Sephadex G-200 according to FLODIN and KILLANDER (46). Ordinate: extinction of the Folin-Lowry reaction.

The gel chromatography of the serum proteins has been covered extensively in the literature. Several publications will be mentioned in Chapter 5. The elution diagram of 10 ml of human serum on a gel bed of 4×35 cm (460 m) Sephadex G-200 may serve as illustration for this type of separations (Fig. 31). The eluent was 0.1 M tris-HCl-buffer (pH 8.0) in 0.2 M sodium chloride (65 to 70 ml/h).

Macromolecules of different molecular weight which are soluble in organic solvents may be separated on the various types of Styragel. These polystyrene gels are applied primarily to the determination of the molecular weight distribution of synthetic polymers (cf. page 120). Several experi-

Table 23. *Polystyrene standards in Figs. 32 and 35*

Designation	Molecular weight ($\bar{M}_w$)	Uniformity ($\bar{M}_w/\bar{M}_n$)
a	1 197 000	1.19
b	570 000	1.05
c	267 000	1.08
d	154 000	1.04
e	82 000	1.05
f	13 850	1.50

ments on the *chromatography of polystyrene standards* (Table 23) on macroporous polystyrene gels (from Table 4, next to the last line) are compiled in Fig. 32.

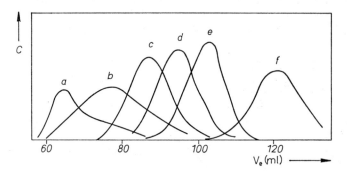

Fig. 32. Superimposed elution curves of polystyrene standards of Table 23 on macroporous polystyrene gels according to MOORE (47). Ordinate: concentration.

The extraordinarily long gel bed (0.775×366 cm $= 172$ ml) was kept under considerable pressure in order to maintain the extremely fast flow (66 ml/h) of toluene which was used as eluent. The concentration of the effluent was determined with the help of a Waters differential refractometer.

This brief account on the potential of gel chromatography (in a narrower sense) should be closed with an example (Fig. 33) of the *separation of particles* on a highly porous agar gel.

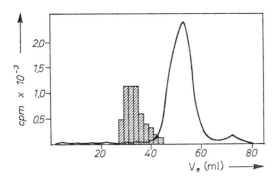

Fig. 33. Separation of polio virus (labeled) and influenza virus (shaded) on 2.5% agar beads according to BENGTSSON and PHILIPSON (48). Ordinate: radioactivity in counts per minute.

The example chosen is a mixture of ^{32}P labeled polio virus type I and influenza virus (SHOPE). The two viruses have a size of 28 and 100 mμ, respectively, which corresponds to "molecular weights" of 6.8×10^6 and 1.7×10^8, respectively. A suspension of 2 ml was chromatographed on a 2×30 cm (94 ml) gel bed of 2.5% agar beads in a combined salt solution (6 ml/h): 0.0081 M KH_2PO_4; 0.0137 M NaCl; 0.0027 M KCl; 0.0009 M $CaCl_2$; 0.0005 M $MgCl_2$, and 0.05% Tween 80. The influenza virus (which was not labeled) was detected by the hemagglutinin test.

Molecular Weight Determination

The molecular weight dependent elution volume of a given substance is easily reproduced on the same column. One may thus in turn determine the molecular weight of an unknown substance from the elution volume. The column has to be calibrated for this purpose, i.e., the elution volumes of test substances have to be correlated with the molecular weights.

Calibration

According to the statements of Chapter 3, it is quite certain that in gel chromatography the separation of macromolecules is brought about by differences in molecular size. With the great differences in structure which we find in macromolecules, the relation between molecular size and molecular weight is, however, different for each type. The substances used for calibration purposes should, therefore, be closely related to the substances to be studied.

Substances suitable for calibration are frequently not available. Only in the group of vinyl polymers one finds a broad spectrum of synthetic polystyrenes of narrow molecular weight distribution which are suitable for the calibration of gel columns for the purpose of molecular weight determination (cf. Table 24). – The proteins occupy a special position among all polymers because they are found in nature with exactly defined molecular weights. They have, therefore, been applied most frequently to the calibration of water-swellable gels (cf. Table 25). It must, however, be borne in

Table 24. *Commercially available polystyrene fractions which are used as molecular weight standards*.*

$\bar{M}_w$	$\bar{M}_w/\bar{M}_n$	Supplier**	$\bar{M}_w$	$\bar{M}_w/\bar{M}_n$	Supplier**
900	1.10	b	97 200	1.06	a, b
2 000	1.10	a	97 200	1.01	c
2 030	1.10	b	160 000	1.06	a, b
3 600	1.10	a	173 000	1.06	c
4 800	1.10	b	411 000	1.10	a
5 000	1.10	c	411 000	1.06	b
10 000	1.06	c	411 000	1.05	c
13 300	1.06	a, b	860 000	1.15	a, b
19 800	1.06	a, b	867 000	1.12	c
19 900	1.01	c	1 800 000	1.25	b
51 000	1.06	a, b	2 145 000	1.20	c
51 000	1.04	c			

*   The manufacturer (c) offers also polypropylene glycol:
    $\bar{M}_n$ = 790, 1220, 2020, 3900.

** (a) ARRO Laboratories, Inc., Joliet, Illinois (USA)
    (b) Pressure Chemical Co., Pittsburgh, Pennsylvania (USA)
    (c) Waters Associates, Framingham, Mass. (USA).

mind that the reported molecular weights of many proteins may deviate considerably. ANDREWS (49) has published a comprehensive review with the aspects of gel chromatography in mind. In addition to the chemical molecular weight, the dimensions of the globular proteins are also frequently known. It is thus possible to obtain information on the radius of action of other molecules from columns which have been calibrated with proteins.

"Molecular Weight Marker Kits" are available from Mann Research Laboratories and from Boehringer. They consist either of proteins or of polystyrene standards for various molecular weight ranges.

It has been pointed out already in Chapter 3 that the elution behavior of a substance in gel chromatography can be described by different variables

Table 25. *Commercially available proteins which have been widely applied as standards for molecular weight determination*

No.*	Protein	Mol.-weight	Supplier**
1	Cytochrome c	13 000	a, b, c, d,
2	Ribonuclease A	13 600	a, b, c, d, e
3	Myoglobin	17 800	c, d
4	Trypsin inhibitor (soybean)	21 500	b, c, d, e
5	α-Chymotrypsin	22 500	a, b, c, d, e
6	Trypsin	24 000	a, b, c, d, e
7	Chymotrypsinogen A	25 000	a, c, d, e
8	Pepsin	35 500	b, c, d, e
9	Egg albumin	45 000	b, c, d, e
10	Serum albumin (bovine, monomer)	67 000	b, c, d
11	Glycerine aldehyde phosphate dehydrogenase	117 000	a, b, d, e
12	Serum albumin (bovine, dimer)	134 000	contained in the monomer
13	Aldolase (yeast)	147 000	a, e
14	γ-Globulin (human)	140 000	b, c, d
15	Alcohol dehydrogenase (yeast)	150 000	a, c, d, e
16	Catalase	230 000	a, b, c, d, e

* The numbers refer to Fig. 34.

** (a) C. F. Boehringer und Söhne G.m.b.H., Mannheim-Waldhof, Germany

    (b) Serva Entwicklungslabor, Heidelberg, Germany

    (c) Mann Research Laboratories, Inc., New York, N.Y.

    (d) Calbiochem, Los Angeles, California, USA

    (e) Worthington Biochemical Corporation, Freehold, New Jersey, USA

which are derived from the elution volume (V_e) (cf. Table 18). These parameters have the advantage that they are independent of the geometry of the column under consideration, thus making it possible to compare two experiments with each other. These relationships are compiled in Table 26. Some of them are empirical (E), some were derived on the basis of theoretical considerations (T) of the *dependence of the elution volume on the molecular weight* (M). Most of these relations have been applied repeatedly and were found to be valid. Furthermore, SANFELIPPO and SURAK (*63*) have deduced the empirical correlation $K_{av} = K_1/\lg M - K_2$ during the chromatography of peptide hormones under different conditions. – The relationship $\lg V_e = k \cdot \lg M$ was applied to a comparison of the molecular weights of ATP-guanidino phosphotransferases (*64*). The corresponding calibration curve was, however, based on only three values. – The application of OGSTON's concept on the gel state to the problems of gel chromatography by LAURENT and KILLANDER (*65*) led to a theoretically highly interesting correlation. Thus far it has, however, found no practical applications. The correlation has been confirmed by SIEGEL and MONTY (*66*) during a critical

Table 26. *Relations between the elution behavior of macromolecules and their molecular weights*

Molecular type	Solvent	Relation (derived)*	Authors
Polysaccharides	Water	$V_e/V_t = k \cdot \lg M$ (E)	GRANATH, FLODIN (50)
Paraffins	Toluene	$V_e - V_o = k \cdot \lg M$ (E)	BREWER (51)
Polysaccharides	Water	$K_d^{1/3} = k_1 - k_2 \cdot M^{1/2}$ (T)	PORATH (52)
Proteins	Water	$K_d^{1/3} = k_1 - k_2 \cdot M^{1/2}$ (E)	WIELAND, DUESBERG, (53) DETERMANN
Proteins	Water	$V_e/V_o = k \cdot \lg M$ (E)	WHITAKER (54)
Oligo-nucleotides	Water	$\ln K_d = k \cdot M$ (E)	HOHN, POLLMANN (55)
Proteins	Water	$V_e = k \cdot \lg M$ (E)	ANDREWS (56)
Oligostyrenes	Chloroform	$K_d^{1/3} = k_1 - k_2 \cdot M^{1/2}$ (E)	DETERMANN, LÜBEN, WIELAND (57)
Proteins	Water	$K_d = f(M^{1/3}/k)$ (T)	ACKERS (58)
Proteins	Water	$(V_e/V_o)^{1/3} = k_1 - k_2 \cdot M^{1/3}$ (T)	SQUIRE (59)
Polyethylenes Polyethers	diff. lipophilic solvents	$V_e = k \cdot \lg$ chain length (E)	MOORE, (60) HENDRICKSON
Cellulose nitrate Polystyrenes Polymethacrylate	Tetrahydrofuran	$V_e = k_1 - k_2 \cdot \lg (M^{1/2} \cdot R)$ $V_e = k_1 - k_2 \cdot \lg (M^{1/2} \cdot [\eta]^{1/3})$ (E,T)	MEYERHOFF (61)
Oligopeptides	Phenol/glacial acetic acid/water	$K_d^{1/3} = k_1 - k_2 \cdot M^{1/2}$ (E)	CARNEGIE (62)
Hydrocarbons	Cyclohexane	$k_1 - k_2 \cdot \lg V_e = M$ (E)	BREWER (169)

* Explanation of symbols: k, k_1, k_2 are constants which have a different value for each formula. (E) refers to the empirical derivation of the formula and (T) to its derivation from theoretical assumptions on the mechanism of gel chromatography.

comparison of several of the relationships from Table 26, using ANDREW's values (49, 56). ANDERSON and STODDART (67) have recently compared the relationships of PORATH (52), LAURENT and KILLANDER (65), and ANDREWS (56).

The linear dependence of the elution volume on the logarithm of the molecular weight is used most frequently in practical applications (cf. 68). Figure 34 shows a number of calibration curves for different Sephadex gels (20). The proteins used for this purpose are to be found in Tables 25 and 27. The data on the elution behavior were obtained in different laboratories. In view of the minor deviations from the straight line as determined by the method of least squares general significance may be attributed to the *equations* of these straight lines (Table 28). Once the volume outside the particles (V_o; determined by the elution volume of a completely

Table 27. *The proteins which - in addition to those mentioned in Table 25 - were applied to the calibration curves of Figs. 34 and 36 (68).*

No.	Protein	Molecular weight
17	Kallikrein inhibitor	6 500
18	Trypsin inhibitor (lima beans)	8 400
19	Methemoglobin	17 000
20	Peroxydase-1	40 000
21	α-Hydroxysteroid dehydrogenase	47 000
22	Phosphoglyceromutase	64 000
23	Malate dehydrogenase	79 000
24	Enolase	80 000
25	Creatine phosphokinase	81 000
26	Pyruvate kinase	230 000
27	Xanthine oxydase	320 000

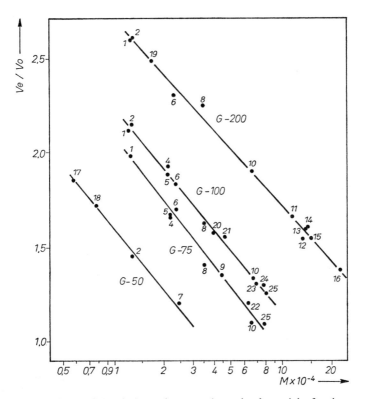

Fig. 34. Dependence of the elution volume on the molecular weight for the proteins of Tables 25 and 27; the values were established in different laboratories; the straight lines were obtained by calculating the most probable values (method of least squares); according to DETERMANN and MICHEL (68).

Table 28. *Correlation of the molecular weight and elution volume of globular proteins on Sephadex gels.*

Gel type	Equation	Explanation
G-75	$\lg M = 5.624 - 0.752(V_e/V_o)$	M = molecular weight
G-100	$\lg M = 5.941 - 0.847(V_e/V_o)$	V_e = elution volume
G-200	$\lg M = 6.698 - 0.987(V_e/V_o)$	V_o = exclusion volume
general	$\lg M = M_o - (6.062 - 5.00 \cdot d)(V_e/V_o)$	d = density of the swollen gel

excluded substance) of a Sephadex gel packing is known, the molecular weight of an unknown globular protein may be calculated from the elution volume with the help of these equations. – The values used for the calibra-

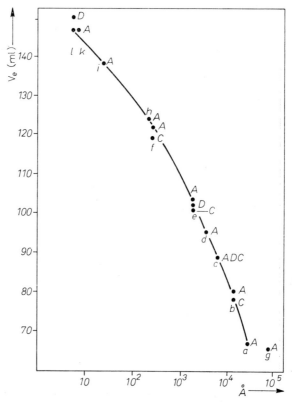

Fig. 35. The elution volume of polystyrene-standards of Table 23 (a–f) and (g) $\bar{M} = 3\,500\,000$, two polyethylene glycols (h) $\bar{M} = 4000$ and (i) $\bar{M} = 400$, (k) ortho-dichloro-benzene and (l) acetone on a 5×10^4 Å polystyrene gel in dependence of the chain length of the polymer in Å (ordinate); gel bed 0.775×366 cm = (172 ml). (A) chromatography in toluene at 90°C; (C) in tetrahydrofuran at 55°C; (D) in tetralin at 125°C according to MOORE and HENDRICKSON (60).

tion curve of Sephadex G-50 were obtained in a single laboratory (69). Its general validity is thus not ascertained. It became, however, feasible to combine the three equations for the Sephadex gels G-75 through G-200 in one general equation (Table 28) since the slope of the curves (Figure 34) was found to be linearly proportional to the gel density (d) (69). This equation may be applied to any type of gel. Only the density of the swollen gel and the elution behavior of a single known protein have to be determined, in order to be able to calculate the molecular weights of unknown proteins.

Other types of macromolecules require other numerical values in the equation since the space filling properties are very different. For the calibration of the GPC-apparatus, curves are used in general which correlate the elution volume with the logarithm of chain length. As an example, the calibration curve for a Styragel column (60) is shown in Figure 35. The curve was in essence determined with the polystyrene standards. It is not linear over the entire range which is probably due to the high number of magnitudes, which are covered.

Technique

The experimental technique for the molecular weight determination is in principle the same as that for the separation of a mixture of substances. All that is required is the determination of the *elution volumes*. As a rule, the solvent volume which leaves the column between the application of the substance to the gel packing and its elution in maximum concentration is considered the elution volume (cf. Chapter 3). This determination will be more accurate for large gel beds. If, however, the cross section is very large, it is necessary (for the analysis in the effluent) to apply a correspondingly large amount of the sample solution (or the calibration substances). In order to prevent this, rather narrow and long columns should be used for the molecular weight determination. While ANDREWS (49, 56) has used Sephadex gel packings of 2.5 × 50 cm, the columns of WHITAKER (54) had dimensions of 1.1 × 200 cm. The column dimensions of the majority of the other authors are within these ranges. The Styragel columns in the GPC-apparatus (70) are an exception. These columns are used exclusively for analytical purposes and have a total length of 370 cm. (The mode of action of this instrument, as applied to the almost completely automatic determination of molecular weight distributions of synthetic polymers, is described on page 40). Similar types of equipment may also be set up for water-soluble polymers (71), whereby the work load for this type of molecular weight determination will also be reduced further.

The equipment for *thinlayer gel chromatography* is considerably less elaborate (cf. Chapter 2). At the end of the experiment the distance between the start and the substance spot – the distance of migration – has to be measured instead of the elution volume (*56*). Similar to the standardization of the results of paper chromatography, where the distance of migration of the substance is compared with the solvent front (R_f-value), it was found useful to compare the distance of migration in thinlayer gel chromatography with the migration of a well defined substance (*72*). The molecular weight determination of proteins – only there thinlayer gel chromatography has so far been applied – may be carried out with only a few micrograms of a substance (*56, 72, 73*). The proteins of Table 25 may be used for comparison. It is demonstrated in Fig. 36 that the migration of different proteins is a linear function of the logarithm of the molecular weight when compared with the distance of migration of cytochrome c. The author has often

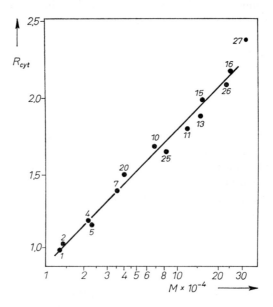

Fig. 36. Relationship between the molecular weights of different proteins of Tables 25 and 27 and the distances of migration on thin layers of Sephadex G-200 (*68*), as compared with the distance of migration of cytochrome c ($R_{cyt} = 1$).

made the experience that the calibration curves are not in all cases valid, i.e. the slope of the curve may vary rather widely from one series of experiments to the next. The results of a molecular weight determination are more accurate, if one applies suitable test proteins to each plate. This is accomplished without difficulty, since on a 20 cm wide plate at least ten samples may be applied simultaneously. Due to the simple instrumentation and the low substance requirements the accuracy of molecular weight determinations may be increased by many individual determinations, approximately 20, thus obtaining a statistical average. Following this approach, only a few percent of deviation have to be expected for the low molecular weight range, while for molecular weights above 100000 the error is frequently somewhat greater.

Molecular Weight Determination of Proteins

Many of the systematic investigations (in aqueous medium) which were discussed in the previous section were conducted with proteins as model substances. There is, indeed, great need for molecular weight determinations of these frequently very sensitive macromolecules which are found in large numbers in nature. Great care must, however, be taken in evaluating the results and several peculiarities have to be kept in mind carefully which are characteristic for this group of macromolecules. Practically all enzymes and serum proteins belong to the group of globular proteins which will be discussed here.

Theory

These protein molecules have – from the standpoint of polymer chemistry – a number of unusual properties: As was mentioned already, each protein has a well defined *unique* molecular weight. The structures of these macromolecules are by and large rigid and rather compact. The partial specific density is the same for almost all species, thus implying that – over a very wide range – each chemical weight unit is associated with a certain space filling property. This, however, is the irrevocable prerequisite for the molecular weight determination by comparison of the space filling requirement with that of standard substances. Therefore, several authors (58, 65) who were guided by theoretical considerations during the quantitative evaluation of the elution behavior of proteins have correlated the Stokes' radius with the elution volume. In almost all of the publications quoted which are concerned with the topic of molecular weight determination by gel chromatography, one notices a certain discomfort about the fact that the established relations require actually protein molecules of uniform shape. The existing differences in the shape of native proteins, however, are evidently not sufficient to effect the separations which are based on size differences. Only SIEGEL and MONTY (66) have described two extreme cases where – on Sephadex G-200 – the higher molecular weight protein, due to its smaller Stokes' radius, was eluted after the low molecular weight one. The proteins of concern (fibrinogen $M = 330000$, ferritin $M = 1300000$, and urease $M = 483000$) are, however, insufficiently studied with regard to their state of aggregation and the content of carbohydrate that the results do not carry enough weight. Furthermore, at least the molecular weight of ferritin reported there (66) is far outside of the fractionation range generally attributed to Sephadex G-200. In cases of extreme deviation of the molecular shape (fibrinogen) from the normal, bulkiness will make diffusion into the gel more difficult and result in "early" elution. – This can also be recognized clearly in experiments with nucleic acids which may be considered rigid rods while proteins have – roughly – the shape of a rugby ball. The exclusion limits of nucleic acids are indeed for all gels considerably lower than those of proteins.

The very careful protein-analytical investigations of ANDREWS (*49*, *56*, *74*) have shown that the *separation range* (cf. Table 5) of Sephadex gels consists of two parts. In the major portion the linear dependence between the elution volume and the logarithm of the molecular weight is in perfect agreement (cf. Fig. 34), while at both ends of the molecular weight scale the curves are no longer linear. For practical purposes, the measured values of a molecular weight determination should best be located in the linear part of the curve. According to that, Sephadex G-100 is suitable for the determination of molecular weights of globular proteins from approximately 10000 up to 150000. The numbers for Sephadex G-200 are accordingly 10000 to 300000.

More recently other proteins have been isolated which in addition to amino acids contain also carbohydrate units. The density of these *glycoproteins* is not the same as that of proteins which are only composed of amino acids. Their elution behavior on dextran gel columns differs considerably from the "normal" proteins (*54*). The structure is, in all likelihood, the more expanded, the higher the carbohydrate content is. Careful studies in this direction have been conducted by ANDREW's (*49*) and by WARD and ARNOTT (*75*).

The structure of proteins may also be influenced by environmental factors. This may result in larger space requirements and find an expression in lower elution volumes. Thus, serum albumin will be split into two peaks in 5 M urea on Sephadex G-200, while normally it has a K_{av}-value of 0.43. The first component is eluted much earlier ($K_{av} = 0.1$), approximately 60% of the protein remains unchanged (*76*). It is entirely possible that a number of the protein molecules are denatured, now having higher space filling requirements. The various steps of protein denaturation may be followed directly with the changes in the elution volume (*77*). Ribonuclease appears on Sephadex G-100 with apparent "molecular weights" which, after various treatments, differ from that of the native protein by the following factors: alkali denaturation, 1.9; performic acid oxidation, 3.0; exposure to 4 M urea, 2.5; exposure to 8 M urea, 4.3. It has been observed on Sephadex G-200 (*160*) that the space filling requirements of serum albumin are considerably increased upon chemical modification (acylation with different reagents).

It has been mentioned already in Chapter 3 that a slight influence of temperature on the elution behavior of proteins has been described repeatedly (*54, 78, 79*). This is perhaps also due to changes in the tertiary structure. Likewise, one may assume (*78*) that in these experiments changes occurred in the gel structure and brought about the differences in elution volume. The dependence of the elution behavior of proteins on the pH-value may also be caused either by a change in the structure of the gel or by partial denaturation.

Results

With the wealth of experimental data one can already draw conclusion on the tertiary structure from an anomalous behavior of a protein. The fact that exact statements about the molecular weight of proteins can be made with the relatively simple means of gel chromatography will in the future not diminish the significance of the ultracentrifuge as analytical tool. With both methods, independent measurements can be carried out and the combination of the results will give deeper insight into the structure of a protein.

The activities of enzymes are of particular interest to the protein chemist. New metabolic reactions are constantly being discovered and the catalyzing enzymes are purified and isolated (cf. Chapter 5). Gel chromatography offers means and ways to determine the molecular weight of impure enzyme preparations (or that of an enzyme of extremely low quantities) if the elution volume is determined by a specific test. Suitable conditions for subsequent isolation steps can easily be established in the same way.

Twenty-nine enzymes are compiled in Table 29 the molecular weights of which were determined by gel chromatography. The deviation from the data obtained by sedimentation and diffusion are remarkably low in most cases. Sometimes, however, the differences are considerable. The gel chromatographic method is very simple and requires only a minimum of experimental effort; the experiments must, however, be carried out carefully before premature conclusions are drawn:

If, for instance, the only protein on a calibration curve happens to be lactate dehydrogenase, the molecular weight of which (135000) is still subject to discussion, then it is difficult to understand why, despite of that, the molecular weights (232000 and 197000) of two phosphatases from rat uterus can be determined so accurately (*94*). Also, if the next following calibration point (glycerine aldehyde phosphate dehydrogenase, 130000) is far away from the protein to be measured, as is the case for 5'-ribonucleotide phosphohydrolase (M = 237000), reservations are in place with regard to the result (*95*).

Several other publications are compiled in Table 30. The molecular weights of these proteins were also estimated by chromatography. The data have not been incorporated in Table 29 because the enzymes are as yet not fully characterized or they are other proteins.

Gel chromatography led already very early to the discovery of *associations* in protein preparations. PEDERSEN (*96*) was able to separate on Sephadex

Table 29. *Molecular weights of enzymes as determined by gel chromatography*

Enzyme	Origin	Gel*	Molecular weight	Reference
Lactate dehydrogenase	diff. iso- and hetero enzymes	G-200	110—120 000	WIELAND et al. (53)
D-lactate dehydrogenase	yeast	G-100	103 000	IWATSUBO et al. (80)
Adenosine deaminase	calf duodenum	G-75; G-100	34 000	ANDREWS (56)
β-Glucoronidase	*Patella barbara*	7% Agarose	300 000	LARGIER et al. (81)
Pantothenic acid synthetase	*E. coli*	G-200	69 000	
Glutamate-pyruvate transaminase	porcine heart	G-200	82 000	AURICCHIO et al. (82)
Aminopeptidase	kidney microsomes	G-200	276 000	
Lipase	porcine pancreas	G-200	38 000	SARDA et al. (83)
Agavain	plant proteinase	G-100	52 500	TIPTON (84)
Renin	various origins	G-100; G-200	42—49 000	KEMP et al. (85)
Xanthine oxydase	milk	G-200	286 000	ANDREWS et al. (86)
Xanthine oxydase	porcine liver	G-200	190 000	
Glutamate dehydrogenase	bovine	G-200	270 000	ROGERS et al. (87)
Carnitin acetyltransferase	pigeon chest muscle	G-100	55 000	CHASE et al. (88)
Glucose-6-phosphate dehydrogenase	yeast	G-100	128 000	
Alkaline phosphatase	bovine duodenum	G-100	130 000	ANDREW (49)
Glycerine dehydrogenase	*Aerobacter aerogenes*	G-100	140 000	
Alkaline phosphatase	milk	G-100	180 000	
Acid phosphatase	prostate	G-100	109 000	OSTROWSKI (89)
Esterase	liver microsomes	G-200	175 000	BOGUTH et al. (90)
Urokinase	human urine	G-75; G-100	35 000	BURGES et al. (91)
Prothrombin	human serum	G-100	68—75 000	LANCHANTIN et al. (92)
Thrombin	prothrombin+citrate	G-200	35 000	
Alanine transaminase	rat liver	G-200	90 500	NIESCHLAG et al. (93)
Sulfite reductase	*Salmonella typhimurium*	G-200	830 000	
Sulfite reductase	*Neurospora crassa*	G-200	540 000	SIEGEL et al. (66)
Hydroxylamine reductase	*Neurospora crassa*	G-200	290 000; 44 000	
6-Phosphogluconate dehydrogenase	Drosophila, man	G-200	79 000	KAZAZIAN (161)
Arginine kinase	lobster muscle	G-100	37 000	VIRDEN et al. (162)

* With one exception Sephadex was used in all cases.

Table 30. *Additional literature on the molecular weight determination of proteins by gel chromatography.*

FEINSTEIN, G., and J. R. WHITAKER: Biochemistry 3, 1050 (1964). On the molecular weights of the proteolytic enzymes of stem bromelain.

DOWNEY, W. K., and P. ANDREWS: Biochem. J. 94, 642 (1965). Gel filtration applied to the study of lipases and other esterases.

SELBY, K., and C. C. MAITLAND: Biochem. J. 94, 578 (1965). The fractionation of *myrothecium verrucaria* cellulase by gel filtration.

DIMIGEN, J., F. KLINK und D. RICHTER: Z. Naturforschung 20 *b*, 924 (1965). Zur Kenntnis des Molekulargewichtes von Peptidsynthetasen aus Leber und Hefe.

RIEKKINEN, P. J., T. O. EKFORS, and V. K. HOPSU: Biochim. biophys. Acta 118, 604 (1966). Purification and characteristics of an alkaline protease from rat-submandibular gland.

JUNGWIRTH, C., und G. BODO: Biochem. Z. 339, 382 (1964). Bestimmung des Molekulargewichts von Interferon durch Gelfiltration.

BURKE, D. C., and J. ROSS: Nature 208, 1297 (1965). Molecular weight of chick interferon.

SCHONNE, E.: Biochim. biophys. Acta 115, 429 (1966). Properties of rat-tumor interferon.

DELLACHA, J. M., M. A. ENERO, and I. FAIFERMAN: Experientia 22, 16 (1966). Molecular weight of bovine growth hormone.

MORRIS, C. J. O. R.: Acta endocrinol. Suppl. 90, 163 (1964). On the molecular weight of pregnant mare's serum gonadotrophin.

HNILICA, L. S., and L. G. BESS: Analyt. Biochem. 12, 421 (1965). The heterogeneity of arginine-rich histones.

PŘISTOUPIL, T. I.: J. Chromatog. 19, 64 (1965). Gel filtration of modified bovine serum on Sephadex G-200.

NAKAYAMA, F., and H. MIYAKE: J. Lab. clin. Med. 65, 638 (1965). Cholesterol complexing by macromolecular fractions in human gall bladder bile.

THOMPSON, E. O. P., and I. J. O'DONELL: Aust. J. biol. Sci. 18, 1207 (1965). Studies on reduced wool.

SOROF, S., E. M. YOUNG, R. A. McBRIDE, and C. B. COFFEY: Arch. Biochem. Biophys. 113, 83 (1966). Size classes of soluble liver macromolecules.

SIMONS, K., and T. WEBER: Biochim. biophys. Acta 117, 201 (1966). The vitamin B_{12}-binding protein in human leukocytes.

PULIDO, P., J. H. R. KÄGI, and B. L. VALLEE: Biochemistry 5, 1768 (1966). Isolation and some properties of human matallothionein.

G-150 the pure dimer of serum albumin from old preparations and characterized it. The components which were represented by earlier peaks were the trimer and the tetramer of serum albumin (cf. *163*). When pure ribonuclease was lyophilized from 50% acetic acid and the protein afterwards chromatographed on Sephadex G-75 several active fractions were obtained. The material represented by the main peak corresponded to the original monomeric protein while the elution volumes of the other components indicated again aggregations (*97*). The observations of SIEGEL and MONTY (*98*) for urease are reminiscent of those earlier made for serum albumin. Gel chromatography on Sephadex G-200 enabled the authors to separate from the crystalline enzyme (Sigma, Type C1) several more rapidly migrating fractions. The Stokes' radius was calculated from the elution volume with the help of the equation of ACKERS (58) and together with sedimentation data the molecular weight. Thus the remarkable fact was established that from this preparation, in addition to urease ($M = 483000$), also its dimer and the trimer could be isolated. A form of the enzyme of even higher aggregation is supposed to have been isolated.

Association Equilibria

The results of the gel chromatography of reversibly associating systems are of particular interest and importance because it is not easy to study these systems in the ultracentrifuge. With gel chromatography, however, very dilute solutions can still be analyzed. This is true in particular for enzymes, when biochemical tests are applied to the effluent. ANDREWS has already shown for hemoglobin and beta-lactoglobulin on Sephadex G-200 that the "molecular weight" decreased with increasing dilution and approached an ultimate value that was one half of that generally accepted (56). It can be demonstrated by gel chromatography on Sephadex G-75 (164) and G-100 (165; cf. 166) that the dissociation of hemoglobin is widely dependent upon the state of oxidation. Very dilute solutions of glutamate dehydrogenase gave elution volumes on Sephadex G-200 which, when extrapolated to indefinite dilution, suggested the value 250000 as molecular weight for the sub-unit (49). In view of the reversible dissociation of high molecular weight proteins one can only speak of molecular weight once the experimental conditions are exactly defined.

Many proteins are subject to reversible aggregation. This phenomenon was very impressively demonstrated for α-amylase from *Bacterium subtilis* ($M = 48200$) by a group of Japanese authors (99). In the presence of zinc ions a concentration dependent equilibrium exists between the dimer (zinc containing enzyme) and the monomeric (zinc free) form. Fig. 37 shows (A), as a result of two experiments (superimposed), one chromatogram each of the enzyme in zinc containing (a) and the zinc free (b) solvent on Sephadex G-100.

Upon rechromatography of the complex (a) in a zinc-free solvent (B), one obtains an additional peak for the monomer. In this way the amount of zinc in the dimer can be determined and one finds that for a monomer 0.5 Zn-atoms are required. (The dimerization appears, however, to have no effect on the enzymatic activity.) – ANDREWS (100) used a calibrated Sephadex G-100 column and succeeded after careful analysis of the elution curves of different growth hormones (in dependence on the pH-value and the concentration) in determining the molecular weight of the monomers. According to that the following molecular weights can be given for growth

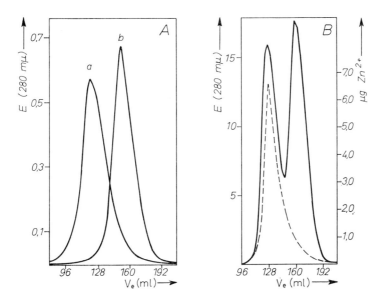

Fig. 37. A: Chromatography of Bacillus subtilis α-amylase (2 ml 1.1% solution) on Sephadex G-100 (2.5×54 cm = 260 ml) in (a) 0.1 M sodium chloride, 0.5 M Ca-acetate and 5×10⁻⁶ M Zn-acetate at pH 7.0 and (b) in 0.1 M NaCl and 1×10⁻³ M EDTA at pH 7.0. B: Chromatography of a complex as in (a) (2 ml 11.8% solution) on a similar gel packing in 0.1 M NaCl pH 7.0. The dashed curve represents the concentration in zinc ion. According to KAKIUCHI et al. (99).

hormones: human 20500, monkey 21000, bovine 26000, porcine 22500, sheep 24000.

The molecular weight of the monomeric unit may be estimated from the elution diagrams of a gel column with the help of the "Gilbert Theory" (101) which was originally developed for the analysis of sedimentation diagrams (102, 103, 167). The monomer must only be noticable as a "tail" which follows the associate. After a mathematical analysis of the results one may even calculate the constant of the association equilibrium (104; cf. 105, 168).

A publication by FRITZ, TRAUTSCHOLD, and WERLE (69) on various protease inhibitors is of particular interest in this connection. The molecular weight of a number of new inhibitors was first determined on Sephadex G-50. Upon chromatography of the 1:1 complex of trypsin ($M = 24000$) and trypsin-inhibitor ($M = 6500$) on Sephadex G-75 this complex is eluted in a position which corresponds to a molecular weight of 26000 (instead of 30500). The authors assume a particularly compact structure (the inhibitor is said to partially penetrate the enzyme). – The inhibitor which is not bound in the complex can naturally be separated on Sephadex G-50 from the mixture of complex and protease. The authors determined the individual components and were thus able to calculate the dissociation constant of the complex under different conditions. (Spreading due to subsequent dissociation on the column was not observed in this case.) AURICCHIO (106) has demonstrated the existence of enzyme/substrate complexes by closely related procedures. Trypsin in the presence of casein is earlier eluted ("M" = 100000) from Sephadex G-100 than trypsin without substrate. The elution patterns of other proteins are not effected by casein.

The Study of Polydisperse Systems

On page 117 several cases have been discussed in which protein molecules had combined with each other. The oligomeric mixture thus formed was separated by gel chromatography into several fractions from which one could obtain the more or less pure oligomers and characterize them. Oligosaccharides of cellulose (107) and a homologous series of oligomeric peptides (43, 108) may be separated on more strongly cross-linked Sephadex gels. A separation of this type is shown in Figure 28 and described there in detail. Upon plotting the reduced elution volume of these oligomeric pentapeptides (108) against the logarithm of their molecular weights, one obtains also a perfectly straight line. This demonstrates that the separation in the denser gel is evidently also based on the same principle as in porous gels. However, the cases are rare in which individuals can be isolated from mixtures of homologous polymers. They are restricted to very low degrees of polymerization (cf. Fig. 26, separation of oligomeric ethylene glycols on Sephadex G-10). On the other hand it is possible to accomplish a very effective and reproducible separation of ionically polymerized relatively low molecular weight polystyrenes by repeated chromatography on polymethacrylate gel (57). The fractions isolated in this case were not homogeneous with regard to molecular weight (particularly not above a polymerization degree of 5). Nevertheless, distinct peaks were present in the elution diagram and the elution volumes were directly proportional to the logarithm of the molecular weight ($\bar{M}_n$).

General Principles (cf. 109)

Synthetic high-polymers contain so many individual components of different molecular weight that it is beyond hope – by even the most effective method – to obtain from them fractions of uniform molecular size. Polymers are in general characterized by the average molecular weight ($\bar{M}$). The average values may differ, depending upon the analytical method applied. The *weight average* ($\bar{M}_w$) is the molecular weight of a (fictive) homogeneous polymer which, with regard to light scattering or sedimentation, would have the same properties as the pertinent mixture. An average molecular weight which is close to the weight average is also obtained when the increase in viscosity in the solvent is measured. – Accordingly the number average ($\bar{M}_n$) of the molecular weight is obtained upon application of colligative methods (e.g. osmotic measurements or end group analyses). It can easily be seen that $\bar{M}_n$ is always smaller than $\bar{M}_w$, since in polydisperse mixtures the smaller individuals make a larger contribution upon counting the molecules. In the case of methods which lead to the weight average the low molecular weight components will contribute to a lesser degree. The quotient $\bar{M}_w/\bar{M}_n$ is thus a measure for the inhomogeneity of the mixture. It assumes the value of 1 only for homogeneous polymers; polymers of very narrow molecular weight distribution (e.g. living-polystyrenes) have values of approximately 1.05 to 1.2 and the technical block polymers may reach a quotient of approximately 10 (and higher).

These values are, however, not sufficient for the characterization of a given polymer preparation. While they are an expression for the molecular weight range covered by the components of the polymer, there is no account for the distribution over this range. Information on that is only to be obtained from the distribution function of the molecular weight. For that purpose, the polymer has to be separated into suitable fractions and their weights have to be plotted against the molecular weight determined in each fraction. For analytical reasons, it was found advisable to plot on the ordinate the sum of the weight of all fractions (in % or as fraction of the total) up to the molecular weight which is plotted on the abscissa (cf. Fig. 38).

If the weight of the fractions (c_i) is known, and their corresponding molecular weight (M_i), i.e. the pattern of the distribution curve, then the average molecular weights may be calculated from it (more accurately than from the data of the unfractionated polymers) e.g. according to the definition equation (cf. *109*).

$$\bar{M}_n = \frac{c_1 + c_2 + c_3 + \dots}{c_1/M_1 + c_2/M_2 + c_3/M_3 + \dots} = \frac{\Sigma\, c_i}{\Sigma\, c_i/M_i} \qquad \text{number average}$$

$$\bar{M}_w = \frac{c_1 M_1 + c_2 M_2 + c_3 M_3 + \dots}{c_1 + c_2 + c_3 + \dots} = \frac{\Sigma\, c_i M_i}{\Sigma\, c_i} \qquad \text{weight average}$$

In order to obtain such distribution curves one has thus far taken advantage of the fact that the solubility of polymers is a function of the molecular weight. Upon *fractional precipitation* one first obtains the high molecular weight fractions in the precipitate, while upon fractional dissolution the low molecular weight components will go first into solution. Besides the solvent system composition the temperature plays an important role. The combination of these two effects makes possible the fractionation in the so-called Baker-Williams columns (*110*, *111*; cf. *170*). Fractional precipitation was frequently used before the introduction of gel chromatography (cf. *109*). The technique is rather elaborate in all of its forms and a careful analysis of one polymer required many days.

Gel Chromatography

Gel chromatography accomplishes within a few hours, maximally in one day, the separation of a polymer into any number of fractions of increasing molecular weight. This is exactly what is required for the construction of a distribution curve: many fractions, preferably of equal size, are isolated on a preparative scale; the weight and the molecular weight are determined and the distribution curves are constructed as earlier (e. g. from the fractional precipitation). In doing so, GRANATH and FLODIN (*50*) established for the first time the distribution of three dextran preparations by gel chromatography (on Sephadex). HEUFER and BRAUN (*112*) fractionated on a preparative scale on a combined packing (1.4×489 cm) of two different ethyleneglycol dimethacrylate gels a polystyrene sample (200 mg) and constructed the distribution function from the viscosimetrically determined molecular weights. It was (except for the very low molecular weight range) in good agreement with the distribution curve which had been obtained for the same sample by conventional fractional precipitation. – Similarly, ALT-GELT (*113*) applied a packing (2×180 cm) of the two polystyrene gels of page 24 to compare on a sample of polyisobutylene the resolution of the Baker-Williams fractionation with the separation by gel chromatography. The author determined the molecular weight in the corresponding fractions with a vapor pressure osmometer and obtained in both cases exactly the same distribution curve. More recently a microtechnique has been developed by GRANATH (*114*) according to which one can obtain the entire molecular weight distribution by gel chromatography on a mixture of Sephadex G-200 and G-100 on samples of 1 to 2 mg of a dextran. ENGEL et al. (*171*) have separated on Sephadex G-50 the reaction products of the polycondensation of a tripeptide (prolyl-glycyl-proline). $\bar{M}_w$ and $\bar{M}_n$ were determined for individual fractions in order to construct the (differential) molecular weight distribution curve.

The molecular weight distribution curve may be constructed more conveniently if calibration substances (cf. Table 24) are available: The elution diagram of a polydisperse polymer on a *calibrated gel column* provides the data which are essential for its characterization and no additional measurements are required. The (integral) distribution curve and thus all other values may be calculated directly from the (differential) elution curve: The concentration is usually determined in a suitable way and plotted on the ordinate of the elution diagram (it must be observed during the algebraic calculation that the chosen parameter of the concentration is linearly proportional). The corresponding molecular weights are obtained from the volume data of the abscissa (with the help of the calibration curve: cf. e. g. Fig. 35). Now one has to plot the corresponding area under the elution curve up to the chosen molecular weight section versus the molecular weight and construct in this way an integral distribution curve.

This is the basis for obtaining the molecular weight distribution by gel permeation chromatography (60). The application of special equipment (70), the so-called GPC (cf. page 40) is not absolutely required for this, purpose. However, the introduction and wide-spread acceptance of this integral unit has made the gel chromatographic representation of a distribution curve a standard method of today's polymer chemistry. In order to obtain reproducible results it may very well be advisable to use an instrument that offers so many conveniences. The GPC apparatus incorporates all components which are essential for gel chromatography in a suitable combination. One characteristic feature of the GPC system cannot be adopted with simple means, namely the short duration of the experiment. The high flow rate applied requires high pressures and thus special equipment. Another great advantage of GPC is the possibility to maintain all corresponding parts at high temperature (up to 140°C). In this way poorly soluble polymers can also be handled.

It must be stressed once more at this point that it is possible to obtain the distribution function of polymers which are soluble at room temperature with the simple means of gel chromatography as long as the instructions given in Chapter 2 are observed. The time required may be one day maximally while the analysis from GPC would be available already after 3 to 4 hours.

Evaluation of Gel Permeation Chromatograms

The scheme for the *calculation of the distribution curve from the elution diagram* has already been indicated above. The GPC apparatus gives by way of its differential refractometer a measure which is directly proportional to the concentration. The equipment is so calibrated that a certain molecular weight is associated with each elution volume. The integral molecular weight distribution is obtained by plotting (in steps as small as possible) the sum of the concentrations (in % or as fraction of the total concentration) versus molecular weight up to a certain molecular weight.

One would naturally like to know whether the result is in agreement with the data obtained by other methods. The distribution functions of the same polymer may be compared for this purpose. It is of great importance to bear the following three things in mind:

For one thing, the *permeability of the gel* used must be optimally adapted to the polymer under study. Because of this the components of a polymer with a very wide molecular weight distribution will not be separated completely. This is probably the reason for the difference between the two distribution curves which HARMON (115) obtained by (incomplete) solvent fractionation and with the GPC apparatus for cis-1.4-polybutadiene. In Figure 38, on the other hand, MEYERHOFF (61) has demonstrated with the integral mass distribution of a technical (very polydisperse) polystyrene good agreement between the curves obtained by gel chromatography and the values from combined precipitation and dissolution fractionation. The two curves were obtained with combinations of columns which differed in permeability. Other values are incorporated in the curves.

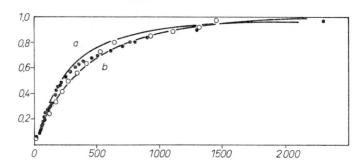

Fig. 38. Integral molecular weight distribution curves of polystyrene III from BASF according to MEYERHOFF (*61*); solid lines represent measurements in the GPC when 4 columns, each of different permeability, were switched in series (in Å, cf. Table 10); (a) 10^5, 10^4, and 9×10^2, (b) 10^6, 10^5, 2×10^4, and 10^3; solid circles: Baker-Williams fractionation (with temperature gradient); open circles: solution-precipitation fractionation on the filler. Abscissa: molecular weight ($\times 10^{-3}$); ordinate: sum of the masses of the fractions as fraction of the total mass.

The deviations may yet have other reasons which lead us to the second point of significance. As earlier observed with the proteins – we are faced with the problem of the correlation between *molecular shape* and molecular weight. The inhomogeneous polymers have normally no superstructure, i.e. they are present in solution as random coils. It may be assumed for the homologous series of chain molecules that the density of the random coil is independent of the molecular weight; the size of the random coil increases steadily with the molecular weight. The calibration of this type of gel column is based on this fact. The situation is different when macromolecules of different structure are compared. This is always the case when the distribution curve of a given polymer is determined on a gel packing which has been calibrated with one of the polystyrene standards (Table 24). In view of this difficulty it has been recommended to compare the chain length of the stretched polymers instead of the molecular weight (cf. Fig. 35). HENDRICKSON and MOORE (*116*) have studied on a relatively dense polystyrene gel the low molecular compounds of a large number of types of compounds and determined correction factors for the commonly encountered structural elements. – MEYERHOFF (*61*) has approached the problem of different molecular configuration in a different way. The author selected different polymers, such as polystyrene, polymethylmethacrylate, and cellulose trinitrate in GPC, and determined the correlation between the elution volume on the one hand, and the molecular weight (M), the viscosity number $[\eta]$, as well as the calculated diameter of the coil, on the other hand, and found that a different calibration curve is obtained for each type of polymer. The two vinyl polymers were, as was to be expected, more closely related than the rigid cellulose molecules which showed a rather different calibration curve. MEYERHOFF was, however, able to compensate the differences to a great extent by the combination of two parameters (weight and space filling) and made the recommendation to plot instead of the chain length the expressions $M^{1/2} \cdot R$ or $M^{1/2} \cdot [\eta]^{1/3}$ as function of the elution volume (cf. Table 26).

The *third problem* in the evaluation is that of widening of the elution profile due to longitudinal diffusion in the column (cf. Chapter 3) which is observed in each type of chromatography. It is well known that the elution pattern of a homogeneous substance from a gel bed is also a bell shaped curve the basis of which is in each case broader than that of the originally applied band. In the case of a polydisperse mixture, this may lead to difficulties in the evaluation. It is quite clear that for a given elution volume not only the corresponding fraction is eluted in maximum concentration but also certain portions of the neighboring fractions. These quantities are added inevitably to the fraction for which the distribution curve is constructed. The error is not as great as it may initially appear to be, since all fractions are by and large subject to the same error. TUNG (117) has proposed a calculation method which takes into consideration the effects which are brought about by spreading of the band. This uncertainty may be eliminated by determining the spreading of bands due to diffusion, e.g. by allowing a polymer to migrate to the middle of the gel packing and then back again. The separation which the porous structure of the gel had caused will be reversed. The undesired widening of the elution profile, for which the porosity of the gel is not responsible, can be measured (118). The careful evaluation of the gel chromatographic analysis of polydisperse polymers requires extensive calculations. Particularly the application of the GPC apparatus may require more calculations than actual attention during the fractionation. CANTOW et al. (119, 120) have developed a *computer program* which requires as input the reading of the recording refractometer and the elution volume. In the output of the computer are contained the molecular weight distribution function as well as direct values for $\bar{M}_n$ and $\bar{M}_w$. In addition one obtains all other information associated with the molecular weight distribution. Another method of calculation was outlined by HESS and CRATZ (185).

Results

The reader unfamiliar with the chemistry of macromolecules may question the necessity of knowing the molecular weight distribution of polydisperse polymers and other factors. There are in essence two reasons for the interest in these parameters: On the one hand, the *properties* of the solid or dissolved polymer are highly dependent upon the molecular weight distribution. It has therefore become common practice to specify the various molecular weight average values of plastic materials. But, even without mathematical evaluation the identity of, e. g., different production batches may be established by the mere comparison of the elution diagrams as obtained under standard conditions. – On the other hand, *polymerisation kinetics* and molecular weight distribution are related fundamentally. Conclusions on the kinetics of the reaction may be drawn from the knowledge of the distribution of the product and the reaction conditions. The knowledge of the kinetics is of scientific as well as of practical significance.

Multiple analyses are inevitable in both cases in view of the heterogeneous nature of the mixtures of polymers. It is, therefore, very important that the many days of cumbersome operations in the laboratory are now reduced to a few hours within which the complete analysis of a polydisperse polymer is obtained. The interest in this area is mainly with industrial laboratories and – understandably – only a limited amount of data has been published thus far. Most scientific publications deal with methods of calculation or with the comparison of different methods of fractionation (cf. above). This comparison must not necessarily be carried out with the graphic distribution curves. The numerical values of the molecular weights from different methods may also be compared. This has been done in Table 31.

Considerable deviations between the directly determined values and those obtained by fractionation are frequently observed for the $\bar{M}_n$-values and in particular for very disperse mixtures. In addition the data obtained by gel chromatography are dependent upon the permeability of the gel applied. In a theoretical investigation (*122*) a new average value ($\bar{M}$ GPC) has been defined which in its magnitude is between the weight average and the number average. The new value is obtained from the location of the maximum of the elution curve of a polydisperse polymer under the assumption of a linear relationship between the elution volume and the logarithm of the molecular weight. A new mathematical model has recently been proposed with which average molecular weights are accessible from nomograms (*174*).

The gel chromatographic behavior of polybutadiene has been carefully studied by ADAMS, FARHAT, and JOHNSON (*173*). The authors constructed the distribution curves of a series of polymer samples under different conditions and calculated the average molecular weights (cf. Table 31). The distribution determined by gel chromatography is comparatively broad. The authors recommend only moderate flow rates for the GPC-apparatus (1 ml/min.). A number of publications have been compiled in Table 32

Table 31. *Comparison of average molecular weight values (as obtained by a variety of methods)*

Polymer	Direct determination $\bar{M}_n \times 10^{-3}$	$\bar{M}_w$	$\bar{M}_w/\bar{M}_n$	Fractionation $\bar{M}_n \times 10^{-3}$	$\bar{M}_w$	$\bar{M}_w/\bar{M}_n$	Gel permeation chromatography $\bar{M}_n \times 10^{-3}$	$\bar{M}_w$	$\bar{M}_w/\bar{M}_n$	Column combination	Ref.
Polystyrene III (BASF)	10	400	40	50	420	8.4	55	420	7.6	$10^5, 10^4, 9\times10^2$	(61)
							55	370	6.7	$10^6, 10^5, 2\times10^4, 10^3$	
Polystyrene NBS 706	136.5	257.8	1.89	—	—	—	162	273	1.74	4 columns à $1,6\times10^4$	(61)
							173	231	1.35	$10^6, 10^5, 10^4, 10^3$	
							72	220	3.06	$10^5, 10^4, 10^2$	
Polystyrene S-108 (Dow)	—	267	1.08	—	—	—	—	—	1.06	7 columns à 5×10^4	(60)
Polyisobutane B	1.10	2.35	2.14	1.17	1.67	2.14	1.72	2.89	1.68	$10^6, 10^5, 10^4, 10^3$	(121)
C	2.45	6.40	2.61	2.81	5.39	2.61	2.50	5.80	2.32		
D	4.50	—	—	4.49	10.0	2.23	5.06	10.4	2.06		
E	—	40*	—	19.9	47.3	2.38	19.6	48.1	2.45		
F	—	62*	—	—	—	—	20.5	66.0	2.22		
G	—	800*	—	—	—	—	612	956	1.56		
lin. polyethylene	—	—	—	11.3	30.1	2.66	13.7	34.1	2.49	$10^5, 10^4, 10^3, 10^2$	(172)
lin. polyethylene	—	—	—	16.2	123.0	7.59	16.4	110.2	6.72	$10^5, 10^4, 10^3, 10^2$	
							20.2	108.3	5.37	$10^5, 10^4, 10^3, 10^2$	
Polybutadiene	207	230	1.11	201	202	1.01	137	254	1.85	$10^6, 10^4, 10^4, 10^3$	(173)
Polybutadiene	140	310	2.21	154	180	1.17	143	320	2.21	$10^6, 10^4, 10^4, 10^3$	

* from the increase in viscosity

Table 32. *Additional literature on the determination of the molecular weight distribution by gel chromatography*

SEIDE, H., und G. LANGHAMMER: Plaste und Kautschuk **9**, 573 (1962). Fraktionierung von Polyvinylpyrrolidon.

FRITZSCHE, P., und V. GRÖBE: IUPAC Symp. Macromol. Chem., Preprint P 422, Prag 1965. Gelfiltration von Polyacrylnitril an vernetztem Polyacrylnitril.

DE VRIES, A. J.: IUPAC Symp. Macromol. Chem., Preprint P 618, Prag 1965. Sur la détermination de la répartition moleculaire des polymères au moyen de la »chromatographie sur gel«.

ALTGELT, K. H.: Makromol. Chem. **88**, 75 (1965). Gel permeation chromatography of asphalts and asphaltenes.

MAYLEY, L. E.: J polymer Sci., Part C **8**, 253 (1965). Application of gel permeation chromatography to high and low molecular weight polymers.

EDWARDS, G.: J. appl. polymer Sci. **9**, 3845 (1965). Estimation of molecular weight of epichlorhydrin-bis-phenol polymers by gel permeation chromatography.

BREWER, P. I.: Polymer **6**, 603 (1965). Fractionation of low molecular weight polymers by liquid chromatography.

RODRIGUEZ, F., R. A. KULAKOWSKI, and O. K. CLARK: I & EC Prod. Res. Develop. **5**, 121 (1966). Characterization of silicones by gel permeation chromatography.

COLOMBO, P., J. FONTANTA, L. E. KUKACKA, and M. STEINBERG: J. appl. polymer Sci. **9**, 3123 (1965). Characterization studies for polyethylene formed by Co-60 γ-radiation under constant conditions in a non-flow system.

HARMON, D. J., and H. L. JACOBS: J. appl. polymer Sci. **10**, 253 (1966). Degradation of natural rubber during mill mastication.

---

which, in addition to those quoted already, report applications of the gel chromatographic determination of molecular weights to special problems. The experience made in many other laboratories has been condensed in

Table 33. *Solvents which are used in the GPC-apparatus and their properties*

Solvent*	Boiling Point (° C)	Temperature** (° C)	Polymer
Tetrahydrofuran	65	25—45	all polymers which are soluble at room temperature; the most frequently used solvent
Trichlorobenzene	213	135—140	polyolefines of all types and natural rubber
Dimethylformamide	153	25—135	polyester, polyurethanes, polyacrylnitrile polyvinylacetate, polystyrene
Toluene	110	25—90	various polyolefines, polyethers, dimethyl-polysiloxanes, polyurethanes
m-Cresol	202	80—135	all types of polyamides, polyesters

* various chlorinated hydrocarbons and ketones have also been used

** it is advisable to work at high temperature for most solvents (except tetrahydrofuran and toluene) in order to reduce the viscosity of the solvent.

reports which have been presented at the occasion of two conferences (International Seminar on Gel Permeation Chromatography, Boston, September 1965, and Geneva, May 1966. Pertinent information is available from Waters Associates, Framingham, Massachusetts, USA). The solvents which are most frequently used in the GPC apparatus and the Styragels together with their properties are compiled in Table 33. It is evident that suitable solvents are available for most macromolecular substances of technical significance.

Separation without Differences in Size

The interactions between solutes and the gel have been discussed in Chapter 3. These phenomena are superimposed on the differences in molecular size; they may sometimes interfere with the separation on the basis of molecular weight differences. If, however, molecules of (approximately) the same size show *different affinities* to the gel this effect may be utilized with advantage for separation. Many very useful applications are indicated for particularly the low molecular weight range some of which will be discussed here.

There are in essence two different types of interactions: Coulomb forces between charged molecules and charged groups of the matrix of the gel, dispersion forces between the solutes and the phase of the swollen gel (cf. Chapter 3). The latter are particularly strong if the solvent in the gel pores has a different composition from the freely flowing solvent. In this case gel chromatography does not differ very much from partition chromatography on other inert carriers (e.g. cellulose or silica gels). For practical purposes the material has been organized by the eluent applied.

Chromatography in Aqueous Media

The retardation of aromatic compounds by dextran gels (cf. page 82), may be applied to the isolation and identification of these substances. The phenolic group shows particularly strong affinity to Sephadex gels (in neutral solution). An important clinical-chemical application of gel chromatography is based on this fact: The determination of free thyroxine, labeled iodine, and protein-bound hormone in serum while testing the function of the thyroid gland. Numerous publications dealing with this problem are compiled in Chapter 5. All are based upon the fact that labeled thyroxine together with triiodothyronine is always strongly retarded by Sephadex G-25; subsequently, however, it is quantitatively eluted. The two iodinated tyrosines may be identified by paper chromatography.

Of all the amino acids, tryptophan has the strongest effect on the affinity of peptides to Sephadex gels. Tryptophan containing peptides from partial (e.g. tryptic) hydrolyzates of protein (e.g. *pseudomonas* cytochrom c-551) are most strongly retarded during gel chromatography and eluted separately (*123*). A classic example for this effect is offered by the chemistry of the tyrocidines. This group of cyclic decapeptides with antibiotic activity consists of components with two tryptophan residues (tyrocidine C), one residue of tryptophan (tyrocidine B), and no tryptophan (tyrocidine A). These peptides are easily separated in 10% acetic acid on a 1 × 200 cm column of Sephadex G-25 (*124*) as is evident from Fig. 39. Fragments for the determination of the sequence of tyrocidine C which contained the aromatic residues were also separated on the basis of their different affinities for the dextran gel (*125*).

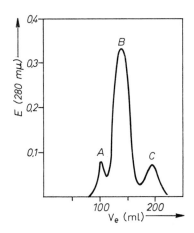

Fig. 39. Chromatogram of 4 mg "tryocidine" on Sephadex G-25 (0.9 × 150 cm = 95 ml); eluent 10% acetic acid (10 ml/hr.); A, B, C = tyrocidine A, B, C; according to RUTTEN-BERG et al. (*125*).

Derivatives of tryptophan are also responsible for the interactions of the toxic cyclopeptides from *Amanita phalloides* with Sephadex gels. The isolation of these natural products was greatly improved and the number of constituents considerably increased by the appropriate application of gel chromatography (*175, 176*). Indol derivatives are so strongly retarded on gel packings of Sephadex G-10 that they can be desalted by elution of the heterocyclic compounds after the salt (*177*).

Two separations on Sephadex G-25 from the field of preparative organic chemistry are of particular interest: Many aromatic sulfonic acids (*178*) display differences in affinity and can be separated just as effectively as the mixture of the keto and enolic tautomers of phenylpyruvic acid (*179*). Additional information on the low molecular weight compounds from different classes of substances which are separated by gel chromatography is

Table 34. *Additional literature on the separation of substances due to interaction with the gel in water*

STREULI, H.: Chimia **16**, 371 (1962). Fraktionierung von Farb- und Geschmacksstoffen des Röstkaffees mittels Sephadex G-25.

NILSSON, A.: Acta chem. scand. **16**, 31 (1962). Fractionation of some plant estrogens and their animal excretion metabolites on dextran gels.

BOSER, H., K.W. VON EICKSTEDT und H. GIERTZ: Ärztliche Forschung **16**, 199 (1962). Über die Herzwirkung hochkondensierter Flavane.

WOOF, J. B.: Nature **195**, 184 (1962). Investigation of phenolic components of brewing materials by gel filtration.

WUCHERPFENNIG, K., und I. FRANKE: Zschr. Lebensmitt.-Untersuch. Forschung **124**, 22 (1963). Trennung von Inhaltsstoffen des Weines mittels Gelfiltration. Vgl. auch: Die Weinwissenschaft **19**, 362 (1964).

SOUKUP, M.: Collect. Czechoslov. chem. Commun. **29**, 3182 (1964). Separation of humic substances by gel filtration on Sephadex.

GJESSING, E. T.: Nature **208**, 1091 (1965). Use of Sephadex gel for the estimation of molecular weight of humic substances in natural water.

WRIGHT, jr., H. E., W. W. BURTON, and R. C. BERRY, jr.: Nature **202**, 1210 (1964). Isolation of tryptophan from air cured tobacco by gel filtration.

SCHLOSSBERGER, H. G., H. KUCH und I. BUHROW: Z. physiol. Chem. **333**, 152 (1963). Abtrennung von Indol-Derivaten aus Urin mittels Sephadex G-25.

BOLDT, P.: Naturwissenschaften **51**, 265 (1964). Zur Kenntnis des Trichosiderins, eines Pigments aus roten Haaren.

SÖCHTIG, H.: Landbauforschung Volkenrode **16**, 25 (1966). Zur Fraktionierung von Humusstoffen durch Gelfiltration I. Das Verhalten von anorganischen Ionen aus der Asche und den Lösungen von Humusstoffen an Sephadex-Gelen.

VIHKO, R.: Acta endocrinol. **52**, Suppl. **109**, 15 (1966). Methylated Sephadex and Sephadex LH-20 in steroid separations.

contained in Table 34. It may also be assumed that the affinity of the gel phase plays more often a decisive role for the success of a separation than generally noticed and explicitly recorded.

Sephadex G-25 is used in clinical chemistry very effectively for the isolation and purification of the conjugated oestrogens in urine of pregnant women. *(126)* The total amount of oestrogens from 10 ml of urine may be obtained in a total of 3 ml of solution if one elutes the sample on a 1 × 50 cm Sephadex column with distilled water. The method is in principle based upon the fact that the steroid hormones are associated with acidic oligosaccharides which are initially strongly retarded due to their great affinity for the gel bed. They are therefore not only separated from macromolecular substances present in urine but also from the salts and are eluted in pure distilled water. Here, however, *ion exlcusion* due to the low negative charge of Sephadex plays a role; the conjugated oestrogens migrate particularly fast and pass the zone of salts. This is constantly repeated, whereby the zone

is sharpened. The hormones were finally eluted from the column in two
very narrow fractions.

The exclusion of negatively charged low molecular weight substances
in distilled water may also be applied to the isolation of nucleotides and
similar substances. Small amounts of N-1-(5'-phosphoribosyl)-adenosine
triphosphate were excluded on Sephadex G-25 and separated from low
molecular weight accompanying substances (*127*).

Salt formation between cations and strongly cross-linked Sephadex gels
in distilled water was applied to the isolation of different proteins. Very
small quantities of ribonuclease and lysozyme (*128, 129*) as well as of trypsin
and bovine serum albumin (*129*) in distilled water were quantitatively retarded by the gel; dilute NaCl-solution eluted the proteins completely. A
very dilute solution of ribonuclease was concentrated 40-fold in this way
(*129*). The toxic, basic proteins from the venom of the scorpion were
separated from other proteins during gel chromatography on Sephadex
G-25 by reversible adsorption (*128*). – Certain proteins show *specific interactions* with polysaccharides. The typical retardation of amylases on porous
Sephadex gels (*130*) is believed to be due to similarities with amylase substrates (*131*). Concavalin A is a plant protein which can be precipitated with
all polysaccharides which contain α-D-glucopyranose- or α-D-manopyranose
bonds. Consequently it is also bound quantitatively by all porous Sephadex
gels and can be eluted again with 0.1 M glucose. Binding does not occur
on strongly cross-linked gels (*132*).

Chromatography with Organic Solvents

In aqueous systems the gel phase shows only in certain cases (normally for
aromatic compounds) noticable affinity for dissolved molecules. According
to statements made in Chapter 3 one must, however, always expect considerable affinity in organic solvents when the eluent is less polar than the
substances to be separated.

Chromatography in *pure organic solvents* requires gels which swell in
these solvents. Mixtures of substances are separated on these organophilic
gels on the basis of differences in polarity between the components. A clean
separation between α- and β-carotene, chlorophyll a and b, as well as
xantophyll (*133*) is, for instance, obtained upon chromatography of spinach
extract (18 mg) on polymethylmethacrylate (0.7 × 60 cm). Sephadex LH-20
is capable of retarding low molecular weight substances in chloroform on
the basis of the presence of hydroxyl or carboxyl groups, while in hydroxyl-
containing solvents the elution observed was in the order of decreasing
molecular weights (*42*). It can be seen from Figure 27 for the chromatography of different glycerides in chloroform that the elution volume is
dependent upon the number of free hydroxyl groups. The methylether of
Sephadex shows similar affinities to the bile acids (*134*), phospholipids,

triglycerides, cholesterin, and related substances (*135*) which can be separated by gel chromatography in organic solvents.

The differences between the stationary phase of the swollen gel grains and the mobile eluent are naturally increased by differences in the solvent composition of the two phases. This is the case for the so-called *partition chromatography*: If one suspends a hydrophylic xerogel, e. g. in a large excess of water-saturated butanol then it accepts from the mixture predominantly water and swells to a certain degree. The swelling process may be completed by treating the gel repeatedly with new solvent until equilibrium has been reached. At the end, however, the gel is clearly less swollen than in pure water. It may be assumed that, finally, butanol-saturated water is present in the pores while water-saturated butanol is present outside. During chromatography partition takes place between these two phases, when the gel matrix acts frequently only as the inert carrier. On such gel columns, it should be possible to carry out all separations on a preparative scale which are known from paper chromatography. By contrast to cellulose powder, Sephadex has the great advantage that the flow rates are better and that the stationary phase penetrates indeed the gel grains. This is the reason for the tremendous capacity of this type of partition columns.

TANAKA et al. (*136*) were among the first to apply successfully the principle described above. Transfer ribonucleic acids had thus far been separated by countercurrent distribution. These authors attempted the same on Sephadex G-25 and succeeded in demonstrating considerable initial successes with a solvent system of complex composition (cf. Table 35). In view of the importance of these ribonucleic acids the procedure has been applied frequently. BERGQUIST et al. (*137*) have suggested a modification in which Sephadex G-25 was equilibrated with the lower phase of the solvent system (cf. Table 35) and then eluted with the upper phase. The amount of n-butylether was gradually lowered.

The separation is evidently not governed by the base composition but rather by the coding-properties (*180*). A total of 10 l of a Sephadex G-25 gel packing swollen firstly in the lower phase of 1.25 M potassium phosphate (pH 6.88)/2-ethoxyethanol/2-butoxyethanol/triethylamine(+mercaptoethanol) (6/2/1/0.01). A t-RNA-mixture (3.5 g) was separated in the upper phase by gradually increasing the triethylamine content to 0.05 parts (*181*).

The partition chromatography of native and synthetic oxytocin by YAMASHIRO (*138*) was also a substitute for the commonly practiced countercurrent distribution. A gel packing (2.18 × 115 cm) of Sephadex G-25 was prepared in 0.2n acetic acid and first equilibrated with the lower phase and then with the upper phase of the solvent system (Table 35). The contaminants which remained on the column after the chromatography of the crude hormone could be removed by repeating the cycle mentioned above.

Table 35. *Experimental conditions for partition chromatography on Sephadex*

Substances	Gel Type	Column dimensions (cm)	Solvent systems (volume ratios)	Ref.
s-RNA	G-25	3×36	n-butanol/water/tri-n-butylamine/glacial acetic acid/di-n-butylether (100/130/10/2.5/27)	(136)
s-RNA	G-25	4.5×55	as above, however with gradient, see text	(137)
Desalting of peptides	G-25	4.5×65	glacial acetic acid/pyridine/water (60/15/25)	(140)
Peptide hormones	G-25	—	glacial acetic acid/pyridine/water (55/15/30)	(141)
Oxytocin and analogs	G-25	2.2×115	n-butanol/benzene/pyridine/0,1% acetic acid (6/2/1/9)	(138, 142)
Oxytocin-analogs	G-25	2.2×120	n-butanol/n-propanol/3.5% glacial acetic acid+1.5% pyridine (2/1/3) pH of the lower phase: 4.1	(143)
Oxytocin-analogs	G-25	—	n-butanol/n-propanol/0.2n glacial acetic acid (2/1/3)	(144)
Oxytocin-analogs	G-25	1.1×110	n-butanol/benzene/3,5% glacial acetic acid+1,5% pyridine (1/1/2)	(145)
Desamino-oxytocin	G-25	1.1×110	n-butanol/benzene/3,5% acetic acid+1,5% pyridine (1/1/2)	(182)
Oxytocin-diastereomers	G-25	2.17×118	n-butanol/benzene/pyridine/0,1% acetic acid (6/2/1/9)	(183)
Actinomycin C	G-25	3.5×40	Di-n-butylether/n-butanol/9% Na-metakresotinate (3/2/5)	(139)
Various Peptides	G-75	—	phenol/glacial acetic acid/water (1/1/1)	(146)
Diastereomeric dipeptides	G-25; G-50	1.5×100	pyridine/water (molar ratio 1:1)	(147)
Protein partial hydrolyzate	G-25	2.0×120 to 1.0×70	n-butanol/n-propanol/3% acetic acid+3% pyridine (2/1/3) n-butanol/n-propanol/benzene/3% acetic acid+3% pyridine (4/1/1/6); (8/1/3/12) n-butanol/benzene/3% acetic acid+3% pyridine (1/1/2)	(148)
Sugars, aminosugars	G-25	5—10 ml	n-butanol/acetic acid/water (62/15/25) ethanol/1M ammonium acetate pH 7,5 (7/3)	(149)
Alkalichlorides	G-25	1×42	methanol/water (75/25)	(150)
DNP-amino acids	G-25	1.5×80	n-butanol/acetic acid/water (4/1/1)	(108)

This column is immediately ready for use. The solvent system used for this and other problems has been modified numerous times (cf. Table 35).

A very informative demonstration of partition chromatography of peptides on Sephadex G-25 is the separation of the three main components of actinomycin C (actinomycins C_1, C_2, and C_3) (cf. Fig. 40). The gel packing was also prepared in the hydrophilic phase of the solvent system (Table 35) and then equilibrated with the lipophilic phase (139). Other solvent systems which are incorporated in Table 35 were applied to the partition chromato-

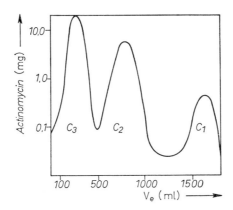

Fig. 40. Partition chromatography of 320 mg of actinomycin C on Sephadex G-25 (3.5×40 cm = 384 ml); eluent di-n-butylether/n-butanol/9% Na-meta-kresotinate (3/2/5) (18 ml/hr); after Schmidt-Kastner (139).

graphy of other substances on Sephadex gels. Partition chromatography on Sephadex G-25 – predominantly in mixtures of butanone and water – was applied extensively to the isolation of the toxins (cyclic oligopeptides) of *Amanita phalloides* (176).

The *group separation* of *lipophilic and hydrophilic* substances of extracts of natural products may also be considered as partition chromatography: Upon pouring a column of Sephadex G-25 in a mixture of chloroform/methanol/water (60/3/4.5) and filtering through it a lipid soluble extract, all polar contaminants are retarded by the Sephadex while the lipids pass the packing without delay (151, 184). The water soluble components can be eluted subsequently with methanol/water (1:1).

Fractional Precipitation

The solvent composition on a Sephadex G-25 column may be changed in such a way that some of the components to be separated will be insoluble and thus be retarded while the other components are eluted. This is the case for instance during the differentiation between the so-called euglobulins and pseudoglobulins of human serum according to EPSTEIN and TAN (152): a sample of serum in 1 *M* NaCl is applied to a G-25 column which is equilibrated with a very dilute buffer. Upon elution with the buffer the proteins are separated from the salt. The pseudoglobulins (the major portion of the serum proteins) which are also easily soluble in dilute salt solution are eluted long before the salt. The euglobulins, however, become insoluble as soon as they are separated from the salt. In the subsequent course of the elution they are again dissolved by the moving salt zone and so forth. They leave the column together with the salt. PORATH (153) has extended the principle and produced a steadily increasing salt gradient from top to bottom of a gel packing (Sephadex G-100). During the elution of a protein mixture with water its components will migrate more rapidly than the salt gradient. The proteins are precipitated – according to their solubility in salt solution – on different locations of the column and again dissolved and so forth. Proteins of identical size but different solubility may be separated in this way (zone precipitation).

References

1. FLODIN, P.: J. Chromatog. 5, 103 (1961).
2. CONNELL, G. E., and R.W. SHAW: Canad. J. Biochem. Physiol. 39, 1013 (1961).
3. LIÉBECQ, C., and M. J. DEGUELDRE-GUILLAUME: J. Chromatog. 7, 130 (1962).
4. SINGER, M. F., and G. TOLBERT: Biochemistry 4, 1319 (1965).
5. MATHEKA, H.-D., und G. WITTMANN: Zbl. Bakt. 182, 169 (1961).
6. OBENAUS, R., und H.-J. NEUMANN: Naturwissenschaften 52, 131 (1965).
7. RINGERTZ, N. R., and P. REICHARD: Acta chem. Scand. 14, 303 (1960).
8. SCHLUBACH, H. H., und M. GREHN: Liebigs Ann. Chem. 668, 180 (1963).
9. UZIEL, M., and W. E. COHN: Biochim. biophys. Acta 103, 539 (1965).
10. SHEPHERD, G. R., and D. F. PETERSEN: J. Chromatog. 9, 445 (1962).
11. LESTER, G., and A. BYERS: Biochem. biophys. Res. Commun. 18, 725 (1965).
12. HOERMAN, K. C., A.Y. BALEKJIAN, and V. J. BERZINSKAS: Anal. Biochem. 12, 403 (1965).
13. STEGEMANN, H., und V. LOESCHCKE: Z. Naturforschg. 18 b, 195 (1963).
14. BEISS, U., und R. MARX: Naturwissenschaften 49, 142 (1962).
15. MARSHALL, CH. S.: Biochim. biophys. Acta 74, 158 (1963).
16. KISLIUK, R. L.: Biochim. biophys. Acta 40, 531 (1960).
17. BASSETT, E. W., S. M. BEISER, and S.W. TANENBAUM: Science 133, 1475 (1961).
18. MILLER, K. D., and A. P. MARIN: Proc. Soc. exp. Biol. Med. 118, 961 (1965).
19. Brochure: Sephadex LH-20, Gel Filtration in Organic Solvents, Uppsala 1965.
20. ENEST, B., und H. SCHILL: Acta biologica et medica germanica 15, 527 (1965).
21. ANFINSEN, C. H. B., and E. HABER: J. biol. Chem. 236, 1361 (1961).
22. NEUMANN, H., R. F. GOLDBERGER, and M. SELA: ibid. 239, 1536 (1964).
23. STEINER, R. F.: Biochim. biophys. Acta 100, 111 (1965).
24. DIXON, H. B. F., and V. MORET: Biochem. J. 94, 463 (1965).
25. ENGLANDER, S.W.: Biochemistry 2, 798 (1963).
26. —, and J. J. ENGLANDER: Proc. natl. Acad. Sci. USA 53, 370 (1965).

27. PRINTZ, M. P., and P. H. VON HIPPEL: ibid. **53**, 363 (1965).
28. KÖSSEL, H., und S. DOEHRING: Z. physiol. Chem. **340**, 221 (1965).
29. LINDNER, E. B., A. ELMQVIST, and J. PORATH: Nature **184**, 1565 (1959).
30. DAISLEY, K.W.: Nature **191**, 868 (1961).
31. HUMMEL, J. P., and W. J. DREYER: Biochim. biophys. Acta **63**, 530 (1962).
32. MUDD, S. H., und J. D. MANN: J. biol. Chem. **238**, 2164 (1963).
33. LEE, M., and J. R. DEBRO: J. Chromatog. **10**, 68 (1963).
34. DE MOOR, P., K. HEIRWEGH, and O. STEENO: Arch. Biochem. Biophys. **103**, 506 (1963).
35. HABER, E., L. B. PAGE, and G. A. JACOBY: Biochemistry **4**, 693 (1965).
36. HARTMANN, G., U. COY und G. KNIESE: Z. physiol. Chem. **330**, 227 (1963).
37. LIERSCH, M., und G. HARTMANN: Biochem. Z. **340**, 390 (1964); **343**, 16 (1965).
38. HERRIES, D. G., W. BISHOP, and F. M. RICHARDS: J. phys. Chem. **68**, 1842 (1964).
39. THUREBORN, E.: Nature **197**, 1301 (1963).
40. BORGSTRÖM, B.: Biochim. biophys. Acta **106**, 171 (1965).
41. GELOTTE, B., and J. PORATH: in HEFTMANN (Ed.) Chromatography, New York 1966.
42. JOUSTRA, M. K.: Protides Biol. Fluids **14**, 533 (1967).
43. DETERMANN, H., und R. KÖHLER: Liebigs Ann. Chem. **690**, 197 (1965).
44. GELOTTE, B.: Acta chem. Scand. **18**, 1283 (1964).
45. AEBI, H., C. H. SCHNEIDER, H. GANG und U. WIESMANN: Experientia **20**, 103 (1964).
46. FLODIN, P., and J. KILLANDER: Biochim. biophys. Acta **63**, 403 (1962).
47. MOORE, J. C.: J. Polym. Sci., Part A **2**, 835 (1964).
48. BENGTSSON, S., and L. PHILIPSON: Biochim. biophys. Acta **79**, 399 (1964).
49. ANDREWS, P.: Biochem. J. **96**, 595 (1965).
50. GRANATH, K., and P. FLODIN: Makromol. Chem. **48**, 160 (1961).
51. BREWER, P. I.: Nature **190**, 625 (1961).
52. PORATH, J.: Pure Appl. Chem. **6**, 233 (1963).
53. WIELAND, TH., P. DUESBERG und H. DETERMANN: Biochem. Z. **337**, 303 (1963).
54. WHITAKER, J. R.: Anal. Chem. **35**, 1950 (1963).
55. HOHN, TH., und W. POLLMANN: Z. Naturforschung **18 b**, 919 (1963).
56. ANDREWS, P.: Biochem. J. **91**, 222 (1964).
57. DETERMANN, H., G. LÜBEN und TH. WIELAND: Makromol. Chem. **73**, 168 (1964).
58. ACKERS, G. K.: Biochemistry **3**, 723 (1964).
59. SQUIRE, P. G.: Arch. Biochem. Biophys. **107**, 471 (1964).
60. MOORE, J. C., and J. G. HENDRICKSON: J. Polymer. Sci., Part C **8**, 233 (1965).
61. MEYERHOFF, G.: Makromol. Chem. **89**, 282 (1965); Ber. d. Bunsenges. physikal. Chem. **69**, 866 (1965).
62. CARNEGIE, P. R.: Nature **206**, 1128 (1965).
63. SANFELIPPO, P. M., and J. G. SURAK: J. Chromatog. **13**, 148 (1964).
64. VAN THOAI, N., R. KASSAB, and L. A. PRADEL: Biochim. biophys. Acta **110**, 532 (1965).
65. LAURENT, T. C., and J. KILLANDER: J. Chromatog. **14**, 317 (1964).
66. SIEGEL, L. M., and K. J. MONTY: Biochim. biophys. Acta **112**, 346 (1966).
67. ANDERSON, D. M.W., and J. F. STODDART: Anal. chim. Acta **34**, 401 (1966).
68. DETERMANN, H., und W. MICHEL: J. Chromatog. **25**, 303 (1966).
69. FRITZ, H., I. TRAUTSCHOLD und E. WERLE: Z. physiol. Chem. **342**, 253 (1965).
70. MALEY, L. E.: J. Polymer. Sci., Part C **8**, 253 (1965).
71. ROUBAL, W. T., and A. L. TAPPEL: Analyt. Biochem. **9**, 211 (1964).
72. MORRIS, C. J. O. R.: J. Chromatog. **16**, 167 (1964).
73. DETERMANN, H., und W. MICHEL: Z. Anal. Chem. **212**, 211 (1965).
74. ANDREWS, P.: Protides biol. Fluids **14**, (1966).
75. WARD, D. N., and M. S. ARNOTT: Analyt. Biochem. **12**, 296 (1965).
76. OLESEN, H., and P. O. PEDERSEN: Protides biol. Fluids **14**, (1966).

77. DE LA LLOSA, P., C. TERTRIN, and M. JUTISZ: Biochim. biophys. Acta 115, 464 (1966).
78. SELBY, K., and C. C. MAITLAND: Biochem. J. 94, 578 (1965).
79. LEACH, A. A., and P. C. O'SHEA: J. Chromatog. 17, 245 (1965).
80. IWATSUBO, M., et A. CURDEL: Comptes rendues Acad. Sci., Paris 256, 5224 (1963).
81. LARGIER, J. F., and A. POLSON: Biochim. biophys. Acta 79, 626 (1964).
82. AURICCHIO, F., und C. B. BRUNI: Biochem. Z. 340, 321 (1964).
83. SARDA, L., M. F. MAYLIÉ, J. ROGER et P. DESNUELLE: Biochim. biophys. Acta 89, 183 (1964).
84. TIPTON, K. F.: ibid. 92, 341 (1964).
85. KEMP, E., and I. RUBIN: Acta chem. scand. 18, 2403 (1964).
86. ANDREWS, P., R. C. BRAY, P. EDWARDS, and K.V. SHOOTER: Biochem. J. 93, 627 (1964).
87. ROGERS, K. S., L. HELLERMAN, and T. E. THOMPSON: J. biol. Chem. 240, 198 (1965).
88. CHASE, J. F. A., D. J. PEARSON, and P. K. TUBBS: Biochim. biophys. Acta 96, 162 (1965).
89. OSTROWSKI, W., and J. RYBARSKA: ibid. 105, 196 (1965).
90. BOGUTH, W., K. KRISCH und H. NIEMANN: Biochem. Z. 341, 149 (1965).
91. BURGES, R. A., K.W. BRAMMER, and J. D. COOMBES: Nature 208, 894 (1965).
92. LANCHANTIN, G. F., J. A. FRIEDMANN, and D.W. HART: J. biol. Chem. 240, 3276 (1965).
93. NIESCHLAG, E., und K. OTTO: Z. physiol. Chem. 340, 46 (1965).
94. SCHANE, H. P.: Analyt. Biochem. 11, 371 (1965).
95. LISOWSKI, J.: Biochim. biophys. Acta 113, 321 (1966).
96. PEDERSEN, K. O.: Arch. Biochem. Biophys. Suppl. 1, 157 (1962).
97. CRESTFIELD, A. M., W. H. STEIN, and S. MOORE: ibid. 1, 217 (1962).
98. SIEGEL, L. M., and K. J. MONTY: Biochim. biophys. Res. Commun. 19, 494 (1965).
99. KAKIUCHI, K., S. KATO, A. IMANISHI, and T. ISEMURA: J. Biochem., Tokyo, 55, 102 (1964).
100. ANDREWS, P.: Nature 209, 155 (1966).
101. GILBERT, G. A.: Discuss. Faraday Soc. 20, 68 (1956).
102. WINZOR, D. J., and H. A. SCHERAGA: Biochemistry 2, 1263 (1963).
103. — — J. phys. Chem. 68, 338 (1964).
104. ACKERS, G. K., and I. E. THOMPSON: Proc. natl. Acad. Sci. 53, 342 (1965).
105. GILBERT, G. A.: Nature 210, 299 (1966).
106. AURICCHIO, F.: Biochem. J. 98, 290 (1965).
107. FLODIN, P., and K. ASPERG: in Biological Structure and Function, 1, 345. New York 1961.
108. DETERMANN, H.: Liebigs Ann. Chem. 690, 182 (1965).
109. VOLLMERT, B.: Grundriß der makromolekularen Chemie, Berlin, Göttingen, Heidelberg: 1962.
110. BAKER, C. A., and R. J. P. WILLIAMS: J. chem. Soc. 1956, 2352.
111. SCHULZ, G.V., K. C. BERGER und A. G. R. SCHOLZ: Ber. Bunsenges. physikal. Chem. 69, 856 (1965).
112. HEUFER, G., and D. BRAUN: Polymer Letters 3, 495 (1965).
113. ALTGELT, K. H.: J. appl. polymer Sci. 9, 3389 (1965).
114. GRANATH, K.A., and B. E. KVIST: J. Chromatog., in the press.
115. HARMON, D. J.: J. polymer. Sci., Part C 8, 243 (1965).
116. HENDRICKSON, J. G., and J. C. MOORE: J. polymer Sci., Part A 1, 4, 167 (1966).
117. TUNG, L. H.: J. appl. polymer Sci. 10, 375 (1966).
118. —, J. C. MOORE, and G. W. KNIGHT: J. appl. polymer Sci., 10, 1261 (1966); vgl. auch ibid. 10, 1271 (1966).
119. PICKETT, H. E., M. J. R. CANTOW, and J. F. JOHNSON: J. appl. polymer Sci., 10, 917 (1966).

120. CANTOW, M. J. R., R. S. PORTER, and J. F. JOHNSON: Angew. Chemie **78**, 609 (1966).
121. — — — IUPAC Symposium on macromolecular Chemistry, Preprint P 618, Prag. 1965.
122. BERGER, H. L., and A. SCHULTZ: J. polymer Sci. Part A **2**, 3643 (1965).
123. AMBLER, R. P.: Biochem. J. **89**, 349 (1963).
124. MACH, B., and E. L. TATUM: Proc. natl. Acad. Sci. **52**, 876 (1964).
125. RUTTENBERG, M. A., T. P. KING, and L. C. CRAIG: Biochemistry **4**, 11 (1965).
126. BELING, C. G.: Nature **192**, 326 (1961).
127. AMES, B. N., R. G. MARTIN, and B. J. GARRY: J. biol. Chem. **236**, 2019 (1961).
128. MIRANDA, F., H. ROCHAT et S. LISSITZKY: J. Chromatog. **7**, 142 (1962).
129. GLAZER, A. N., and D. WELLNER: Nature **194**, 862 (1962).
130. WILDING, P.: Clin. chim. Acta **8**, 918 (1963).
131. GELOTTE, B.: Acta chem. scand. **18**, 1283 (1964).
132. AGRAWAL, B. B., and L. J. GOLDSTEIN: Biochem. J. **96**, 23C (1965).
133. WIELAND, TH., G. LÜBEN und H. DETERMANN: Naturwissenschaften **51**, 138 (1964).
134. NYSTRÖM, E., and J. SJÖVALL: J. Chromatog. **17**, 574 (1965).
135. — — Analyt. Biochem. **12**, 235 (1965).
136. TANAKA, K., H. H. RICHARDS, and G. L. CANTONI: Biochim. biophys. Acta **61**, 846 (1962).
137. BERGQUIST, P. L., B. C. BAGULEY, J. M. ROBERTSON, and R. A. RALPH: Biochim. biophys. Acta **108**, 531 (1965).
138. YAMASHIRO, D.: Nature **201**, 76 (1954).
139. SCHMIDT-KASTNER, G.: Naturwissenschaften **51**, 38 (1964).
140. PORATH, J., and E. B. LINDNER: Nature **191**, 69 (1961).
141. —, and A. V. SCHALLY: Endocrinology **70**, 738 (1962).
142. DRABAREK, S., and V. DUVIGNEAUD: J. Amer. Chem. Soc. **87**, 3974 (1965).
143. — ibid. **86**, 4477 (1964).
144. KLIEGER, E., und E. SCHRÖDER: Tetrah. Letters **25**, 2067 (1965).
145. JARVIS, D., B. M. FERRIER et V. DUVIGNEAUD: J. biol. Chem. **240**, 3553 (1965).
146. BAGDASARIAN, M., N. A. MATHESON, R. L. M. SYNGE, and M. A. YOUNGSON: Biochem. J. **91**, 91 (1964).
147. WIELAND, TH., und H. BENDE: Chem. Ber. **98**, 504 (1965).
148. MAHOWALD, T. A.: Biochemistry **4**, 732 (1965).
149. ZELEZNICK, L. D.: J. Chromatog. **14**, 139 (1964).
150. SPITZY, H.: Angew. Chem. **78**, 721 (1966).
151. WELLS, M. A., and J. C. DITTMER: Biochemistry **2**, 1259 (1963).
152. EPSTEIN, W.V., and M. TAN: J. Chromatog. **6**, 258 (1961).
153. PORATH, J.: Nature **196**, 47 (1962).
154. GOLDBERGER, R. F., and C. B. ANFINSEN: Biochemistry **1**, 401 (1962).
155. CRESTFIELD, A. M., S. MOORE, and W. H. STEIN: J. biol. Chem. **238**, 622 (1963).
156. FASELLA, P., G. G. HAMMES, and P. R. SCHIMMEL: Biochim. biophys. Acta **103**, 708 (1965).
157. FAIRCLOUGH, jr., G. F., and J. S. FRUTON: Biochemistry **5**, 673 (1966).
158. NAKAYAMA, F., and H. MIYAKE: J. Lab. clin. Med. **67**, 78 (1966).
159. —, Clin. chim. Acta **13**, 212 (1966).
160. HABEEB, A. F. S. A.: Biochim. biophys. Acta **121**, 21 (1966).
161. KAZAZIAN, jr., H. H.: Nature **212**, 197 (1966)
162. VIRDEN, R., D. C. WATTS, R. L. WATTS, D. B. GAMMACK, and J. H. RAPER: Biochem. J. **99**, 155 (1966).
163. ANDERSSON, L.-O.: Biochim. biophys. Acta **117**, 115 (1966).
164. BANERJEE, R., and R. CASSOLY: C. R. Acad. Sc., Paris, **262**, 1375 (1966).
165. MERRETT, T.: Biochim. biophys. Acta **124**, 389 (1966).

166. WINTERHALTER, K. H.: Nature **211**, 932 (1966).
167. WINZOR, D. J.: Arch. Biochem. Biophys. **113**, 421 (1966).
168. GILBERT, G. A.: Nature **212**, 296 (1966).
169. BREWER, P. I.: Polymer **6**, 603 (1965).
170. SCHULZ, W. W., J. P. SCHELZ, and W. C. PURDY: Separation Science **1**, 113 (1966).
171. ENGEL, J., J. KURTZ, E. KATCHALSKI, and A. BERGER: J. mol. Biol. **17**, 255 (1966).
172. TAKAGI, T.: 3rd Intern. Seminar on Gel Permeation Chromatog. Geneva 1966.
173. ADAMS, H. E., K. FARHAT, and B. L. JOHNSON: I & EC Prod. Res. Develop. **5**, 126 (1966).
174. RODRIGUEZ, F., and O. K. CLARK: I & EC Prod. Res. Develop. **5**, 118 (1966).
175. WIELAND, Th., H. SCHIEFER und U. GEBERT: Naturwissenschaften **53**, 39 (1966).
176. WIELAND, Th., D. REMPEL, U. GEBERT, A. BUKU und H. BOEHRINGER: Liebigs Ann. Chem. in the press.
177. CONTRACTOR, S. F., and P. JOMAIN: Clin. chim. Acta **14**, 535 (1966).
178. STEUERLE, H.: Z. anal. Chem. **220**, 413 (1966).
179. HAAVALDSEN, R., and T. NORSETH: Anal. Biochem. **15**, 536 (1966).
180. NATHENSON, S. G., F. C. DOHAN, jr., H. H. RICHARDS, and G. L. CANTONI: Biochemistry **4**, 2412 (1965).
181. MUENCH, K. H., and P. BERG: Biochemistry **5**, 970 (1966).
182. FERRIER, B. M., D. JARVIS, and V. DU VIGNEAUD: J. biol. Chem. **240**, 4264 (1965).
183. YAMASHIRO, D., D. GILLESEN, and V. DU VIGNEAUD: J. Am. chem. Soc. **88**, 1310 (1966).
184. WUTHIER, R. A.: J. Lipid. Res. **7**, 558 (1966).
185. HESS, M., and R. F. KRATZ: J. polymer Sci. A-2 **4**, 731 (1966).

Chapter 5

Results

In the preceding chapter representative experiments had been selected in order to demonstrate potential applications of gel chromatography. Methodical aspects had been the guiding principle for these selections. Experimental procedures had been chosen irrespective of the class of substances to which the investigated compounds belonged. This was possible because the methods are essentially the same for different classes of substances. Many of the results of "gel filtration", and particularly those of "molecular weight determination", have already been incorporated in the corresponding chapters. However, the chapter on "gel chromatography" contains only a fraction of the vast amount of experimental data which is to be found predominantly in the biochemical literature. The results compiled in the present chapter are, therefore, derived from experiments which, in a narrower sense, were covered in the preceding chapter as "gel chromatography". More or less complex mixtures of substances are separated by chromatography on relatively long gel packings, as these substances do not show great differences in molecular weight.

The results are organized by classes of substances and topics. Naturally, such classification is frequently rather arbitrary; it may, therefore, be advisable to consult the chapters on related areas for doubtful cases. In order to be able to accomodate as much information as possible on as little space as possible, only a limited number of publications has been discussed while others are cited by their titles. In spite of that, it became also a necessity for this chapter to select published experimental data and many interesting publications had to be left unmentioned. In accordance with the purpose of this book as an introduction to the new technique, preference was given to reports in which gel chromatographic techniques are described in greater detail and in which relatively well defined substances were involved. In order to keep individual sections within limits the results of many publications cannot be discussed (particularly those which describe the separation of serum proteins and enzymes).

Enzymology

Isolation of Enzymes

In recent years a large number of enzymes has been purified or isolated in the pure state by gel chromatography. The application of the new technique does not replace the familiar steps of protein purification (e. g. precipitation with solvents or ammonium sulfate or ion exchange chromatography). However, these techniques are very effectively supplemented by gel chromatography. The gels find application in three different ways, namely, the removal of low molecular weight components by "gel filtration" (cf. Chapter 4), the separation of contaminating proteins by chromatography on gels of suitable porosity, and finally in the estimation of molecular weights (Tables 29 and 30). In Tables 36, 37, and 38 publications are compiled in which gel chromatography represented an essential step in the isolation of phosphoesterases, different other esterases, dehydrogenases, transferases, and other enzymes.

Table 36. *Phosphoesterases*

VON HOFSTEN, B., and J. PORATH: Biochim. biophys. Acta **64**, 1 (1962). Purification and some properties of an acid phosphatase from E.coli.

ESTBORN, B.: Z. klin. Chem. **2**, 53 (1964). Separation of phosphatase isoenzymes by gel filtration.

ENGSTRÖM, L.: Biochim. biophys. Acta **92**, 71 (1964). Studies on bovine-liver alkaline phosphatase, purification, phosphate incorporation.

OSTROWSKI, W., and J. RYBARSKA: Biochim. biophys. Acta **105**, 196 (1965). Studies on human prostatic acid phosphomonoesterase. Further purification and molecular weight of the enzyme.

SINGER, M. F., and G. TOLBERT: Biochemistry **4**, 1319 (1965). Purification and properties of potassium-activated phosphodiesterase from E.coli.

ANDERSON, J. H., and C. E. CARTER: Biochemistry **4**, 1102 (1965). Acid soluble ribosomal ribonuclease of E.coli.

NABER, J. E., A. M. SCHEPMAN, and A. RÖRSCH: Biochim. biophys. Acta **99**, 307 (1965). Purification of E.coli endonuclease by agarose chromatography.

BJÖRK, W.: Biochim. biophys. Acta **95**, 652 (1965). Purification of two endonucleases from potato tubers.

Table 37. *Various esterases*

BJÖRK, W., and J. PORATH: Acta chem. scand. **13**, 1256 (1959). Fractionation of snake venom by the gel filtration method.

BJÖRK, W.: Biochim. biophys. Acta **49**, 195 (1961). Partial purification of phosphodiesterase, 5'-nucleotidase, lecithinase A, and acetylcholine esterase from ringhalscobra venom.

RIESEN, W. H., and E. J. HAWRYLEWICZ: Biochim. biophys. Acta **90**, 372 (1964). Fractionation of Indian cobra venom by column chromatography. I. Dextran gels.

SARDA, L., M. F. MAYLIÉ, J. ROGER et P. DESNUELLE: Biochim. biophys. Acta **89**, 183 (1964). Comportement de la lipase pancréatique sur Sephadex. Application à la purification et à la détermination du poids moléculaire de cet enzyme.

GELOTTE, B.: Acta chem. scand. **18**, 1283 (1964). Separation of pancreatic enzymes by gel filtration.

DOWNEY, W. K., and P. ANDREWS: Biochem. J. **94**, 642 (1965). Gel filtration applied to the study of lipases and other esterases.

FRAZER, G. P., and A. D. NICOL: Clin. chim. Acta **13**, 552 (1966).

Table 38. *Various enzymes*

DELIN, S., and J. PORATH: Biochim. biophys. Acta **67**, 197 (1963). Purification of α- and β-hydroxysteroid dehydrogenases from *pseudomonas testosteroni* by gel filtration.

CHERSI, A.: Science Tools **11**, 1 (1964). The purification of lactic dehydrogenase by recycling chromatography.

FLATMARK, T.: Acta chem. scand. **18**, 1517 (1964). Studies on the peroxidase effect of cytochrome c. II. Purification of beef heart cytochrome c by gel filtration.

SCHREIBER, G., U. U. ECKSTEIN, A. OESER und H. HOLZER: Biochem. Z. **340**, 13 (1964). Anreicherung einer Aspartataminotransferase aus Bierhefe.

GASIOR, E., and K. MOLDAVE: J. biol. Chem. **240**, 3346 (1965). Resolution of aminoacyl-transfering enzymes from rat liver by molecular sieve chromatography.

CHASE, J. F. A., D. J. PEARSON, and P. K. TUBBS: Biochim. biophys. Acta **96**, 162 (1965). The preparation of crystalline carnitine acetyltransferase.

BOLL, M., und H. HOLZER: Biochem. Z. **343**, 504 (1965). Untersuchungen zur Serinhydratase-Reaktion in Hefe.

MAASS, D., H. PELZER und W. WEIDEL: Z. Naturforschung **19b**, 413 (1964). Reinigung, Eigenschaften und Substratspezifität einer N-Acetylglucosaminidase aus E.coli B.

BUDDECKE, E., und D. PLATT: Z. physiol Chem. **343**, 61 (1965). Untersuchungen zur Chemie der Arterienwand, VIII. Nachweis, Reinigung und Eigenschaften der Hyaluronidase aus der Aorta des Rindes.

Among the *proteases* pepsin was one of the first enzymes to be purified by gel chromatography on Sephadex G-50 (*1*). – Prior to the crystallization of agavain (*2*) and pinguinain (*3*) – two new plant proteases – gel chromatography (on Sephadex G-100) was a decisive step. Autolysis and the molecular weight were also studied on the same gel. – Various bromelains from the stem and fruit of pineapple (*4*) and a cathepsin from cod muscle (*5*) were considerably purified on Sephadex G-75 and G-200. The yield and purity of a bacterial collagenase (*6*) was better after passage over G-200 than over DEAE-Sephadex. The enzyme was homogeneous after chromatography of a commercial preparation on Sephadex G-100 (*126*). The conversion of prothrombin to thrombin under the influence of sodium citrate (*7*) could be followed on Sephadex G-100 (cf. also Table 29). Sephadex G-100 was of great importance in the isolation of urokinase, the plasminogen activator from human urine (*127*). A particularly long packing of Sephadex G-100, superfine (2.2 × 180 cm), was used for the purification of renin from hog kidneys (*128*). A dipeptidase from dog kidneys was isolated with the help of Sephadex G-200 (*129*); two different dipeptidases may be obtained from bakers yeast on the same gel (*130*). During the investigation of inhibitors of trypsin (*8*, *9*) and chymotrypsin (*10*) it was found that the proteins which had been considered to be homogeneous (*8*, *10*) could be purified considerably by gel chromatography. Chromatography on dextran gels was an important tool in the isolation of the trypsin inhibitor from pancreatic tissue and secretions of the dog (*11*).

Enzymes of the carbohydrate metabolism, i.e. cellulases from different bacteria have been studied repeatedly by gel chromatography *(12, 13, 14)*. The activity always appeared in several isolated fractions; this raised the suspicion that a low molecular enzyme was perhaps bound to carrier proteins of different molecular weight *(13)*. β-Galactosidase from *E.coli* K 12 was purified on Sephadex G-200 (10×40 cm) and isolated in 80% yield from 4 g (precipitated with ammonium sulfate) of crude extract *(15)*; various types from *N. crassa* were also separated on Sephadex G-200 *(16)*. Two inactive components of a lactose synthetase from milk are separated on Bio-Gel P-30; the mixture, however, has full activity *(17)*. A mannosidase specific for the analysis of α-D-mannoside bonds in glycoproteins was purified on Bio-Gel P-200 *(18)*. A pure α-amylase has been isolated from human saliva *(19)*.

Enzymatic Reactions

In Chapter 4 we have already demonstrated with two examples (page 97) that Sephadex G-25 may be applied to the determination of the number of binding sites in enzymes and also to the binding affinity between enzymes and reactants as well as to the study of the influence of cofactors on enzymes (page 92). An equivalent weight of 30–40000 was determined in a similar fashion for seven dehydrogenases by measuring the DPNH-binding capacity *(20)*. Sometimes stable complexes are formed from enzymes and reactants, e.g. upon the action of Zn-free carboxypeptidase on a peptide substrate *(21)*. The complex, which can be separated from the excess of substrate by gel chromatography, cannot be reactivated subsequently by the addition of Zn-ions. The purification by "gel filtration" on Sephadex G-50 is the method of choice before the metal analysis of carboxypeptidase (cf. *22*). – Lysozyme forms an insoluble complex with the product of its action on a certain glycopeptide. The dissociation of the complex (in sodium chloride solution) and the subsequent analysis by gel chromatography on Sephadex G-75 and G-25 provides information on the kinetics of the enzymatic reaction *(23)*. – Upon addition of cytochrome oxidase to excess cytochrome c and subsequent gel chromatography on Sephadex G-200 one finds under certain conditions a very high molecular weight fraction which contains both enzymes in the same molar ratios and which, so to say, represents a portion of the respiratory chain *(24)*. – The $^{14}CO_2$-labeled enzymes from several biotin enzymes of the citric acid cycle were obtained after reaction with suitable substrates and by subsequent purification on Sephadex G-50; following degradation with pronase the biotin-binding sites were determined *(25, 26)*. – Traces of enzymatic activities (e.g. from tissue extracts) can be demonstrated in the following way: A Sephadex column is equilibrated with a suitable substrate (which should have a cern affinity for the gel); the extract is allowed to pass over the column. Due to enzymatic action, a certain amount of product is formed which is much greater than the substrate concentration in the buffer; its presence in the effluent is an indication for the presence of the enzyme (27). – Mononucleotides are formed immediately (beginning at the terminus) by the action of exonucleases on denatured deoxyribonucleic acid and can be separated on Sephadex G-100 from the high molecular weight residue; if, however, an endonuclease, which would cleave in central locations, is present, a gradual decrease in molecular weight can be observed. Both types of enzymes can thus be identified by gel chromatography (28).

Endocrinology

"Gel filtration" on Sephadex was from the beginning associated with the isolation of peptide hormones from the *pituitary gland*. We have already seen in Figure 25 a classical example utilizing complex formation for the isolation of oxytocin and vasopressin from the posterior lobe (29). Formic acid (70%) was used for the dissociation of the protein complex but does actually not seem to be required. Weaker acid (0.1 N) is claimed also to be sufficient (30, 31). – Lysine-vasopressin forms a dimer which can be separated from higher polymers by chromatography on Sephadex G-25 (2.2 × 200 cm) in 1 N acetic acid (32). – A new inactive product was formed upon treatment of oxytocin with 80% acetone (presumably the isopropylidene compound) which was purified by partition chromatography on Sephadex G-25 in one of the solvent systems mentioned in Table 35 for oxytocine (33). A retroplacental oxytocinase removes at least the first three amino acids from the hormone thus forming an inactive peptide which can be isolated on Sephadex G-25 (34). Recently a polypeptide of 48 amino acids was isolated in the crystalline state from the posterior lobe of the pituitary gland by repeated gel chromatography (35); the peptide shows very weak hormone activity (cf. Table 35 on the purification of sythnetic analogs of oxytocin).

Gel chromatography was very useful in the isolation and purification of hormones of the *anterior lobe of the pituitary*. The isolation of growth hormone of high activity on porous Sephadex gels is of particular interest; more details are to be found in the publications of Table 39. Other proteins from the anterior lobe which are less well characterized can also be purified on Sephadex, as is evident from the publications of Table 40. Several peptides of the intermediate lobe of the pituitary gland have been isolated by chromatography on Sephadex G-25; these are structurally and in their activity related to β-MSH; however, they are not identical with it (36).

146 Results

Table 39. *Growth hormone, isolation and labeling*

PAPKOFF, H., C. H. LI, and W.-K. LIU: Arch. Biochem. Biophys. **96**, 216 (1962). The isolation and characterization of growth hormone from porcine pituitaries.

REISFELD, R. A., B. G. HALLOWS, D. E. WILLIAMS, N. G. BRINK, and S. L. STEELMAN: Nature **197**, 1206 (1963). Purification of human growth hormone on Sephadex G-200.

ROOS, P., H. R. FEVOLD, and C. A. GEMZELL: Biochim. biophys. Acta **74**, 525 (1963). Preparation of human growth hormone by gel filtration.

DELLACHA, J. M., and M. SONENBERG: J. biol. Chem. **239**, 1515 (1964). Purification of bovine growth hormone.

REUSSER, F., and H. KO: Experientia **22**, 310 (1966). Fractionation of highly purified bovine growth hormone on Sephadex G-25 gel.

SAXENA, B. B., and P. H. HENNEMAN: Endocrinology **78**, 561 (1966). Preparation and properties of growth hormone from equine pituitary glands.

HUNTER, W. M.: Biochem. J. **97**, 199 (1965). Homogeneity studies on human growth hormone.

HÅNSON, L. A., P. ROOS, and L. RYMO: Nature **212**, 948 (1966). Heterogeneity of human growth hormone preparations by immuno gel filtration and gel filtration electrophoresis.

DELLACHA, J. M., M. A. ENERO, and I. FAIFERMAN: Experientia **22**, 16 (1966). Molecular weight of bovine growth hormone.

GREENWOOD, F. C., W. M. HUNTER, and J. S. GLOVER: Biochem. J. **89**, 114 (1963). The preparation of [131]J-labelled human growth hormone of high specific radioactivity.

COLLIPP, P. J., S. A. KAPLAN, D. C. BOYLE, and C. S. N. SHIMIZU: J. biol. Chem. **240**, 143 (1965). ^{14}C-acetyl bovine growth hormone. Physiological and antigenic properties.

LEAVER, F. W.: Proc. Soc. exptl. Biol. Med. **122**, 188 (1966). Evidence for the existence of human growth hormone-ribonucleic acid complex in the pituitary.

Table 40. *Protein hormones of the anterior lobe of the pituitary gland*

JUTISZ, M., C. HERMIER, A. COLONGE et R. COURRIER: C. R. Acad. Sci. (Paris) **256**, 3922 (1963). Isolement des hormones hypophysaires: purification de l'hormone folliculo stimulante de Mouton par filtration sur gel Sephadex.

SQUIRE, P. G., B. STARMAN, and C. H. LI: J. Biol. Chem. **238**, 1389 (1963). Studies of pituitary lactogenic hormone. XXII. Analysis of the state of aggregation of the ovine hormone by ultracentrifugation and exclusion chromatography.

SLUYSER, M., and C. H. LI: Nature **200**, 1007 (1963). Preparation of a low molecular weight component with lactogenic activity from a limited chymotryptic digest of ovine prolactin.

SANFELIPPO, P. M., and J. G. SURAK: J. Chromatog. **13**, 148 (1964). The behavior of hormonally-active proteins and peptides of the anterior pituitary on cross-linked dextran polymer gels.

MORRIS, C. J. O. R.: Acta endocr. Suppl. **90**, 163 (1964). On the molecular weight of pregnant mare's serum gonadotropin.

WARD, D. N., and M. S. ARNOTT: Anal. Biochem. **12**, 296 (1965). Gel filtration of proteins with particular reference to the glycoprotein, luteinizing hormone.

REICHERT, jr. L. E., und N. S. JIANG: Endocrinology **77**, 78 (1965). Comparative gel filtration and density gradient centrifugation studies in heterologous pituitary luteinizing hormones.

The publications of Table 41 describe the purification of extracts of the *parathyroid and thyroid glands*. The application of Sephadex G-25 in the test on the function of the thyroid gland is discussed in the section on "clinical chemistry".

Table 41. *Proteins and peptides of the thyroid glands*

RASMUSSEN, H., and L. C. CRAIG: J. biol. Chem. **236**, 759 (1961). Isolation and characterization of bovine parathyroid hormone.

— — Biochim. biophys. Acta **56**, 332 (1962). Purification of bovine parathyroid hormone by gel filtration.

AURBACH, G. D., and J. T. POTTS, jr.: Endocrinology **75**, 290 (1964). Partition of parathyroid hormone on Sephadex G-100.

RASMUSSEN, H., Y.-L. SZE, and R. YOUNG: J. biol. Chem. **239**, 2852 (1964). Further studies on the isolation and characterization of parathyroid polypeptides.

SALVATORE, G., M. SALVATORE, H. J. CAHNMANN, and J. ROBBINS: J. biol. Chem. **239**, 3267 (1964). Separation of thyroidal jodoproteins and purification of thyroglobulin by gel filtration and density gradient centrifugation.

—, G. VECCHIO, M. SALVATORE, H. J. CAHNMANN and J. ROBBINS: J. biol. Chem. **240**, 2935 (1965). Thyroid proteins.

NUNEZ, J., J. MAUCHAMP, V. MACCHIA et J. ROCHE: Biochim. biophys. Acta **107**, 247 (1965). Biosynthèse in vitro d'hormones doublement marquées dans des coupes de corps thyroïde. II. Biosynthèse d'une préthyroglobuline non iodée.

TENENHOUSE, A., C. ARNAUD, and H. RASMUSSEN: Proc. natl. Acad. Sci. **53**, 818 (1965). The isolation and characterization of thyrocalcitonin.

FRIEDMAN, J., and L. G. RAISZ: Science **150**, 1465 (1965). Thyrocalcitonin: Inhibitor of bone resorption in tissue culture.

HAWKER, C. D., J. D. GLASS, and H. RASMUSSEN: Biochemistry **5**, 344 (1966). Further studies on the isolation and characterization of parathyroid polypeptides.

The aggregation of *insulin* molecules frequently makes their exact localization during gel chromatography difficult. However, in suitable solvents the isolation of crystalline insulin can be accomplished with the help of dextran gels, e. g. from a fish (*37*), from 10–20 g of bovine pancreas (*38*), or from a single cat pancreas (*39*). Insulin which was labeled with $^{131}I_2$ (e.g. *40*) was applied to the identification of antibody reactions. The complex from serum is separated from "free" insulin on Sephadex G-75 (*41*). On Sephadex G-200 one can see that there are at least two proteins to which insulin is bound (*42*). An insulin inhibitor from the albumin fraction was partially purified on a preparative scale (*43*). On the other hand there is insulin activity in serum which can not be inhibited; the carrier was characterized more closely by intensive chromatography on different dextran gels (*44*). – The insulin molecule may be split reductively in urea into the two chains which can be separated from each other (on Sephadex G-75 in 50% acetic acid) and also from excess of reagents after alkylation (*131*).

Following oxidative sulfitolysis the A- and B-chains of insulins (as copper complexes of the S-sulfo derivatives) may be separated on Sephadex G-50 (*45*) or also in 50% acetic acid as S-sulfonic acids on Sephadex G-75 (*132*). During attempts to combine the liberated inactive mercaptan chains by oxidation large proportions of the reaction product consisted of polymers which again could be separated conveniently on Sephadex G-75 (*46*). – After the synthesis of the partially protected A-chain of this hormone the heneicosipeptide was contaminated with the nonapeptide component which had been applied in excess. The solubility difficulties were overcome; the A-chain was eluted (in tris buffer) on Sephadex G-25 before the contaminant (*47*). – Cf. (*48*) on the isolation of a high molecular weight *gastrin* on Sephadex.

Chemistry of Plasma Proteins

The fact that serum proteins can be separated on a preparative scale by chromatography on water swellable gels was very stimulating to the research in this area of protein chemistry. It is shown in Fig. 31 how the *fractionation of serum* on Sephadex G-200 progresses. Similar elution diagrams were obtained or can be found in most of the publications of Table 42. *Fluorescent labeling* with fluorescein isothiocyanate and the separation of the excess of reagent constitute an important application of "gel filtration" (cf. Table 20). – Numerous pharmaceuticals and certain metals form *complexes with serum proteins* (cf. Table 22); likewise, there are components in plasma which possess particular affinity for steroid hormones. In Table 43 investigations are compiled in which such complexes have been studied.

Table 42. *Fractionation of plasma proteins*

FLODIN, P.: Dissertation, Uppsala, 1962. Dextran Gels and their Applications in Gel Filtration.

GELOTTE, B., P. FLODIN, and J. KILLANDER: Arch. Biochem. Biophys., Suppl. **1**, 319 (1962). Fractionation of human plasma proteins by gel filtration and zone electrophoresis or ion-exchange chromatography.

FLODIN, P., and J. KILLANDER: Biochim. biophys. Acta **63**, 403 (1962). Fractionation of human serum proteins by gel filtration.

KILLANDER, J.: Protides biol. Fluids **11**, 446 (1963). Fractionation of antibodies of 19 S, 7 S and »intermediate« types by gel filtration and ion exchange chromatography or preparative electrophoresis.

ROSENQUIST, G. L., and R.V. GILDEN: Biochim. biophys. Acta **78**, 543 (1963). Chicken antibodies to bovine serum albumin. Molecular size and sensitivity to 2-mercaptoethanol.

KILLANDER, J., and C. F. HÖGMAN: Scand. J. clin. Lab. Invest. **15**, 130 (1963). Fractionation of human blood group antibodies by gel filtration.

BROMAN, L., and K. KJELLIN: Biochim. biophys. Acta 82, 101 (1964). A rapid semi-continuous method for purification of ceruloplasmin from human serum.

TERR, A. I., and J. D. BENTZ: J. Allergy 35, 206 (1964). Gel filtration of human skin sensitizing antibody and β_{2A}-globuline.

PORATH, J., and N. UI: Biochim. biophys. Acta 90, 324 (1964). Chemical studies on immunoglobulins I. A new preparative procedure for γ-globulins employing glycine-rich solvent systems.

KILLANDER, J., S. BENGTSSON, and L. PHILIPSON: Proc. Soc. exp. Biol. Med. 115, 861 (1964). Fractionation of human plasma macroglobulins by gel filtration on pearl-condensed agar.

GOT, R.: Clin. chim. Acta 11, 432 (1965). Fractionation of human lactoserum proteins.

CHAN, J. Y. S., and E. T. MERTZ: Can. J. Biochem. 44, 475 (1966). Studies on plasminogen. V. Purification of bovine and human plasminogens by Sephadex chromatography.

FRANZINI, C.: Clin. chim. Acta 14, 576 (1966). Gel filtration behaviour of human serum lipoproteins.

COHEN, I. R., and L. C. NORINS: Science 152, 1257 (1966). Natural human antibodies to gram-negative bacteria: immunoglobulins G, A and M.

JACOBSEN, S.: Nature 210, 98 (1966). Separation of two different substrates for plasma kinin-forming enzymes.

ALLAN, D., and M. MALKINSON: Nature 211, 493 (1966). Spectrophotometric detection and measurement of sensitizing antibodies.

WERNER, M.: J. Chromatog. 25, 63 (1966). Fractionation of lipoproteins from blood by agarose gel filtration.

PŘISTOUPIL, T. I., and S. ULRYCH: J. Chromatog. 25, 58 (1966). Study of modified bovine serum by gel filtration on pearl-condensed agar.

PHILIP, B. A., P. HERBERT, and J.W. HOLLINGSWORTH: Proc. Soc. eptl. Biol. Med. 123, 576 (1966). Separation of contaminating pyrogen materials from commercial bovine serum albumin.

Table 43. *Complexes of plasma proteins with steroid hormones*

DE MOOR, P., K. HEIRWEGH, J. F. HEREMANS, and M. DECLERCK-RASKIN: J. clin. Invest. 41, 816 (1962). Protein binding of corticoids studied by gel filtration.

QUINCEY, R.V., and C. H. GRAY: J. Endocrinol. 26, 509 (1963). A comparison of protein-binding of cortisol as measured by equilibrium dialysis and gel filtration.

DE MOOR, P., R. DECKX, and O. STEENO: J. Endocrinol. 27, 355 (1963). Influence of various steroids in the specific binding of cortisol.

—, K. HEIRWEGH, and O. STEENO: Arch. Biochem. Biophys. 103, 506 (1963). Protein binding of progesterone studied by gel filtration.

BOULOUARD, R., et Y. A. FONTAINE: C. R. Acad. Sci. (Paris) 257, 1379 (1963). Sur l'état de la corticostérone plasmatique chez le rat. Etude par filtration sur gels Sephadex G-100 et G-200.

TALWAR, G. P., S. J. SEGAL, A. EVANS, and O.W. DAVIDSON: Proc. natl. Acad. Sci. 52, 1059 (1964). The binding of estradiol in the uterus: A mechanism for derepression of RNA synthesis.

MURPHEY, B. E. P., and CH. J. PATTEE: J. clin. Endocrinol. Metab. 24, 919 (1964). Determination of plasma corticoids by competitive protein-binding analysis using gel filtration.

Complexes of serum proteins with other proteins may also be isolated by gel chromatography as has already been shown in Fig. 16 for the hemoglobin-haptoglobin-complex *(49)*. The quantitative determination of the "hemoglobin binding capacity" on Sephadex G-100 is much simpler *(50)*. – The macroglobulin fraction (isolated on Sephadex G-200) evidently contains proteins which bind trypsin *(51, 52)*. The activity is partially retained *(51)*, to some extent it is lost *(52)*. – *Antigen-antibody complexes* have frequently been isolated on porous Sephadex gels and the components were studied after dissociation; additional data are to be found in Table 44. In the

Table 44. *Antigen-antibody complexes*

BASSETT, E. W., S. M. BEISER, and S. W. TANENBAUM: Science **133**, 1475 (1961). Purification of antibody to galactosyl-protein conjugates.

GRAMLICH, F., D. MOHRING und H. E. MÜLLER: Naturwissenschaften **49**, 451 (1962). Reinigung von Antikörpern durch Gelfiltration.

GIVOL, D., S. FUCHS, and M. SELA: Biochim. biophys. Acta **63**, 222 (1962). Isolation of antibodies to antigens of low molecular weight.

BENNETT, J. C., and E. HABER: J. biol. Chem. **238**, 1362 (1963). Studies on antigen conformation during antibody purification.

HABER, E., L. B. PAGE, and G. A. JACOBY: Biochemistry **4**, 693 (1965). Synthesis of antigenic branch-chain copolymers of angiotensin and poly-L-lysine.

—, L. B. PAGE, and F. F. RICHARDS: Anal. Biochem. **12**, 163 (1965). Radio immunoassay employing gel filtration.

STEMKE, G.W.: Immunochemistry **2**, 359 (1965). A study of soluble complexes and uncombined material in antigen-antibody reactions involving allotypic specificities of purified rabbit γ-globulin.

BOYNS, A. R., and J. HARDWICKE: Immunology **10**, 57 (1966). The isolation of soluble antigen-antibody complexes on Sephadex G-200.

previous section the potential of studying *soluble* immunocomplexes had already been shown for insulin. Immunological techniques in combination with gel chromatography have played an important role in the structural elucidation of γ-globulins. Excellent studies on the reductive cleavage, the isolation of the L- and H-chains, the recombination, the limited action of papain, and finally on the immunological properties of fragments and the intact molecule are to be found in publications on this topic compiled in Table 45.

The difficulties in solving these problems were greatly reduced when it was recognized that the so-called Bence-Jones proteins, which are found in urine during certain diseases, originate from γ-globulins. These proteins can be isolated on a preparative scale on G-100 *(53–56, 133)*. The analytical detection in urine is of great diagnostic significance (cf. Table 52).

Table 45. *Fragments of γ-globulins*

HANSON, L. Å., and B. G. JOHANSSON: Nature **187**, 599 (1960). Presence of immunologically active fragments after proteolytic degradation of human γ-globulin.

FLEISCHMANN, J. B., R. R. PORTER, and E. M. PRESS: Biochem. J. **88**, 220 (1963). The arrangement of the peptide chains in γ-globulin.

HANSON, L. Å., and B. G. JOHANSSON: Acta chem. scand. **17**, 2701 (1963). Studies on the antigenic complexity of human **7**S γ-globulin.

— — Clin. chim. Acta **8**, 66 (1963). Isolation of immunologically active fragments of normal human γ-globulin after tryptic degradation.

TAN, M., and W. V. EPSTEIN: Science **139**, 53 (1963). Purification of γ-globulin fragments by gel filtration.

METZGER, H., and S. J. SINGER: Science **142**, 674 (1963). Binding capacity of reductively fragmented antibodies to the 2,4-dinitrophenyl group.

GOODMAN, J.W.: Biochemistry **3**, 857 (1964). Immunologically active fragments of rabbit γ-globulin.

JAMES, K., C. S. HENNEY, and D. R. STANWORTH: Nature **202**, 563 (1964). Structural changes occurring in 7 S γ-globulins.

FOUGEREAU, M., and G. M. EDELMAN: Biochemistry **3**, 1120 (1964). Resemblance of the gross arrangement of polypeptide chains in reconstituted and native γ-globulins.

UTSUMI, S., and F. KARUSH: Biochemistry **3**, 1329 (1964). The subunits of purified rabbit antibody.

CRIDDLE, R. S.: Arch. Biochem. Biophys. **106**, 101 (1964). Dissociation and separation of γ-globulin into subunits.

FRANĚK, F., and J. ZIKÁN: Collect. czech. chem. Commun. **29**, 1401 (1964). Limited cleavage of disulphide bonds of pig γ-globulin by S-sulphonation.

KOTÝNEK, O., and F. FRANĚK: Collect. czech. chem. Commun. **30**, 3153 (1965). Unequal importance of different polypeptide chains for the determination of antibody specificity in bovine anti-dinitrophenyl antibodies.

YONEZAWA, D., P. J. MIGLIORE, S. C. CAPETILLO, and B. JIRGENSONS: Makromol. Chem. **77**, 191 (1964). Structural studies on human serum γ-globulins and myeloma proteins. II. Cleavage of the disulfide bonds of the globulins with sulfite and recombination of the fragments.

JIRGENSONS, B., M. E. ADAMS-MAYNE, V. GORGURAKI, and P. J. MIGLIORE: Arch. Biochem. Biophys. **111**, 283 (1965). III. Oxidative sulfitolysis of myeloma globulins and reconstitution of the macromolecules.

INMAN, F. P., and A. NISONOFF: J. biol. Chem. **241**, 322 (1966). Reversible dissociation of fragment Fc of rabbit γG-immunoglobin.

SJÖQVIST, J.: Nature **210**, 1182 (1966). Heterogeneity of heavy chain preparations from human γ-G-immunoglobulins.

LANCKMAN, M.: Nature **210**, 1379 (1966). Structural heterogeneity of L-chains in antibodies of restricted specificity.

FRANĚK, F.: Collect. Czechoslov. chem. Commun. **31**, 1142 (1966). Study of the polypeptide chain arrangement in pig γ-G-globulin through molecular and peptide map characteristics of individual polypeptide chains and higher subunits.

Structural Elucidation of Proteins

It is an essential part of the elucidation of the primary structure of proteins to cleave the macromolecules into poly- and oligopeptides which have to be separated as quantitatively as possible. Not only the fragments of (the above mentioned) γ-globulins were separated on porous gels, but relatively large *polypeptides* can also be obtained from other proteins and represent important intermediates in structural work. Upon the action of proteases on serum albumin (*57*) as well as on β-lactoglobulin and α-lactalbumin (*58*) immunologically active fragments are formed which can be separated on Sephadex G-75 and G-50. Due to the high selectivity of the action of cyanogen bromide on proteins these are only split (at methionine) into large, well defined partial sequences. Already with the introduction of this technique (*59*) the fragments of ribonuclease were separated on Sephadex G-25. The same gel and (for larger fragments) Sephadex G-75 were applied to the isolation and characterization of the fragments of sperm whale (*60*) and horse heart (*61*) myoglobin and of cytochromes of the same organ (*61*); all fragments had also been obtained by treatment with cyanogen bromide. As has already been described for insulin and globulins, α-chymotrypsin (*62*) and even wool (*63*) can be fragmented by cleavage of the disulfide bridges; the fragments were separated subsequently by gel chromatography. – Upon exposure of ribonuclease to γ-radiation, fragments are formed which can be made visible by gel chromatography (*64*). Partial hydrolysis of the same enzyme with subtilisin leads to the formation of two fragments, the so-called S-peptide and S-protein. The two fragments may be obtained in 70% yield simply by chromatography on Sephadex G-25 (*134*). If upon enzymatic hydrolysis of a protein a high molecular weight residue (the so-called core) remains, this core may be separated on Sephadex G-25 before a "finger print" is taken (*135*).

Examples have already been presented on page 135 in which e.g. tryptophan-containing peptides had been retarded on Sephadex G-25. Such interactions play a great role during the *separation of oligopeptides* of the (predominantly enzymatic) partial hydrolysates of proteins. The separation of the peptide mixture is normally the result of a combination of various effects on the gel column. Publications reporting the separation of regular oligopeptides are compiled in Table 46.

In the publications of Table 47 so-called labeled peptides have been isolated in the pure state, i.e. those in which an amino acid (either by a chromophor or by radioactive labeling) had been modified; in Table 48 publications on the isolation of glycopeptides on Sephadex G-25 are compiled. – In a mixture of phenol/glacial acidic acid/water (1/1/1) there is no interaction of peptides with the Sephadex gel, so that, for instance, the tryptic peptides of the α-chain of hemoglobin are separated exactly ac-

Table 46. *Separation of oligopeptides for the purpose of sequence determination of proteins*

BENNICH, H.: Biochim. biophys. Acta **51**, 265 (1961). Gel filtration of tryptic hydrolysates of α-casein.

STEPANOV, V., D. HANDSCHUH und F. A. ANDERER: Z. Naturforschung **16b**, 626 (1961). Tryptische Spaltpeptide von Tabak-Mosaik-Virus.

GUIDOTTI, G., R. J. HILL, and W. KONIGSBERG: J. biol. Chem. **237**, 2184 (1962). The structure of human hemoglobin. II. The separation and amino acid composition of the tryptic peptides from the α- and β-chains.

AMBLER, R. P.: Biochem. J. **89**, 349 (1963). The amino acid sequence of pseudomonas cytochrome c-551.

GRASSMANN, W., K. HANNIG und A. NORDWIG: Z. physiol. Chem. **333**, 154 (1963). Über die apolaren Bereiche des Kollagenmoleküls.

CHERNOFF, A. I., and N. PETTIT: Biochim. biophys. Acta **97**, 47 (1965). The amino acid composition of hemoglobin. VI. Separation of the tryptic peptides of hemoglobin *knox-ville* No. 1 on Dowex 1 X2 and Sephadex.

SIEBERT, G., A. SCHMITT und R. V. MALORTIE: Z. physiol. Chem. **342**, 20 (1965). Reinigung und Eigenschaften von Dorschmuskel-Kathepsin.

PFLEIDERER, G., und A. KRAUSS: Biochem. Z. **342**, 85 (1965). Die Wirkungsspezifität von Schlangengiftproteasen.

EAKER, D. L., T. P. KING, and L. C. CRAIG: Biochemistry **4**, 1479 (1965). Des-lysyl-glutamyl- and des-lysyl-pyroglutamyl-ribonucleases II, structural studies.

MAROUX, S., et M. ROVERY: Biochim. biophys. Acta **113**, 126 (1966). Contribution à l'étude de la structure de la chymotrypsine α de bœuf. La chaîne C et son core trypsique.

Table 47. *Isolation of labeled peptides from protein partial hydrolysates*

PORATH, J.: Biochim. biophys. Acta **39**, 193 (1960). Gel filtration of proteins, peptides and amino acids.

MAHOWALD, T. A.: Biochemistry **4**, 732 (1965). The amino acid sequence around the »reactive« sulfhydryl groups in adenosine triphosphocreatine phosphotransferase.

FASOLD, H.: Biochem. Z. **342**, 295 (1965). Zur chemischen Untersuchung der Tertiärstruktur von Proteinen. II. Abbau des Azoglobins, Auftrennung und Identifizierung einzelner Brückenpeptide.

HIRS, C. H.W., and J. H. KYCIA: Arch. Biochem. Biophys. **111**, 223 (1965). Identification of initial reaction sites in the dinitrophenylation of pancreatic ribonuclease A.

HARRIS, J. I., and L. POLGÁR: J. mol. Biol. **14**, 630 (1965). Amino acid sequence around a reactive lysine in glyceraldehyde 3-phosphate dehydrogenase.

HAYASHI, K., T. IMOTO, G. FUNATSU, and M. FUNATSU: J. Biochem. (Japan) **58**, 227 (1965). The position of the active tryptophan residue in lysozyme.

HOLBROOK, J. J., G. PFLEIDERER, J. SCHNETGER, and S. DIEMAIR: Biochem. Z. **344**, 1 (1966). Preparation of the tryptic peptides containing the essential cysteine residues of lactate dehydrogenase I and V.

---

154 Results

Table 48. *Isolation of glycopeptides*

NOLAN. C., and E. L. SMITH: J. biol. Chem. **237**, 446 (1962). Glycopeptides. Isolation and properties of glycopeptides from rabbit γ-globulin.

— — J. biol. Chem. **237**, 453 (1962). Glycopeptides. Isolation and properties of glyco-peptides from a bovine globulin of colostrum and from fraction II-3 of human globulin.

MARKS, G. S., R. D. MARSHALL, A. NEUBERGER, and H. PAPKOFF: Biochim. biophys. Acta **63**, 340 (1962). A simplified procedure for the isolation of glycopeptides from glyco-proteins.

LEE, Y. CH., and R. MONTGOMERY: Arch. Biochem. Biophys. **97**, 9 (1962). Glycopeptides from ovalbumin: the structure of the peptide chains.

MONTGOMERY, R., and Y. CH. WU: J. biol. Chem. **238**, 3547 (1963). The carbohydrate of ovomucoid. Isolation of glycopeptides and the carbohydrate protein linkage.

NEUBERGER, A., and H. PAPKOFF: Biochem. J. **87**, 581 (1963). Carbohydrates in protein. 7. The nature of the carbohydrate in ovomucoid.

CARSTEN, M. E., and J. G. PIERCE: J. biol. Chem. **238**, 1724 (1963). Chemical studies on thyrotropin preparations and related pituitary glycoproteins.

GHUYSEN, J.-M., and J. L. STROMINGER: Biochemistry **2**, 1110 (1963). Structure of the cell wall of Staphylococcus aureus, Strain Copenhagen. I. Preparation of fragments by enzymatic hydrolysis.

PLUMMER, jr., T. H., and C. H.W. HIRS: J. biol. Chem. **239**, 2530 (1964). On the structure of bovine pancreatic ribonuclease B. Isolation of a glycopeptide.

BOURRILLON, R., et J. L. VERNAY: Biochim. biophys. Acta **117**, 319 (1966). Deux glyco-peptides à hydroxyproline dans l'urine humaine normale.

DEMAILLE, J., M. DAUTREVAUX, R. HAVEZ et G. BISERTE: Bull. Soc. Chim. biol. **48**, 45 (1966). Isolement d'une fraction glycopeptidique de l'α₂-macroglobuline du sérum de porc.

cording to size (*65*). Water insoluble peptides from the degradation of a bacteriophage coat protein could be separated on Sephadex G-50 in 88% formic acid (*136*). Peptides may also be desalted by gel chromatography (following ion exchange chromatography), in certain cases even on Sepha-dex G-25 (cf. *66*). – The isolation of (few) amino acids from a mixture of peptides and proteins is a difficult problem. A gel has been suggested which is obtained upon preparing copper hydroxide in Sephadex G-25 (*67*). Only the amino acids (as dextran-copper-amino acid complex) are retarded. They may be eluted subsequently with 0.2N HCl.

In studies concerned with the cross-linking of protein molecules (in order to determine the tertiary structure) the danger of intermolecular covalent bond formation exists. This can also be controlled by gel chro-matography (*68*).

Nucleic Acid Chemistry

Nucleic Acids

Nucleic acids, as macromolecules, may naturally be separated from low molecular weight contaminants on gels of relatively low porosity. In Fig. 28 we have already become familiar with the extremely important and very effective removal of phenol from desoxyribonucleic acid (*69*). In Table 49 other publications are mentioned all of which report similar procedures.

Table 49. *Removal of low molecular weight substances from nucleic acid solutions*

BRESLER, S. E., KH. M. RUBINA, R. A. GRAEVSKAYA, and N. N. VASIL'EVA: Biochemistry (russ.) **26**, 649 (1961). The separation of ribonucleic and adenosinetriphosphoric acids by chromatography on molecular sieves.

BOMAN, H. G., and S. HJERTÉN: Arch. Biochem. Biophys., Suppl. **1**, 276 (1962). Molecular sieving of bacterial RNA.

HARTMANN, G., U. COY und G. KNIESE: Biochem. Z. **330**, 227 (1963). Zum biologischen Wirkungsmechanismus der Actinomycine. Vgl. auch Biochem. Z. **343**, 16 (1965) und **340**, 390 (1964).

STROHMAIER, K.: Z. Naturforschung **18b**, 788 (1963). Vergleichende Untersuchungen der infektiösen Ribonucleinsäure des Virus der ansteckenden Schweinelähmung (Teschener Krankheit) mit hochmolekularer Gewebe-Ribonucleinsäure.

GROSS, M., B. SKOCZYLAS, and W. TURSKI: Anal. Biochem. **11**, 10 (1965). Separation of phenol and ribonucleic acid by dextran gel filtration.

FRITZ, H.-G., R. DELHEY und H. ROSS: Z. Naturforschung **19b**, 1165 (1964). Zur Gewinnung von infektiöser TMV-RNS aus Pflanzenmaterial mit Hilfe der Gelfiltration.

KÖSSEL, H., und S. DOEHRING: Z. Physiol. Chem. **340**, 221 (1965). Zur Reaktion von Nucleinsäuren mit diazotierter Sulfanilsäure.

Like proteins, various nucleic acids have uniform molecular weights. It should, therefore, be possible, as long as sufficiently large differences exist, to separate them by gel chromatography. The so-called "soluble" or "transfer" or "acceptor" ribonucleic acids (here referred to as s-RNA) are of particular interest to the biochemist on account of their established significance in protein biosynthesis and their structure which have been determined already in three cases. (Cf. Table 35 for the partition chromatography of s-RNA on Sephadex G-25.) The mixture of all soluble ribonucleic acids can be separated from ribosomal RNA on Sephadex G-200 (*70, 71*) and on polyacrylamide gel, 5–5 (*70*). The porosity of Sephadex G-75 earlier was not sufficient for this purpose (*72*); on this gel only the simultaneous removal of mono- and oligonucleotides could be accomplished. Ribosomal RNA, s-RNA and phenol can be separated on Sephadex G-100 (*137*). It has been reported repeatedly (*73, 74, 75, 76*), that various preparations of s-RNA contain in addition to oligonucleotides also high molecular aggregates; their presence was shown by chromatography on Sephadex G-100. In addition to ribonucleic acid (4S), which transfers amino acids, "ribosomal RNA" from *E.coli* (*138*) and liver cells (*139*) contain yet another inactive (5S) ribonucleic acid. The second one is possibly the precursor of the first one. Both can be separated on Sephadex G-100. A careful study (*140*) of s-RNA from rat liver did not confirm any separation on Sephadex G-200.

ZACHAU (*75*), in his report on the chromatography of soluble ribonucleic acid and the cleavage products on Sephadex, comprehensively reviews the literature and with the help of own investigations, gives a preview on the potential and the limitations of the new method for the fractionation of nucleic acids. According to this author, the situation in this field is not as clear as with the proteins because the behavior of nucleic acids is much more dependent upon conformational changes, aggregations, and affinities for the gel. Thus, serine specific s-RNA is eluted much earlier once charged with the amino acid than prior to being charged (*75*). It is unlikely that this is due to the difference in molecular weight. Nevertheless, it is possible to utilize these effects for separation. The soluble ribonucleic acids of *E.coli* were separated into two groups on Sephadex G-100 when a special elution gradient of decreasing ionic strength was applied (*76*). This separation is supposed to be brought about by the fact that individual soluble ribonucleic acids respond to changes in their environment to a different degree by conformational changes and thus space occupation. Whether such effects play also a role in the separation of "peptidyl-s-RNA" from free s-RNA on Sephadex G-200 (*141*) is presently an open question. Infectious RNA from polio virus also undergoes conformational changes; despite its very high molecular weight, it may be separated from the virus under certain conditions on Sephadex G-200 (*77*) and on 2% agarose (*78*). – Hybrides of RNA and DNA have been purified on Sephadex G-100; they had been prepared with excess RNA which, for the purpose of separation, had been degraded to oligonucleotides by the action of ribonuclease (*79*). The so-called "replicative intermediate" which supposedly contains still a double stranded "core" can be separated from a single stranded bacteriophage-RNA on Sepharose 4B (*142*).

Oligonucleotides

The same effects which caused difficulties during the fractionation of high molecular weight nucleic acids are more strongly noticeable in efforts to separate oligonucleotides. Thus, for instance, the longer chain (8–10 membered) oligonucleotides, which are of particular interest for structural elucidation, can barely be separated on Sephadex G-200 from s-RNA unless special precautions are observed (*75*). The situation is also greatly complicated by the enormous influence of the degree of phosphorylation of the oligonucleotides (*80*). Under such circumstances it is not very meaningful to define for individual gel types exclusion limits (M_{lim}) for nucleotides or nucleic acids.

It is evident from Table 50 that, despite the difficulties described above, several oligonucleotides and their monomers have been separated successfully. – The situation is much clearer for polymers of one nucleotide. In studies concerned with the influence of the chain length of oligonucleo-

Table 50. *Separation of oligonucleotides*

GELOTTE, B.: Naturwissenschaften **48**, 554 (1961). Fraktionierung von Nucleinsäuren und Nucleotiden.

ISHIKURA, H.: Biochim. biophys. Acta **51**, 189 (1961). Fractionation of RNAse I core by gel filtration and its relation to streptolysin S'-forming activity.

ZADRAŽIL, S., Z. ŠORMOVÁ, and F. ŠORM: Collect. czech. chem. Commun. **26**, 2643 (1961). Separation of nucleic acid components on Sephadex.

INGRAM, V. M., and J. G. PIERCE: Biochemistry **1**, 580 (1962). Some properties of yeast amino acid acceptor ribonucleic acid and mapping of the oligonucleotides produced by ribonuclease digestion.

ISHIKURA, H.: J. Biochem. (Japan) **52**, 324 (1962). Further studies on the fractionation of RNAse I-core by gel filtration.

HABERMANN, V.: Collect. czech. chem. Commun. **28**, 510 (1963). Studies on deoxyribonucleic acids. II. Degradation of deoxyribonucleic acids to purine nucleotide sequences.

HOHN, TH., und W. POLLMANN: Z. Naturforschung **18b**, 919 (1963). Die Trennung von Nucleinsäure-Bausteinen mit Sephadex.

LIPSETT, M. N.: J. biol. Chem. **239**, 1250 (1964). Aggregation of guanine oligoribonucleotides and the effect of mercuric salts.

STICKLAND, R. G.: Anal. Biochem. **10**, 108, (1965). Separation of 5'-ribonucleotides by two-dimensional thin-layer chromatography.

SCHWARTZ, A. N., A. W. G. YEE, and B. A. ZABIN: J. Chromatog. **20**, 154 (1965). Separation of nucleotides, nucleosides and bases on a new gel filtration material.

UZIEL, M., and W. E. COHN: Biochim. biophys. Acta **103**, 539 (1965). Desalting of nucleotides by gel filtration.

BIRNBOIM, H.: Biochim. biophys. Acta **119**, 198 (1966). The use of gel filtration to distinguish between endonucleolytic and exonucleolytic types of degradation.

---

tides (as artificial messenger-RNA) on protein biosynthesis, oligonucleotides of defined size were required. For this purpose, synthetic polynucleotides were partially hydrolyzed with enzymes and then chromatographed (*81*). From polyuridylic acid, for instance, on Sephadex G-200 fractions of average degrees of polymerization of 42 to 132 and on G-75 those of 5.8 to 42 were isolated.

Virus Separation

Since they are closely related to nucleic acids, the few examples of purification and fractionation of viruses shall be added here. Naturally the viruses are easily separated from low molecular weight contaminations (*82, 83*); protamin must also be considered as such in this context. Protamin is initially used for the precipitation of, for instance, the polyoma-virus. After dissolution in strong sodium chloride solution the virus and protein can be separated on Sephadex G-75 (*84*; cf. also *77, 78*). – In order to separate the various viruses from each other, gels with the largest pores are required for the considerable size of these particles (cf. Chapter 2). Granulated (*85*) or beaded (*86, 87*) agar gels are applicable here as well as the particularly effective porous glass (*88*). Rod-like viruses are then sorted out according to their length. In Fig. 33 an example of a virus separation on agar gel has already been shown.

Carbohydrates

This area of application has been twice reviewed by GRANATH (*89, 90*). Several publications have also been already discussed in the section on molecular weight distribution (page 120). It is actually surprising that relatively few applications of gel chromatography to the separation of compounds of this class of substances are to be found in the literature. This is possibly due to the fact that one is afraid to contaminate the carbohydrates to be separated with traces of dextrans which are continuously bleeding from Sephadex (cf. page 27). The polyacrylamide gels (Bio-Gels) are likely to be better in this respect than dextran gels (*91*) (particularly in the case of quantitative studies) since they do not release traces of carbohydrates. On the other hand, this "background" has evidently thus far not been detrimental to the work with Sephadex gels. Reports on the successful chromatography of oligo- and monosaccharides are compiled in Table 51. The latter can also easily be separated on Sephadex G-10. Of high molecular weight substances, dextrins from starch, have been isolated on Sephadex G-75 (*92*) and those from various glycogenes on Sephadex G-50 (*93*); hemicelluloses from fir wood and acidic polysaccharides of various origin (*95, 96*) have been fractionated on G-100 (*94*). Following the action of pronase on synovial fluid of man, high molecular weight hyaluronic acid (separated from proteins) can be isolated on Sephadex G-200 (*143*). Bacterial polysaccharides have also been isolated by gel chromatography (*144*).

Gel chromatography found very interesting application in the determination of the permeability of membranes in body (*97*). Dextran, *via* the allyl compound, was labeled with $^{131}I_2$ and purified on Sephadex G-200· This material was then applied and after a certain time it could be determined on the same gel that the molecular weight distributions of the dextran in different body fluids differed from each other (cf. below the differentiation

Table 51. *Separation of oligosaccharides*

FLODIN, P., and K. ASPBERG: Biological Structure and Function, New York, 1961, Vol. 1, S. 345. Separation of oligosaccharides with gel filtration.

—, J. D. GREGORY, and L. RODÉN: Anal. Biochem. **8**, 424 (1964). Separation of acidic oligosaccharides by gel filtration.

LEE, Y.-CH., and C. E. BALLOU: Biochemistry **4**, 257 (1965). Preparation of mannobiose, mannotriose and a new mannotetraose from Saccharomyces cerevisiae mannan.

MIETTINEN, T. A.: Scand. J. clin. Lab. Invest. **14**, 380 (1962). Fractionation of urinary mucosaccharides by gel filtration.

LUNDBLAD, A., and I. BERGGARD: Biochim. biophys. Acta **57**, 129 (1962). Gel filtration of the low molecular weight carbohydrate components of normal urine.

ZELEZNICK, L. D.: J. Chromatog. **14**, 139 (1964). The use of Sephadex G-25 in partition column chromatography.

BARRETT, A. J., and D. H. NORTHCOTE: Biochem. J. **94**, 617 (1965). Apple fruit pectic substances.

CIFONELLI, J. A.: Carbohydrate Res. **2**, 150 (1966). Acid hydrolysis of acidic mucopolysaccharides.

LUNDBLAD, A.: Nature **211**, 531 (1966). Low molecular weight carbohydrates in urine from secretors and none-secretors of different blood groups.

between polysaccharides and monosaccharides in body fluids). – The application of gel chromatography to the solution of problems related to the carbohydrate metabolism of plants is described in a series of publications (cf. *98*). – Teichoic acids from the cell walls of different bacteria may be separated from low molecular weight contaminants on Sephadex G-25 (*99*). The polymer from Staphylococcus aureus consists, according to the chromatogram on Sephadex G-50, at best of 40–50 repetitive units (*100, 101*).

Clinical Chemistry

The boundaries of this discipline are chosen rather arbitrarily. Here one could also add enzymology, endocrinology, and the plasma proteins. Therefore, the term should be interpreted in such a way that only those applications will be covered in which gel chromatography was applied as a *diagnostic tool*. With this restrictive aspect in mind, the references on protein labeling with fluorescein or $^{131}I_2$ (Tables 20 and 21) and on the binding of pharmaceuticals or steroid hormones to plasmaproteins (Tables 22 and 43) are of particular interest.

The presence of sugars interferes with the determination of polysaccharides in body fluids. Dextran in serum which had been used as *plasma expander* can easily be separated from glucose by simple "gel filtration" on Sephadex G-25 (*102, 103*). The method has been recommended as standard

technique for the *kidney function test* where the amount of inulin, a poly-
fructosan, in urine has to be determined in the presence of glucose (*104*,
105). The application of gel filtration eliminates the enzymatic degradation
of the sugar which is otherwise required. A polysaccharide suitable for this
test must not associate with plasma proteins. It was shown with Sephadex
G-50 that this requirement is fulfilled for "polyfructosan-S" (*106*).

That the plant protease bromelain is suitable for *substitution therapy* in
the case of digestive difficulties was demonstrated by comparative gel
chromatography of hydrolysates of casein (with bromelain and/or with
gastrointestinal juice and subsequent trypsin treatment) on Sephadex G-25
(*107*). On the other hand, the nutritional value of different fish meals was
determined in a similar fashion by digestive experiments with papain and
pepsin and the comparison of the resulting peptide solutions by gel chromatography (*108*).

Naturally, medicine has taken advantage of the fractionations of plasma
proteins on Sephadex G-200 which are illustrated in Fig. 31 and are supported
by the many examples of Table 42; diseases in which individual proteins
are produced for the first time, appear in large quantities, or not at all, are
quickly diagnozed by these techniques. Clinical chemical publications on
proteins in serum or in other body fluids are compiled in Table 52. Gel chromatography will not replace electrophoresis in this field. However, in many
instances it will be a very effective supplement, since here separation is based
on an entirely different principle. Thus, for instance, morbus Waldenström
(macroglobulinemia) and plasmacytosis cannot be distinguished electro-
phoretically while in gel chromatograms of the serum on Sephadex G-200
the difference is quite considerable. The application of both techniques will
easily discriminate between myeloma and morbus Waldenström. – Using
the "automatic" small column of Sephadex G-50 of Fig. 12b, it is possible
to determine in a sample of 0.1 to 0.3 ml of spinal fluid the amount of
protein without interference from other substances (*109*). On the other
hand, it is possible to isolate the free amino acids from 0.1 ml of blood
plasma (*110*) on a micro column of 350 mg of Sephadex G-25 by separating
the proteins.

The affinity of Sephadex G-25 for 3,5,3'-triiodotyrosine is used with
advantage in the *in vitro thyroid function test* (Hamolsky-method) (*111*, *112*).
Under standard conditions serum is incubated with the labeled hormone
and three components represented by peaks of radioactivity are obtained by
gel chromatography: protein bound and free hormone, and, inbetween,
free $^{131}I_2$ from the radiochemical decomposition of the hormone utilized.
Quantitative determinations are in excellent agreement with those obtained
by other methods, a result that has been confirmed by hundreds of applications (*113*, *114*). The separation of iodinated amino acids, their association
products with proteins and inorganic iodine has already been described

Table 52. *Gel chromatography in the diagnosis of pathological proteins*

VAN EIJK, H. G., C. H. MONFOORT, J. J. WITTE, and H. G. K. WESTENBRINK: Biochim. biophys. Acta **63**, 537 (1962). Isolation and characterization of some Bence-Jones proteins.

EPSTEIN, W. V., and J. M. TAN: J. Lab. clin. Med. **60**, 125 (1962). γ-Globulin interactions in the sera of two patients with rheumatoid arthritis studied by gel filtration.

ROSKES, S. D., and T. E. THOMPSON: Clin. chim. Acta **8**, 489 (1963). A simple molecular sieve technique for detecting macroglobulinemia.

HARBOE, N. M. G., and A. DRIVSHOLM: Protides biol. Fluids **11**, 450 (1963). Characterization of abnormal serum proteins from patients with multiple myeloma and Waldenström's macroglobulinaemia by means of size chromatography.

LEE, M., and J. R. DEBRO: J. Chromatog. **10**, 68 (1963). The application of gel filtration to the measurement of the binding phenol red by human serum proteins.

RATCLIFF, A. P., and J. HARDWICKE: J. clin. Path. **17**, 676 (1964). Estimation of serum hemoglobin-binding capacity (haptoglobin) on Sephadex G-100.

AEBI, H., C. H. SCHNEIDER, H. GANG, and U. WIESMANN: Experientia **20**, 103 (1964). Separation of catalase and other red cell enzymes from hemoglobin by gel filtration.

RICHARD, G. B.: Clin. chim. Acta **11**, 399 (1965). Study of the heterogeneity of myeloma of the β_{2A}-type by Sephadex gel filtration.

WIRTH, K., U. ULLMANN, K. BRAND, K. HUTH und B. HESS: Klinische Wochenschrift **43**, 528 (1965). Analyse von Globulinen mit der Gelfiltration.

RIVERA J.V., E. TORO-GOYCO, and M. L. MATOS: Am. J. med. Sci. **249**, 371 (1965). Molecular sieve in the study of plasma proteins.

HANSON, L. Å., B. G. JOHANSSON, and L. RYMO: Protides biol. Fluids **14**, 579 (1967). Some applications of thin layer chromatographic techniques in molecular sieve chromatography.

AGOSTONI, A., C. VERGANI, and E. CIRLA: Protides biol. Fluids **14**, 625 (1967). Studies on Bence-Jones protein by thin layer gel filtration.

KYLE, R. A., and W. F. McGUCKIN: J. Lab. clin. Med. **67**, 344 (1966). Separation of macroglobulins from myeloma proteins by Sephadex G-200 gel filtration.

PISCATOR, M.: Arch. Environ. Health **12**, 345 (1966). Proteinuria in chronic Cd-poisoning.

McKENZIE, J. M., P. R. FOWLER, and V. FIORICA: Anal. Biochem. **16**, 139 (1966). Semiautomated measurements of hemoglobin and total protein in urine using a molecular sieve module.

HARRISON, J. F., and B. E. NORTHAM: Clin. chim. Acta **14**, 679 (1966). Low molecular weight urine protein investigated by gel filtration.

---

repeatedly (cf. also Table 21) and been utilized for the quantitative determination of ^{131}I-thyronine and ^{131}I-thyroxine (*115, 116, 117*). – In order to determine unlabeled thyroxine, serum is first deproteinized, then a certain amount of the thyroxine-binding globulin fraction is added. This is followed by incubation with a definite amount of ^{131}I-labeled thyroxine and the determination of the activity distribution on Sephadex G-25. In this way the amount of originally present thyroxine is established; it competes with the radioactive hormone for the globulin (*118*). The separation and determination of thyroid hormones have now been worked out for the nanogram level (*119*). – However, objections have also been raised, pointing out that the spontaneous degradation of thyroxine to iodine, the influence of column dimensions on the result and the irreversible adsorption of thyroxine will also have to be considered carefully (*120*).

We had already seen on page 131 that due to a combination of several effects the so-called conjugated oestrogens in urine of pregnant women can be purified and isolated by gel chromatography on Sephadex G-25 (*121*). This effect is utilized in an early pregnancy test (*122, 123*). It was subsequently recommended to remove the acidic carbohydrate component prior to gel chromatography by treatment with enzymes (whereby, however, the concentration effect is lost). In the case of low hormone concentrations, the increase in pigments in the first procedure is claimed to interfere with the quantitative determination (Kober-reaction) (*124, 125*).

Miscellaneous Applications

In closing our inspection of the results of gel chromatography, which have been obtained within the short time that has elapsed since its introduction, several publications will be mentioned in Tables 53 through 58 which are derived from various fields of chemistry.

Table 53. *Toxic proteins*

FRIEDBERG, K. D., H. STEGEMANN und W. VOGT: Naturwissenschaften **50**, 523 (1963). Anreicherung von Anaphylatoxin durch Gelfiltration.

STEGEMANN, H., W. VOGT und K. D. FRIEDBERG: Z. physiol. Chem. **337**, 269 (1964). Über die Natur des Anaphylatoxins.

ALVORD jr., C. E., M.W. KIES, F. N. LeBARON, and R. E. MARTENSON: Science **151**, 821 (1966). Encephalitogenic activity of bovine basic proteins.

TIRUNARAYANAN, M. O., and C. R. SALENSTEDT: Z. Immun.-Forsch. Allergie klin. Immunol. **130**, 54 (1966). Comparison of methods for purification of diphteria toxin with special reference to gel filtration and ion exchange chromatography.

SALENSTEDT, C. R., and M. O. TIRUNARAYANAN: ibid. **130**, 190 (1966).

KOMOROWSKA-RYCERZ, A., A. BRÜHL, and R. KRAUZE: Bull. Acad. Polon. Sci. **14**, 81 (1966).

LATHAM, W. C., C. P. JENNESS, and R. J. K. TIMPERI: J. Immunol. **95**, 487 (1965). Purification of tetanus toxoid by gel filtration.

MILLER, K. D., and A. P. MARIN: Proc. Soc. exp. Biol. Med. **118**, 961 (1965). Gel-filtered media for purification of extracellular toxins.

Table 54. *Structural proteins*

KESSEN, G., und F. AMELUNXEN: Z. Naturforschung **19b**, 346 (1964). Die Ribosomen von Pisum sativum. I. Aminosäureanalyse des Strukturproteins der Ribosomen nach Gelfiltration durch Sephadex.

FRANÇOIS, C., and M. J. GLIMCHER: Biochim. biophys. Acta **97**, 366 (1965). Fractionation of the α- and β-chains of collagen by Sephadex gel filtration.

LUKENS, L. N.: Proc. natl. Acad. Sci. **55**, 1235 (1966). The size of the polypeptide precursor of collagen hydroxyproline.

FOCANT, B., et J. F. PECHÈRE: Arch. int. Physiol. Biochim. **73**, 334 (1965). Contribution a l'étude des protiénes de faible poids moléculaire des myogénes de vertébrés inférieurs.

PECHÉRE, J. F., and B. FOCANT: Biochem. J. **96**, 113 (1965). Carp myogens of white and red muscles.

THOMPSON, E. O. P., and I. J. O'DONELL: Austr. J. biol Sci. **18**, 1207 (1965). Studies on reduced wool.

Table 55. *Miscellaneous proteins*

CRUFT, H. J.: Biochim. biophys. Acta **54**, 611 (1961). The fractionation of histones on Sephadex G-75.

BESS, L. G., and L. S. HNILICA: Anal. Biochem. **12**, 421 (1965). The heterogeneity of arginine-rich histones.

RADOLA, B. J., G. KELLNER, and J. S. FRIMMEL: Nature **207**, 206 (1965). Gel filtration of isotopically labelled ferritin from HeLa cells.

PULIDO, P., J. H. R. KÄGI, and B. L. VALLEE: Biochemistry **5**, 1768 (1966). Isolation and some properties of human metallothionein.

HARDMAN, K. D., E. H. EYLAR, D. K. RAY, L. J. BANASZAK, and F. R. N. GURD: J. biol. Chem. **241**, 432 (1966). Isolation of sperm whale myoglobin by low temperature fractionation with ethanol and metallic ions.

HASEGAWA, K., T. KUSANO, and H. MITSUDA: Agr. Biol. Chem. **27**, 878 (1963). Fractionation of soybean proteins by gel filtration.

ESCRIBANO, M. J., H. KEILOVA, et P. GRABAR: Biochim. Biophys. Acta **127**, 94 (1966). Étude de la gliadine et de la glutenine après réduction ou oxydation.

SOROF, S., E. M. YOUNG, R. A. McBRIDE, and C. B. COFFEY: Arch. Biochem. Biophys. **113**, 83 (1966). Size classes of soluble liver macromolecules.

SIMONS, K., and T. WEBER: Biochim. biophys. Acta **117**, 201 (1966). The vitamin B_{12}-binding protein in human leukocytes.

Table 56. *Miscellaneous peptides*

PHILLIPS, A.W., and P. A. GIBBS: Biochem. J. **81**, 551 (1961). Techniques for the fractionation of microbiologically active peptides derived from casein.

DETERMANN, H., und O. ZIPP: Liebigs Ann. Chem. **649**, 203 (1961). Untersuchungen über die Plastein-Reaktion, III. Isolierung und Charakterisierung von weiteren Plastein-Bausteinen.

CARNEGIE, P. R.: Biochem. J. **89**, 459 (1963). Isolation of a homologue of glutathione and other acidic peptides from seedlings of Phaseolus aureus.

SCHMIDT-KASTNER, G.: Naturwissenschaften **51**, 38 (1964). Die Trennung von Actino-mycin-Gemischen durch Verteilungschromatographie an Sephadex.

MACH, B., and E. L. TATUM: Proc. natl. Acad. Sci. **52**, 876 (1964). Environmental control of amino acid substitutions in the biosynthesis of the antibiotic polypeptide tyrocidine.

HABERMANN, E., und K. G. REIZ: Biochem. Z. **341**, 451 (1965). Ein neues Verfahren zur Gewinnung der Komponenten von Bienengift, insbesonders des zentralwirksamen Peptids Apamin.

SHIBNEV, V. A., and V. G. DEBABOV: Chem. Abstr. **61**, 7097a (1964). Regular polypeptide with glycyl-prolyl-hydroxyprolyl-sequence that is isomorphous with collagen.

ENGEL, J., J. KURTZ, E. KATCHALSKI, and A. BERGER: J. mol. Biol. **17**, 255 (1966). Polymers of tripeptides as collagen models. II. Conformational changes of poly(L-Pro-Gly-L-Pro) in solution.

SCHNEIDER, C. H., and A. L. DE WECK: Nature **208**, 57 (1965). A new chemical aspect of penicillin allergy: the direct reaction of penicillin with ε-aminogroups.

CARNEGIE, P. R., and C. E. LUMSDEN: Nature **209**, 1354 (1966). Encephalitogenic peptides from spinal cord.

Table 57. *Miscellaneous lipids*

THUREBORN, E.: Nature **197**, 1301 (1963). A water-soluble lipid complex obtained in the macromolecular phase by gel filtration of human bile.

NAKAYAMA, F., and H. MIYAKE: J. Lab. clin. Med. **65**, 638 (1965). Cholesterol complexing by macromolecular fractions in human gall bladder bile.

— Clin. chim. Acta **13**, 212 (1966). Nature of cholesterol-complexing macromolecular fractions in bile.

FELDMAN, E. B., and BORGSTRÖM: Biochim. biophys. Acta **125**, 136 (1966). Phase distribution of sterols: studies by gel filtration.

TIPTON, C. L., J.W. PAULIS, and M. D. PIERSON: J. Chromatog. **14**, 486 (1964). Gel filtration of lipid mixtures.

NYSTRÖM, E., and J. SJÖVALL: Anal. Biochem. **12**, 235 (1965). Separation of lipids on methylated Sephadex.

WIELAND, TH., G. LÜBEN und H. DETERMANN: Naturwissenschaften **51**, 138 (1964). Adsorptionschromatographie an vernetzten Polymethylmethacrylat-Gelen.

DAISLEY, K.W.: Nature **191**, 868 (1961). Gel filtration of sea-water: separation of free and bound forms of vitamin B_{12}.

KAKEI, M., and G. B. J. GLASS: Proc. Soc. exp. Biol. Med. **111**, 270 (1962). Separation of bound and free vitamin B_{12} on Sephadex G-25 column.

KWON, T.W., and H. S. OLCOTT: Nature **210**, 214 (1966). Malonaldehyde from the autoxidation of methyl linolenate.

VIHKO, R.: Acta Endocrinol. **52** Suppl. **109**, 15 (1966). Methylated Sephadex and Sephadex LH-20 in steroid separations.

SJÖVALL, J., and R. VIHKO: Acta chem. scand. **20**, 1419 (1966). Chromatography of conjugated steroids on lipophilic Sephadex.

Table 58. *Humic acid and other condensed aromatics*

POSNER, A. M.: Nature **198**, 1161 (1963). Importance of electrolyte in the determination of molecular weights by Sephadex gel filtration, with especial reference to humic acid.

SOUKUP, M.: Collect. czech. chem. Commun. **29**, 3182 (1964). Separation of humic substances by gel filtration on Sephadex.

OBENAUS, R., und H.-J. NEUMANN: Naturwissenschaften **52**, 131 (1965). Entsalzung von Huminsäuren an Sephadex G-25.

GJESSING, E.T.: Nature **208**, 1091 (1965). Use of Sephadex gel for the estimation of molecular weight of humic substances in natural water.

BOLDT, P.: Naturwissenschaften **51**, 265 (1964). Zur Kenntnis des Trichosiderins eines Pigments aus roten Haaren.

ISHIGURO, I., and B. LINZEN: Z. physiol. Chem. **340**, 286 (1965). Preparative isolation and tritium-marking of 3-hydroxy-L-kynurenine.

LINDBERG, J. J., K. PENTTINEN, and C. MAJANI: Suomen Kuuistilekti Sect. B 38, 95 (1965). Gel filtration of lignins obtained by alkaline digestion of spruce wood.

ALTGELT, K. H.: Makromol. Chem. **88**, 75 (1965). Fractionation of asphaltenes by gel permeation chromatography.

— J. appl. Polymer Sci. **9**, 3389 (1965). Fractionation of asphaltenes by gel permeation chromatography.

WILK, M., J. ROCHLITZ und H. BENDE: J. Chromatog. **24**, 414 (1966). Säulenchromatographie von polycyclischen aromatischen Kohlenwasserstoffen an lipophilem Sephadex LH-20.

Table 59. *Gel chromatography in beverage industry*

NUMMI, M., und T.-M. ENARI: Brauwissenschaft **15**, 203 (1962). Die Fraktionierung von Gerstenalbuminen durch Gelfiltration und Papierelektrophorese.

—, R. VILHUNEN, and T.-M. ENARI: Acta chem. scand. **19**, 1793 (1965). Exclusion chromatography of barley β-amylase on Sephadex G-75.

WOOF, J. B.: Nature **195**, 184 (1962). Investigation of phenolic components of brewing materials by gel filtration.

DJURTOFT, R.: European Brewery Convention. Proc. of VIIIth int. Congress, Vienna, 1961, 298. Fractionation of beer constituents by gel filtration.

RAIBLE, K., und J. ENGELHARDT: Brauwissenschaft **18**, 398 (1965). Die Schaumwirkung von Alginaten in Bier.

WUCHERPFENNIG, K., und I. FRANKE: Brauwissenschaft **18**, 132 (1965). Beitrag zur analytischen Kontrolle von Stabilisierungsmaßnahmen bei Bier mit Hilfe der Gelfiltration unter besonderer Berücksichtigung des Eiweißabbaues durch Fermente.

— — Z. Lebensmitt.-Untersuch. Forschung **124**, 22 (1963). Auftrennung von Weininhaltsstoffen durch Gelfiltration.

SOMERS, T. C.: Nature **209**, 368 (1966). Wine tannins-isolation of condensed flavonoid pigments by gel filtration.

WUCHERPFENNIG, K., und I. FRANKE: Die Weinwissenschaft **19**, 362 (1964). Beitrag zur Bestimmung einer Kennzahl für Polyphenole in Weinen durch Gelfiltration.

STREULI, H.: Chimia **16**, 371 (1962). Fraktionierung von Farb- und Geschmacksstoffen des Röstkaffees mittels Sephadex G-25.

OBENAUS, R., H.-J. NEUMANN und D. MÜCKE: Naturwissenschaften **53**, 19 (1966). Bestimmung des Huminsäuregehaltes in Kaffee-Extrakten nach der Gelfiltration an Sephadex G-25.

Table 60. *Gel chromatography in food industry*

DE KONING, P. J.: Neth. Milk and Dairy J. **16**, 210 (1962). Gel filtration, a new method applied for the preparation of lactose-free milk.

LINDQVIST, B.: Proc. XVIth int. Dairy Congress, Copenhagen 1962, S. 673. Preparative separation of high molecular peptides of cheese.

GEORGE, W. H. S.: Nature **195**, 155 (1962). Separation of strontium from milk and protein solutions by gel filtration.

CHANDAN, R. C., and K. M. SHAHANI: J. Diary Sci. **45**, 645 (1962). Purification and characterization of milk lipase.

CORTIS-JONES, B.: Int. Sugar J. **64**, 133 (1962); **64**, 165 (1962). Methods for fractionation of impurities in cane juice and mill syrups.

STINSON, E. E., and C. O. WILLITS: J. Ass. off. agricult. Chem. **46**, 329 (1963). Separation of caramel colour from salts and sugar by gel filtration.

ROTHER, H.: Dtsch. Lebensmittel-Rdsch. **62**, 108 (1966). Über den Nachweis von Zuckerkulör mit Hilfe der Gelfiltration.

WRIGHT jr., H. E., W.W. BURTON, and R. C. BERRY, jr.: Phytochemistry **3**, 525 (1964). Soluble browning reaction pigments of aged Burley tobacco. II. The dialysable fraction. Vgl. auch Nature **202**, 1210 (1964). Isolation of tryptophan from air cured tobacco by gel filtration.

ABBOTT, D. C., and J. A. JOHNSON: J. Food Sci. **31**, 38 (1966). Gel filtration of the water-soluble protein fraction of wheat flour.

References

1. GELOTTE, B., and A. B. KRANTZ: Acta chem. scand. **13**, 2127 (1959).

2. TIPTON, K. F.: Biochim. biophys. Acta **92**, 341 (1964).

3. TORO-GOYCO, E., and M. MATOS: Nature **210**, 527 (1966).

4. OTA, S., S. MOORE, and W. H. STEIN: Biochemistry **3**, 180 (1964).

5. SIEBERT, G., A. SCHMITT und R. v. MALORTIE: Z. physiol. Chem. **342**, 20 (1965).

6. KELLER, S., and I. MANDL: Arch. Biochem. Biophys. **101**, 81 (1963).

7. LANCHANTIN, G. F., J. A. FRIEDMANN, and D.W. HART: J. biol. Chem. **240**, 3276 (1965).

8. JONES, G., S. MOORE, and W. H. STEIN: Biochemistry **2**, 66 (1963).

9. APPEL, W.: Z. physiol. Chem. **330**, 193 (1963).

10. PEANASKY, R. J., and M. M. SZUCS: J. biol. Chem. **239**, 2525 (1964).

11. FRITZ, H., G. HARTWICH und E. WERLE: Z. physiol. Chem. **345**, 150 (1966).

12. PETTERSSON, G., E. B. COWLING, and J. PORATH: Biochim. biophys. Acta **67**, 1 (1963).

13. — Biochim. biophys. Acta **77**, 665 (1963).

14. SELBY, K., and C. C. MAITLAND: Biochem. J. **94**, 578 (1965).

15. CRAVEN, G. R., E. STEERS jr., and C. B. ANFINSEN: J. biol. Chem. **240**, 2468 (1965).

16. LESTER, G., and A. BYERS: Biochem. biophys. Res. Commun. **18**, 725 (1965).

17. BRODBECK, U., and K. E. EBNER: J. biol. Chem. **241**, 762 (1966).

18. LI, Y.-T.: J. biol. Chem. **241**, 1010 (1966).

19. SHAINKIN, R., and Y. BIRK: Biochim. biophys. Acta **122**, 153 (1966).

20. PLEIDERER, G., und F. AURICCHIO: Biochem. biophys. Res. Commun. **16**, 53 (1964).

21. COLEMAN, J. E., and B. L. VALLEE: J. biol. Chem. **237**, 3430 (1962).

22. FOLK, J. E., and J. A. GLADNER: Biochim. biophys. Acta **48**, 139 (1961).

23. COLOBERT, L., and G. DIRHEIMER: Biochim. biophys. Acta **54**, 455 (1961).

24. KUBOYAMA, M., S. TAKEMORI, and T. E. KING: Biochem. biophys. Res. Commun. **9**, 534 (1962).

25. WOOD, H. G., H. LOCHMÜLLER, C. RIEPERTINGER und F. LYNEN: Biochem. Z. **337**, 247 (1963).

26. NUMA, S., E. RINGELMANN und F. LYNEN: Biochem. Z. **340**, 228 (1964).

27. Stoneihill, E. H., and M. E. Balis: Anal. Biochem. **10**, 486 (1965).
28. Birnboim, H.: Biochim. biophys. Acta **119**, 198 (1966).
29. Lindner, E. B., A. Elmqvist, and J. Porath: Nature **184**, 1565 (1959).
30. Hope, D. B., B. A. Schacter, and B. T. B. Frankland: Biochem. J. **93**, 7P (1964); vgl. Brit. J. Pharmacol. **26**, 502 (1966).
31. Ginsburg, M., and M. Ireland: J. Endocrinol. **30**, 131 (1964).
32. Schally, A.V., and R. Guillemin: J. biol. Chem. **239**, 1038 (1964).
33. Yamashiro, D., H. L. Aanning, and V. DuVigneaud: Proc. natl. Acad. Sci. **54**, 166 (1965).
34. Sjöholm, I.: Acta chem. scand. **18**, 889 (1964).
35. Preddie, E. C., and M. Saffran: J. biol. Chem. **240**, 4189 (1965).
36. Lande, S., A. B. Lerner, and G.V. Upton: J. biol. Chem. **240**, 4259 (1965).
37. Humbel, R. E.: Biochem. biophys. Res. Commun. **12**, 333 (1963).
38. Epstein, C. J., and C. B. Anfinsen: Biochemistry **2**, 461 (1963).
39. Davoren, P. R.: Biochim. biophys. Acta **63**, 150 (1962).
40. Abdel Wahab, M. F., and S. A. El-Kinawi: Intern. J. appl. Radiation and Isotopes, **16**, 668 (1965).
41. Manipol, V., and H. Spitzy: Intern. J. appl. Radiation and Isotopes **13**, 647 (1962).
42. Toro-Goyco, E., M. Martinez-Maldonado, and M. Matos: Proc. Soc. exptl. Biol. Med. **122**, 301 (1966).
43. Alp, H., H. Chaplin, and L. Recant: J. clin. endocrinol. Metab. **26**, 340 (1966).
44. Bürgi, H., W. A. Müller, R. E. Humbel, A. Labhart, and E. R. Froesch: Biochim. biophys. Acta **121**, 349 (1966).
45. Leach, S. J., J. M. Swan, and L. A. Holt: Biochim. biophys. Acta **78**, 196 (1963).
46. Zahn, H., B. Gutte, E. F. Pfeiffer und J. Ammon: Liebigs Ann. Chem. **691**, 225 (1966).
47. —, H. Bremer und R. Zabel: Z. Naturforschung **20b**, 653 (1965).
48. Tauber, S., and L. L. Madison: J. biol Chem. **240**, 645 (1965).
49. Killander, J.: Biochim. biophys. Acta **93**, 1 (1964).
50. Lionetti, F. J., C. R. Valeri, J. C. Bond, and N. L. Fortier: J. Lab. clin. Med. **64**, 519 (1963).
51. Mehl, J.W., W. O'Connell, and J. DeGroot: Science **145**, 821 (1964).
52. Ganrot, P. O.: Clin. chim. Acta **13**, 596 (1966).
53. Fireman, P., E. Hershgold, F. Cordoba, K. Schmid, and D. Gitlin: Nature **203**, 78 (1964).
54. Milstein, C.: Nature **205**, 1171 (1965).
55. Hilschmann, N., and L. C. Craig: Biochemistry **4**, 5 (1965).
56. Baglioni, C., M. LaVia, and V. Ventruto: Biochim. biophys. Acta **111**, 479 (1965).
57. Press, E. M., and R. R. Porter, Biochem. J. **83**, 172 (1962).
58. Bengtsson, C., L. Å. Hanson, and B. G. Johansson: Acta chem. scand. **16**, 127 (1962).
59. Gross, E., and B. Witkop: J. biol. Chem. **237**, 1856 (1962).
60. Edmundson, A. B.: Nature **198**, 354 (1963).
61. Black, J. A., and G. Leaf: Biochem. J. **96**, 693 (1965).
62. Biserte, G., et Y. Moschetto: C. R. Acad. Sci. (Paris) **255**, 3263 (1962).
63. van Hoang, D., M. Rovery, and P. Desnuelle: Biochim. biophys. Acta **58**, 613 (1962).
64. Jung, H., und H. Schüssler: Z. Naturforschung **21b**, 224 (1966).
65. Carnegie, P. R.: Nature **206**, 1128 (1965).
66. Anderer, F. A.: Z. Naturforschung **20b**, 462 (1965).
67. Fazakerley, S., and D. R. Best: Anal. Biochem. **12**, 290 (1965).
68. Fasold, H.: Biochem. Z. **342**, 288 (1965).
69. Shepherd, G. R., and D. F. Petersen: J. Chromatog. **9**, 445 (1962).
70. Boman, H. G., and S. Hjertén: Arch. Biochem. Biophys. Suppl. **1**, 276 (1962).

71. Dirheimer, G., J.-H. Weil, and J.-P. Ebel: C. R. Acad. Sci. (Paris) **255**, 2312 (1962).
72. Bosch, L., G. van der Wende, M. Sluyser, and H. Bloemendal: Biochim. biophys. Acta **53**, 44 (1961).
73. Schleich, T., and J. Goldstein: Proc. natl. Acad. Sci. **52**, 744 (1964).
74. Virmaux, N., P. Mandel, and P. F. Urban: Biochem. biophys. Res. Commun. **16**, 308 (1964).
75. Zachau, H. G.: Biochim. biophys. Acta **108**, 355 (1965).
76. Röschenthaler, R., and P. Fromageot: J. mol. Biol. **11**, 458 (1965).
77. Bell, W. C., und R. Engler: Arch. ges. Virusforschung **15**, 109 (1964).
78. Oeberg, B., S. Bengtsson, and L. Philipson: Biochem. biophys. Res. Commun. **20**, 36 (1965).
79. Attardi, G., P. C. Huang, and S. Kabat: Proc. natl. Acad. Sci. **53**, 1490 (1965).
80. Hayes, F. N., E. Hansbury, and V. E. Mitchell: J. Chromatog. **16**, 410 (1964).
81. Jones, O.W., E. E. Townsend, H. A. Sober, and L. A. Heppel: Biochemistry **3**, 238 (1964).
82. Matheka, H.-D., und G. Wittmann: Zbl. Bakt. **182**, 142 (1961).
83. Beiss, U., und R. Marx: Naturwissenschaften **49**, 95 (1962).
84. Inglot, A. D., J. Lisowski, and E. Niedzwiedzka: Acta virol. **8**, 541 (1964).
85. Steere, R. L.: Science **140**, 3571 (1963).
86. Bengtsson, S., and L. Philipson: Biochim. biophys. Acta **79**, 399 (1964).
87. Fridborg, K., S. Hjertén, S. Höglund, A. Liljas, B. K. S. Lundberg, P. Oxelfelt, L. Philipson, and B. Strandberg: Proc. natl. Acad. Sci. **54**, 513 (1965).
88. Haller, W.: Nature **206**, 693 (1965).
89. Granath, K.: in James, Morris (Ed.) New Biochemical Separations, 93. London 1964.
90. — Abhandlungen der dtsch. Akad. Wissensch. (Berlin) **1964**, 91.
91. Anderson, D. M.W., I. C. M. Dea, S. Rahman, and J. F. Stoddart: Chem. Commun. **1965**, 145.
92. Nordin, P.: Arch. Biochem. Biophys. **99**, 101 (1962).
93. Heller, J., und M. Schramm: Biochim. biophys. Acta **81**, 96 (1964).
94. Kringstad, E., und Oe. Ellefsen: Das Papier **18**, 583 (1964).
95. Schmidt, M., und A. Dmochowski: Biochim. biophys. Acta **83**, 137 (1964).
96. Ringertz, N. R., and P. Reichard: Acta. chem. scand. **14**, 303 (1960).
97. Ricketts, C. R.: Nature **210**, 1113 (1966).
98. Schlubach, H. H., und R. Ziegler: Liebigs Ann. Chem. **677**, 165 (1964).
99. Sanderson, A. R., J. L. Strominger, and S. G. Natheson: J. biol. Chem. **237**, 3603 (1962).
100. Ghuysen, J.-M., D. J. Tipper, and J. L. Strominger: Biochemistry **4**, 474 (1965).
101. Wicken, A. J., and J. Baddiley: Biochem. J. **87**, 54 (1963).
102. Oestling, G.: Acta soc. med. Upsaliensis **64**, 222 (1960).
103. Bill, A., N. Marsden, and H. R. Ulfendahl: Scand. J. clin. Lab. Invest. **12**, 392 (1960).
104. Jacobsson, L.: Clin. chim. Acta **7**, 180 (1962).
105. Davidson, W. D., M. A. Sackner, and M. H. Davidson: J. Lab. clin. Med. **62**, 501 (1963).
106. Mertz, D. P., und H. E. Franz: Klinische Wochenschrift **42**, 555 (1964).
107. Hennrich, N., A. Hoffmann und H. Lang: Arzneimittel-Forschung **15**, 434 (1965).
108. Ford, J. E.: Brit. J. Nutr. **19**, 277 (1965).
109. Patrick, R. L., and R. E. Thiers: Clin. Chem. **9**, 283 (1963).
110. McEvoy-Bowe, E., and S. Sarojini Thevi: Clin. Chem. **12**, 144 (1966).
111. Shapiro, B., and J. L. Rabinowitz: J. nuclear Med. **3**, 417 (1962).
112. Stumpf, W., und E. H. Graul: Med. Klin. **58**, 192 (1963).
113. Rabinowitz, J. L., B. Shapiro, and P. Johnson: J. nucl. Med. **4**, 139 (1963).

114. GRAUL, E. H., und W. STUMPF: Dtsch. med. Wschr. 88, 1886 (1963).
115. LISSITZKY, S., and J. BISMUTH: Clin. chim. Acta 8, 269 (1963).
116. MOUGEY, E. H., and J.W. MASON: Anal. Biochem. 6, 223 (1963).
117. LIEWENDAHL, K., and B.-A. LAMBERG: J. clin. Endocrinol. Metab. 25, 991 (1965).
118. MURPHEY, B. E. P., and CH. J. PATTEE: J. clin. Endocrinol. Metab. 24, 187 (1964).
119. MAKOWETZ, E., K. MÜLLER, and H. SPITZY: Microchem. J. 10, 194 (1966).
120. HOCMAN, G.: J. Chromatog. 21, 413 (1966).
121. BELING, C. G.: Nature 192, 326 (1961).
122. — Periodica, Copenhagen 1963.
123. KUSHINSKY, S., and I. OTTERNESS: Steroids 3, 311 (1964).
124. EECHAUTE, W.: Clin. chim. Acta 10, 379 (1964).
125. —, and G. DEMEESTER: J. clin. Endocrinol. Metab. 25, 480 (1965).
126. STRAUCH, L., und W. GRASSMANN: Z. physiol. Chem. 344, 140 (1966).
127. WHITE, W. F., G. H. BARLOW, and M. M. MOZEN: Biochemistry 5, 2160 (1966).
128. PEART, W. S., A. M. LLOYD, G. N. THATCHER, A. F. LEVER, N. PAYNE, and N. STONE: Biochem. J. 99, 708 (1966).
129. CAMPBELL, B. J., Y.-C. LIN, R. V. DAVIS, and E. BALLEW: Biochim. biophys. Acta 118, 371 (1966).
130. FÉLIX, F., et N. BROULLIET: Biochim. biophys. Acta 122, 127 (1966).
131. CRESTFIELD, A. M., S. MOORE, and W. H. STEIN: J. biol. Chem. 238, 622 (1963).
132. VARANDANI, P. T.: Biochim. biophys. Acta 127, 246 (1966).
133. ADAMS-MAYNE, M. E., and B. JIRGENSONS: Arch. Biochem. Biophys. 113, 575 (1966).
134. GROSS, E., and B. WITKOP: Biochem. biophys. Res. Commun. 23, 760 (1966).
135. COOKE, J. P., C. B. ANFINSEN, and M. SELA: J. biol. Chem. 238, 2034 (1963).
136. KONIGSBERG, W., K. WEBER, C. NOTANI, and N. ZINDER: J. biol. Chem. 241, 2579 (1966).
137. MEYER, J. G.: Z. Naturforschg. 21b, 342 (1966).
138. SCHLEICH, T., and J. GOLDSTEIN: J. mol. Biol. 15, 136 (1966).
139. BACHVAROFF, R. J., and V. TONGUR: Nature 211, 248 (1966).
140. DELIHAS, N., and M. STAEHELIN: Biochim. biophys. Acta 119, 385 (1966).
141. BRESLER, S., R. GRAVEJEVSKAJA, S. KIRILOV, E. SAMINSKI, and F. SHUTOV: Biochim. biophys. Acta 123, 534 (1966).
142. ERIKSON, R. L., and J. A. GORDON: Biochim. biophys. Res. Commun. 23, 422 (1966).
143. BARKER, S. A., and N. M. YOUNG: Carbohydrate Res. 2, 49 (1966).
144. BARKER, S. A., S. M. BICK, and J. S. BRIMACOMBE: Carbohydrate Res. 1, 393 (1966).

Bibliography

FLODIN, P., and J. PORATH: Molecular Sieve Process, in HEFTMANN (Ed.): Chromatography, 328. New York 1961.

— »Dextrans Gels and their Applications in Gel Filtration«, Dissertation. Uppsala 1962. Obtainable from AB Pharmacia, Uppsala.

PORATH, J.: Cross-linked Dextrans as Molecular Sieves. Adv. Prot. Chem. **17**, 209 (1962).

TISELIUS, A., J. PORATH, and P.-Å. ALBERTSSON: Separation and Fractionation of Macromolecules and Particles. Science **141**, 13 (1963).

GELOTTE, B.: Fractionation of Proteins, Peptides and Amino Acids by Gel Filtration, in JAMES, MORRIS (Ed.): New Biochemical Separations, 93. London 1964.

GRANATH, K.: Fractionation of Polysaccharides by Gel Filtration, in JAMES, MORRIS (Ed.): New Biochemical Separations, 111. London 1964.

MORRIS, C. J. O. R., and P. MORRIS: Separation Methods in Biochemistry. London 1964.

DETERMANN, H.: Stofftrennung durch Chromatographie an porösen Gelen. Angewandte Chemie **76**, 635 (1964); ibid. Internat. Ed. **3**, 608 (1964).

ANDREWS, P.: Molecular Sieve Chromatography. British Medical Bulletin **22**, 109 (1966).

ALTGELT, K. H., and J. C. MOORE: Gel Permeation Chromatography, in CANTOW (Ed.): Polymer Fractionation. New York 1967.

GELOTTE, B., and J. PORATH: Gel Filtration, in HEFTMANN (Ed.): Chromatography. New York 1966.

Author Index

The numbers in *italics* refer to the references at the end of every chapter and to the bibliography

Aanning, H. L., see Yamashiro, D. 145, *167*

Abbott, D. C., and J. A. Johnson 166

Abdel-Wahab, M. F., and S. A. El-Kinawy 94, 147, *167*

Åberg, B., see Ekman, L. 97

Ackers, G. K. 76, 77, *85*, 108, 113, 118, *137*

—, and I. E. Thompson 119, *138*

—, and R. L. Steere 2, *11*, 76, *85*

Acred, P., D. M. Brown, T. L. Hardy, and K. R. L. Mansford 97

Adams-Mayne, M. E., see Jirgensons, B. 151

—, and B. Jirgensons 150, *169*

Aebi, H., C. H. Schneider, H. Gang, and U. Wiesmann 103, 161, *137*

Agostini, A., C. Vergani, and E. Cirla 55, *62*, 161

Agrawal, B. B., and L. J. Goldstein 132, *139*

Ahrens, jr., E. H., see Craig, L. C. 47, *61*

Albertsson, P.-Å., see Tiselius, A. 79, *85*

Albrecht, E., see Wieland, Th. 2, *11*

Alfrey, jr., T., see Lloyd, W. G. 14, 23, *60*

Allan, D., and M. Malkinson 149

Allison, A. C., and J. H. Humphrey 3, *11*

Alp, H., H. Chaplin, and L. Recant 147, *167*

Altgelt, K. H. 25, 43, *61*, 122, 128, *138* 165

—, and J. C. Moore 73, 76, *84*, *170*

Alvord, jr., C. E., M. W. Kies, F. N. Le Baron, and R. E. Martenson 162

Ambler, R. P. 130, *139*, 153

Amelunxen, F., see Kessen, G. 162

Ames, B. N., R. G. Martin, and B. J. Garry 132, *139*

Ammon, J., see Zahn, H. 148, *167*

Anderer, F. A. 154, *167*

—, see Stepanov, V. 153

Anderson, D. M. W., I. C. M. Dea, S. Rahman, and J. F. Stoddart 158, *168*

—, and J. F. Stoddart 77, 78, *85*, 108, *137*

Anderson, J. H., and C. E. Carter 142

Anderson, N. G., see Barber, A. A. 97

Andersson, L.-O. 117, *139*

Andrews, P. 52, 54, *62*, 106, 108, 111, 112, 114, 116, 118, *137*, *138*, *170*

Andrews, P., see Downey, W. K. 117, 142

—, R. C. Bray, P. Edwards, and K. V. Shooter 116, *138*

Anfinsen, C. B., see Cooke, J. P. 152, *169*

—, see Epstein, C. J. 147, *167*

Anfinsen, C. H. B., and E. Haber 93, *136*

Ansevin, A., see Craig L. C. 2, *11*

Anyas-Weisz, L., see Deuel, H. 9, *12*

Appel, W. 143, *166*

Araki, C. 19, *60*

Arnaud, C., see Tenenhouse, A. 147

Arnott, M. S., see Ward, D. N. 114, *137*, 146

Asperg, K., see Flodin, P. 120, *138*, 159

Attardi, G., P. C. Huang, and S. Kabat 156, *168*

Aurbach, D. G., and J. T. Potts, jr. 147

Auricchio, F. 120, *138*

—, see Pleiderer, G. 144, *166*

—, and C. B. Bruni 116, *138*

Bachvaroff, R. J., and V. Tongur 156, *169*

Baddiley, J., see Wicken, A. J. 159, *168*

Bagdasarian, M., N. A. Matheson, R. L. M. Synge, and M. A. Youngson 83, *85*, 134, *139*

Baglioni, C., M. La Via, and V. Ventruto 151, *167*

Baguley, B. C., see Bergquist, P. L. 133, 134, *139*

Baker, C. A., and R. J. P. Williams 121, *138*

Balekjian, A. Y., see Hoerman, K. C. 91, *136*

Balis, M. E., see Stonehill, E. H. 145, *167*

Ballew, E., see Campbell, B. J. 145, *169*

Ballou, C. E., see Lee, Y.-Ch. 159

Banaszak, L. J., see Hardman, K. D. 163

Banerjee, R., and R. Cassoly 118, *139*

Barber, A. A., C. Dempster, and N. G. Anderson 97

Barker, S. A., S. M. Bick, and J. S. Brimacombe 158, *169*

—, and N. M. Young 158, *169*

Barlow, C. F., H. Firemark, and L. J. Roth 97

Barlow, G. H., see White, W. F. 169

Barrer, R. M. 1, *11*

Barrett, A. J., and D. H. Northcote 159

Bassett, E. W., S. M. Beiser, and S. W. Tanenbaum 92, *136*, 150

Baumann, W. C., see Wheaton, R. M. 9, *12*, 67, 68, *84*

Beiser, S. M., see Bassett, E. W. 92, *136*, 150

Beiss, U., and R. Marx 91, *136*, 158, *168*

Beling, C. G. 131, *139*, 162, *169*

Bell, W. C., and R. Engler 156, 158, *168*

Bende, H., see Wieland, Th. 134, *139*

—, see Wilk, M. 81, *85*

Bengtsson, C., L. Å. Hanson, and B. G. Johansson 152, *167*

Bengtsson, S., see Killander, J. 50, *62*

—, see Oeberg, B. 156, 158, *168*

—, and L. Philipson 20, *60*, 105, *137*, 158, *168*

Bennett, J. C., and E. Haber 150

Bennich, H. 153

—, see Porath, J. 33, 49, 51, *61*, *62*

Bentz, J. D., see Terr, A. I. 149

Berg, P., see Muench, K. H. 133, *140*

Berger, A. see Engel, J. 122, *140*, 164

Berger, H. L., and A. Schultz 126, *139*

Berger, K. C., see Schulz, G. V. 121, *138*

Bergquist, P. L., B. C. Baguley, J. M. Robertson, and R. A. Ralph 133, 134, *139*

Berry, jr., R. C., see Wright, jr., H. E. 166

Berzinskas, V. J., see Hoerman, K. C. 91, *136*

Bess, L. G., see Hnilica, L. S. 117

—, and L. S. Hnilica 163

Best, D. R., see Fazakerley, S. 154, *167*

Bick, S. M., see Barker, S. A. 158, *169*

Bill, A., N. Marsden, and H. R. Ulfendahl 159, *168*

Birk, Y., see Shainkin, R. 144, *166*

Birnboim, H. 145, 157, *167*

Biserte, G., see Demaille, J. 154

—, and Y. Moschetto 152, *167*

Bishop, W., see Herries, D. G. 99, *137*

Bismuth, J., see Lissitzky, S. 161, *169*

Björk, W. 142

—, and J. Porath 10, *12*, 142

Black, J. A., and G. Leaf 152, *167*

Bloemendal, H., see Bosch, L. 155, *168*

Bodo, G., see Jungwirth, C. 117

Boehringer, H., see Wieland, Th. 130, 135, *140*

Boguth, W., K. Krisch, and H. Niemann 116, *138*

Boldt, P. 131, 165

Boll, M., and H. Holzer 143

Boman, H. G., and S. Hjertén 155, *167*

Bond, J. C., see Lionetti, F. 150, *167*

Boocock, G., and D. S. Popplewell 97

Borgström, B, 99, *137*

—, see Feldman, E. B. 164

Bortnick, N., see Kunin, R. 9, *12*, 14, 23, *60*

Bosch, L., G. van der Wende, M. Sluyser, and H. Bloemendal 155, *168*

Boser, H., K. W. von Eickstedt, and H. Giertz 131

Boulouard, R., and Y. A. Fontaine 149

Bourrillon, R., and J. L. Vernay 154

Boyle, D. C., see Collipp, P. J. 146

Boyns, A. R., and J. Hardwicke 150

Brammer, K. W., see Burges, R. A. 116, *138*

Brand, K., see Wirth, K. 48, *61*, 160

Braun, D., see Heufer, G. 22, *60*, 122, *138*

Bray, R. C., see Andrews, P. 116, *138*

Bremer, H., see Zahn, H. 148, *167*

Bresler, S., R. Gravejevskaja, S. Kirilov, E. Saminski, and F. Shutov 156, *169*

Bresler, S. E., Kh. M. Rubina, R. A. Graevskaya, and N. N. Vasil'eva 155

Brewer, P. I. 10, *12*, 79, *85*, 108, 128, *137*, *140*

Brimacombe, J. S., see Barker, S. A. 158, *169*

Brink, N. G., see Reisfeld, R. A. 146

Brodbeck, U., and K. E. Ebner 144, *166*

Broman, L., and K. Kjellin 149

Brönsted, J. N. 78, *85*

Brown, D. M., see Acred, P. 97

Brühl, A., see Komorowska-Rycerz, A. 162

Bruni, C. B., see Auricchio, F. 116, *138*

Buddecke, E., and D. Platt 143

Buhrow, I., see Schlossberger, H. G. 131

Buku, A., see Wieland, Th. 130, 135, *140*

Burges, R. A., K. W. Brammer, and J. D Coombes 116, *138*

Bürgi, H., W. A. Müller, R. E. Humbel, A. Labhart, and E. R. Froesch 147, *167*

Burke, D. C., and J. Ross 117

Burton, W. W., see Wright, jr., H. E. 131, 166

Byers, A., see Lester, G. 91, *136*, 144, *166*

Cahnmann, H. J., see Salvatore, G. 147

Campbell, B. J., Y.-C. Lin, R. V. Davis, and E. Ballew 143, *169*

Cantoni, G. L., see Nathenson, S. G. 133, *140*

—, see Tanaka, K. 133, *139*

Cantow, M. J. R., see Pickett, H. E. 125, *138*

—, R. S. Porter, and J. F. Johnson 125, *139*

Capetillo, S. C., see Yonezawa, D. 151

Carnegie, P. R. 83, *85*, 108, *137*, 154, 163, *167*

—, and C. E. Lumsden 163

—, and G. Pacheco 55, *62*

Carsten, M. E., and J. C. Pierce 154

Carter, C. E., see Anderson, J. H. 142

Cassoly, R., see Banerjee, R. 118, *139*

Chan, J. Y. S., and E. T. Mertz 149

Chandan, R. C., and K. M. Shahani 166

Chaplin, H., see Alp, H. 147, *167*

Chase, J. F. A., D. J. Pearson, and P. K. Tubbs 116, *138*, 143

Chernoff, A. I., and N. Pettit 153

Chersi, A. 50, *62*, 143

Cifonelli, J. A. 159

Cirla, E., see Agostini, A. 55, *62*, 161

Clark, R. T. 9, *12*

Clark, O. K., see Rodriguez, F. 126, *140*

Coffey, C. B., see Sorof, S. 48, *62*, 117, 163

Cohen, I. R., and L. C. Norins 149

Cohn, W. E., see Uziel, M. 90, *136*, 157

Coleman, J. E., and B. L. Vallee 144, *166*

Collipp, P. J., S. A. Kaplan, D. C. Boyle, and C. N. S. Shimizu 146

Colobert, L., and G. Dirheimer 144, *166*

Colombo, P., J. Fontana, L. E. Kukacka, and M. Steinberg 128

Colonge A., see Jutisz, M. 146

Connell, G. E., and R. W. Shaw 88, *136*

Contractor, S. F., and P. Jomain 130, *140*

Cooke, J. P., C. B. Anfinsen, and M. Sela 152, *169*

Coombes, J. D., see Burges, R. A. 116, *138*

Cordoba, F., see Fireman, P. 151, *167*

Cortis-Jones, B. 10, *12*, 23, *61*, 82, *85*, 166

Courrier, R., see Jutisz, M. 146

Cowling, E. B., see Petterson, G. 59, *62*, 144, *166*

Coy, U., see Hartmann, G. 98, *137*, 155

Craig, L. C. 2, *11*

—, see Eaker, D. L. 153

—, see Hilschmann, N. 151, *167*

Craig, L. C., see Rasmussen, H. 147

—, see Ruttenberg, M. A. 130, *139*

—, and A. Ansevin 2, *11*, 82, *85*

—, E. J. Harfenist, and A. C. Paladini 2, *11*

—, W. Hausmann, E. H. Ahrens, jr., and E. J. Harfenist 47, *61*

—, and T. P. King 2, *11*

—, and W. Konigsberg 2, *11*

—, and A. O. Pulley 2, *11*

Craven, G. R., E. Steers, jr., and C. B. Anfinsen 47, *61*, 144, *166*

Crestfield, A. M., S. Moore, and W. H. Stein 94, *139*, 147, *169*

—, W. H. Stein, and S. Moore 117, *138*

Criddle, R. S. 151

Cruft, H. J. 163

Curdel, A., see Iwatsubo, M. 116, *138*

Curtain, C. C., and W. G. Nayler 18, 44, *60*, *61*

Daisley, K. W. 59, *62*, 96, *137*, 173

van Dam, A. F., see Zwaan, J. 93

Dautrevaux, M., see Demaille, J. 154

Davidson, G. W., see Talwar, G. P. 149

Davidson, M. H., see Davidson, W. D. 160, *168*

Davidson, W. D., M. A. Sackner, and M. H. Davidson 160, *168*

Davis, B. J. 3, *11*

Davis, R. V., see Campbell, B. J. 143, *169*

Davoren, P. R. 147, *167*

Dea, J. C. M., see Anderson, D. M. W. 158, *168*

Debabov, V. G., see Shibnev, V. A. 164

Debro, J. R., see Lee, M. 98, *137*, 160

Deckx, R., see de Moor, P. 149

Declerck-Raskin, M., see de Moor, P. 149

Deffner, G., see Grassmann, W. 83, *85*

De Groot, J., see Mehl, J. W. 150, *167*

Degueldre-Guillaume, M. J., see Liébecq, C. 88, *136*

Delhey, R., see Fritz, H.-G. 155

Delihas, N., and M. Staehelin 48, *62*, 156, *169*

Delin, S., and J. Porath 143

Dellacha, J. M., M. A. Enero, and I. Faiferman 117, 146

—, and M. Sonenberg 146

Demaille, J., M. Dautrevaux, R. Havez, and G. Biserte 154

Demeester, G., see Eechaute, W. 162, *169*

Dempster, C., see Barber, A. A. 97

Desnuelle, P., see van Hoang, D. 152, *167*
—, see Sarda, L. 116, *138*, 142
Determann, H. 7, *12*, 21, 51, 55, *60*, *62*, 120, 134, *138*, *170*
—, see Wieland, Th. 2, *11*, 108, 116, 132, *137*, *139*, 164
—, and B. Gelotte 65, *84*
—, and R. Köhler 101, 120, *137*
—, G. Lüben, and Th. Wieland 10, *12*, 22, *60*, 108, 120, *137*
—, and W. Michel 52, 53, 54, *62*, 78, *85*, 108, 109, 112, *137*
—, and I. Walter 82, 83, *85*
—, and O. Zipp 163
Deuel, H., and H. Neukom 9, *12*
—, J. Solms, and L. Anyas-Weisz 9, *12*
Deutsch, B., R. D. Levere, and J. Levine 59, *62*
Diemair, S., see Holbrook, J. J. 153
Dimigen, J., F. Klink, and D. Richter 117
Dirheimer, G., J.-H. Weil, and J.-P. Ebel 155, *168*
—, see Colobert, L. 144, *166*
Dittmer, J. C., see Wells, M. A. 135, *139*
Dixon, H. B. F., and V. Moret 94, *136*
Djurtoft, R. 165
Dmochowski, A., see Schmidt, M. 158, *168*
Doehring, S., see Kössel, H. 95, *137*, 155
Dohan, F. C., see Nathenson, S. G. 133, *140*
Downey, W. K., and P. Andrews 117, 142
Drabarek, S., and V. Du Vigneaud 134, *139*
Dreyer, W. J., see Hummel, J. P. 97, *137*
Drivsholm, A., see Harboe, N. M. G. 160
Duesberg, P., see Wieland, Th. 108, 116, *137*
Dušek, K. 14, *60*

Eaker, D. L., T. P. King, and L. C. Craig 153
Ebel, J.-P., see Dirheimer, G. 155, *168*
Ebner, K. E., see Brodbeck, U. 144, *166*
Eckstein, U. U., see Schreiber, G. 143
Edelman, G. M., see Fougereau, M. 48, *61*, 151
Edmundson, A. B. 152, *167*
Edwards, G. 128
Edwards, R., see Andrews, P. 116, *138*
Edwards, M. R., see Gordon, M. A. 93
Eechaute, W. 162, *169*
—, and G. Demeester 162, *169*
von Eickstedt, K. W., see Boser, H. 131

van Eijk, H. G., C. H. Monfoort, J. J. Witte, and H. G. Westenbrink 160
Ekfors, T. O., see Riekkinen, P. J. 117
Ekman, L., E. Valmet, and B. Åberg 97
El-Kinawi, S. A., see Abdel Wahab, M. F. 99, 147, *167*
Ellefsen, Oe., see Kringstad, E. 158, *168*
Elmqvist, A., see Lindner, E. B. 96, *137*, 145, *167*
Emnéus, A., see Gelotte, B. 56, *62*
Enari, T.-M., see Nummi, M. 165
Ende, H. A., see Hermans, J. J. 1, *11*
Enero, M. A., see Dellacha, J. M. 117, 146
Enest, B., and H. Schill 93, 108, *136*
Engel, J., J. Kurtz, E. Katchalski, and A. Berger 122, *140*, 164
Engelhardt, J., see Raible, K. 165
Englander, J. J., see Englander, S. W. 95, *136*
Englander, S. W. 94, *136*
—, and J. J. Englander 95, *136*
Engler, R., see Bell, W. C. 156, 158, *168*
Engström, L. 142
Epstein, C. J., and C. B. Anfinsen 147, *167*
Epstein, W. V., see Tan, M. 151
—, and M. Tan 136, *139*, 160
Eriksson, K. E., see Widén, R. 43, *61*
Erikson, R. L., and J. A. Gordon 156, *169*
Escribano, M. J., H. Keilova, and P. Grabar 163
Estborn, B. 142
Evans, A., see Talwar, G. P. 149
Everall, P. H., see Grant, G. H. 55, *62*
Eylar, E. H., see Hardman, K. D. 163

Faiferman, I., see Dellacha, J. M. 117, 146
Fairclough, jr., G. F., and J. S. Fruton 98, *139*
Farhat, K., see Adams, H. E. 126, 127, *140*
Fasella, P., G. G. Hammes, and P. R. Schimmel 98, *139*
Fasold, H. 153, 154, *167*
—, G. Gundlach, and F. Turba 7, *11*
Fawcett, J. S., and C. J. O. R. Morris 19, 33, *60*, 76, *85*
Fazakerley, S., and D. R. Best 154, *167*
Feinstein, G., and J. R. Whitaker 117
Feldman, E. B., and Borgström 164
Félix, F., and N. Broulliet 144, *169*
Felix, K., see Rauen, H. M. 8, *12*
Ferrier, B. M., see Jarvis, D. 134, *139*
—, D. Jarvis, and V. Du Vigneaud 134, *140*

Fevold, H. R., see Roos, P. 146
Fiorica, V., see McKenzie, J. M. 161
Fireman, P., E. Hershgold, F. Cordoba, K. Schmid, and D. Gitlin 150, *167*
Firemark, H., see Barlow, C. 97
Fisher, S. A., see Kunin, R. 11, *12*, 14, 23, *60*
Flatmark, T. 143
Fleischmann, J. B., R. R. Porter, and E. M. Press 151
Flodin, P. 10, *12*, 15, 16, 17, 42, 58, *60*, *61*, 64, 67, 71, 72, 73, *84*, 88, *136*, 148
—, see Gelotte, B. 148
—, see Porath, J. 7, 10, *11*, 71, *84*
—, and K. Asperg 120, *138*, 159
—, B. Gelotte, and J. Porath 59, *62*
—, J. D. Gregory, and L. Rodén 159
—, and J. Killander 103, *137*, 148
—, and J. Porath 170
Focant, B., see Pechère, J. F. 163
—, and J. F. Pechère 163
Folk, J. E., and J. A. Gladner 144, *166*
Fontaine, Y. A., see Boulouard, R. 149
Fontanta, J., see Colombo, P. 128
Ford, J. E. 160, *168*
Fortier, N. L., see Lionetti, F. J. 150, *167*
Fothergill, J. E., and R. C. Nairn 93
Fougereau, M., and G. M. Edelman 48, *61*, 151
Fowler, P. R., see McKenzie, J. M. 161
François, C., and M. J. Glimcher 48, *62*, 162
Franěk, F. 151
—, see Kotyñek, O. 151
—, and J. Zikán 151
Franke, I., see Wucherpfennig, K. 131, 165
Frankland, B. T. B., see Hope, D. B. 145, *167*
Free, C. A., see Pierce, J. G. 2, *11*
Franz, H. E., see Mertz, D. P. 160, *168*
Franzini, C. 149
Frazer, G. P., and A. D. Nicol 142
Fridborg, K., S. Hjertén, S. Höglund, A. Liljas, B. K. S. Lundberg, P. Oxelfelt, L. Philipson, and B. Strandberg 158, *168*
Friedberg, K. D., see Stegemann, H. 162
—, H. Stegemann, and W. Vogt 162
Friedman, J., and L. G. Raisz 147
Friedmann, J. A., see Lanchantin, G. F. 116, *138*, 143, *166*
Frimmel, J. S., see Radola, B. J. 163
Frisch, V., see Kunin, R. 11, *12*, 14, 23, *60*
Frisch, H. L., see Si Jung Yeh 81, *85*
Fritz, H., G. Hartwich, and E. Werle 143, *166*

Fritz, H., I. Trautschold, and E. Werle 111, 119, *137*
Fritz, H.-G., R. Delhey, and H. Ross 155
Fritzsche, P., and V. Gröbe 23, *61*, 128
Fromageot, P., see Röschenthaler, R. 155, *168*
Froesch, E. R., see Bürgi, H. 147, *167*
Fruton, J. S., see Fairclough, jr., G. F. 98, *139*
Fuchs, S., see Givol, D. 150
Funatsu, G., see Hayashi, K. 153
Funatsu, M., see Hayashi, K. 153

Gabert, A., H. Seide, and G. Langhammer 17, *60*
Gammack, D. B., see Virden, R. 116, *139*
Gang, H., see Aebi, H. 103, *137*, 160
Ganrot, P. O. 150, *167*
Garry, B. J., see Ames, B. N. 132, *139*
Gasior, E., and R. Moldave 143
Gebert, U., see Wieland, Th. 130, *140*
Gelotte, B. 80, 84, *85*, 102, 132, *137*, *139*, 142, 157, *170*
—, see Determann, H. 67, *84*
—, see Flodin, P. 59, *62*
—, see Laurent, T. C. 75, *85*
—, and A. Emnéus 56, *62*
—, P. Flodin, and J. Killander 148
—, and B. Krantz 143, *166*
—, and J. Porath 33, *61*, 83, *85*, 100, *137*, *170*
Gemzell, C. A., see Roos, P. 146
George, W. H. S. 83, *85*, 166
George, W., and K. W. Walton 93
Ghuysen, J.-M., and J. L. Strominger 154
—, D. J. Tipper, and J. L. Strominger 159, *168*
Gibbs, P. A., see Phillips, A. W. 163
Giddings, J. C., and K. L. Mallik 72, *85*
Giertz, H., see Boser, H. 131
Gilbert, G. A. 119, *139*, *140*
Gilden, R. V., see Rosenquist, G. L. 148
Gillesen, D., see Yamashiro, D. 134, *140*
Ginsburg, M., and M. Ireland 145, *167*
Gitlin, D., see Fireman, P. 151, *167*
Givol, D., S. Fuchs, and M. Sela 150
Gjessing, E. T. 131, 164
Gladner, J. A., see Folk, J. E. 144, *166*
Glass, G. B. J., see Kakei, M. 164
Glass, J. D., see Hawker, C. D. 147
Glazer, A. N., and D. Wellner 132, *139*
Glimcher, M. J., see François, C. 48, *62*
Glover, J. S., see Greenwood, F. C. 146

Glueckauf, E. 70, *84*

Goldberger, R. F., see Neumann, H. 94, 95, *136*

—, and C. B. Anfinsen 94, *139*

Goldstein, J., see Schleich, T. 155, 156, *168*, *169*

Goldstein, L. J., see Agrawal, B. B. 132, *139*

Goodman, J. W. 151

Gordon, J. A., see Erikson, R. L. 156, *169*

Gordon, M. A., M. R. Edwards, and V. N. Tompkins 93

Gorguraki, V., see Jirgensons, B. 151

Got, R. 149

Grabar, P., see Escribano, M. J. 163

Graevskaja, R. A., see Bresler, S. E. 155

Graham, T. H. 2, *11*

Gramlich, F., D. Mohring, and H. E. Müller 150

Granath, K. 16, 27, 60, 65, *84*, 158, *168*, *170*

Granath, K. A., and P. Flodin 68, *84*, 108, 122, *137*

—, and B. E. Kvist 122, *138*

Grant, G. H., and P. H. Everall 55, *62*

Gräsbeck, R., and R. Karlsson 47, *61*

Grassmann, W., see Strauch, L. 143, *169*

—, and G. Deffner 83, *85*

—, K. Hannig, and A. Nordwig 153

Graul, E. H., and W. Stumpf 161, *169*

—, see Stumpf, W. 161, *169*

Gravejevskaja, R., see Bresler, S. 156, *169*

Gray, C. H., see Quincey, R. V. 149

Greenwood, F. C., see Hunter, W. M. 94

—, W. M. Hunter, and J. S. Glover 146

Gregory, J. D., see Flodin, P. 159

Grehn, M., see Schlubach, H. H. 90, *136*

Gröbe, V., see Fritzsche, P. 23, *61*, 128

Gross, E., and B. Witkop 152, *167*, *169*

Gross, M., B. Skoczylas, and W. Turski 155

Guidotti, G., R. J. Hill, and W. Konigsberg 153

Guillemin, R., see Schally, A. V. 145, *167*

Gundlach, G., see Fasold, H. 7, *11*

Gurd, F. R. N., see Hardman, K. D. 163

Gutte, B. see Zahn, H. 148, *167*

Guy, J. L., see Potter, G. D. 97

Haahti, E., and T. Nikkari 39, *61*

— —, and J. Kärkkäinen 39, *61*

Haavaldsen, R., and T. Norseth 130, *140*

Habeeb, A. F. S. A. 114, *139*

Haber, E., see Anfinsen, C. H. B. 93, *136*

—, see Bennett, J. C. 150

Haber, E., L. B. Page, and G. A. Jacoby 98, *137*, 150

— —, and F. F. Richards 150

Habermann, E., and K. G. Reiz 163

Habermann, V. 157

Haller, W. 25, *61*, 158, *168*

Hallows, B. G., see Reisfeld, R. A. 146

Hammes, G. G., see Fasella, P. 98, *139*

Handschuh, D., see Stepanov, V. 152

Hänni, H., see Signer, R. 2, *11*

Hannig, K., see Grassmann, W. 153

Hansbury, E., see Hayes, F. N. 83, *85*, 157, *168*

Hanson, L. Å., see Bengtsson, C. 152, *167*

—, and B. G. Johansson 151

— —, and L. Rymo 55, *62*, 160

Hånson, L. A., P. Roos, and L. Rymo 146

Harboe, N. M. G., and A. Drivsholm 161

Hardman, K. D., E. H. Eylar, D. K. Ray, L. J. Banaszak, and F. R. N. Gurd 163

Hardwicke, J., see Boyns, A. R. 150

—, see Ratcliff, A. P. 161

Hardy, T. L., see Acred, P. 97

—, and K. R. L. Mansford 97

Harfenist, E. J., see Craig, L. C. 2, *11*

Harmon, D. J. 123, *138*

—, and H. L. Jacobs 128

Harris, J. I., and L. Polgár 153

Harrison, J. F., and B. E. Northam 161

Hart, D. W., see Lanchantin, G. F. 116, *138*, 143, *166*

Hartmann, G., see Liersch, M. 98, *137*

—, U. Coy, and G. Kniese 98, *137*, 155

Hartwich, G., see Fritz, H. 143, *166*

Hasegawa, K., T. Kusano, and H. Mitsuda 48, *62*, 163

Hausmann, W., see Craig, L. C. 47, *61*

Havez, R., see Demaille, J. 154

Hawker, C. D., J. D. Glass, and H. Rasmussen 147

Hawrylewicz, E. J., see Riesen, W. H. 142

Hayashi, K., T. Imoto, G. Funatsu, and M. Funatsu 153

Hayes, F. N., E. Hansbury, and V. E. Mitchell 83, *85*, 157, *168*

Heirwegh, K., see de Moor, P. 98, *137*, *149*

Heitz, W., H. Ullner, and H. Höcker 22, 23, 60

Heller, J., and M. Schramm 158, *168*

Hellerman, L., see Rogers, K. S. 116, *138*

Hellsing, K. 76, *85*

—, see Laurent, T. C. 75, *85*

Hendrickson, J. G., see Moore, J. C. 72, *84*, 108, 110, 111, 123, 127, *137*
—, and J. C. Moore 124, *138*
Henneman, P. H., see Saxena, B. B. 146
Henney, C. S., see James, K. 151
Hennrich, N., A. Hoffmann, and H. Lang 160, *168*
Heppel, L. A., see Jones, O. W. 157, *168*
Herbert, P., see Philip, B. A. 149
Heremans, J. F., see de Moor, P. 149
Hermans, P. H. 3, *11*
Hermans, J. J., and H. A. Ende 1, *11*
Hermier, C., see Jutisz, M. 146
Herries, D. G., W. Bishop, and F. M. Richards 99, *137*
Hershgold, E., see Fireman, P. 151, *167*
Hess, B., see Wirth, K. 48, *61*, 160
Hess, M., and R. F. Kratz 125, *140*
Heufer, G., and D. Braun 22, *60*, 122, *138*
Hicks, G. P., and S. J. Updike 45, *61*
Hill, R. J., see Guidotti, G. 153
Hilschmann, N., and L. C. Craig 151, *167*
von Hippel, P. H., see Printz, M. P. 95, *137*
Hirs, C. H. W., see Plummer, jr., T. H. 48, *62*, 154
—, and J. H. Kycia 153
Hjertén, S. 10, *12*, 18, 20, *60*
—, and R. Mosbach 7, *12*, 18, *60*
—, see Boman, H. G. 155, *167*
—, see Fridborg, K. 158, *168*
Hnilica, L. S., see Bess, L. G. 163
—, and L. G. Bess 117
van Hoang, D., M. Rovery, and P. Desnuelle 152, *167*
Höcker, H., see Heitz, W. 22, 23, *60*
Hocman, G. 162, *169*
—, M. Kutka and V. Licko 94
Hoerman, K. C., A. Y. Balekjian, and V. J. Berzinskas 91, *136*
Hoffmann, A., see Hennrich, N. 160, *168*
von Hofsten, B., and J. Porath 142
Höglund, S., see Fridborg, K. 158, *168*
Högman, C. F., see Killander, J. 148
Hohn, Th., and W. Pollmann 78, *85*, 108, *137*, 157
Holbrook, J. J., G. Pfleiderer, J. Schnetger, and S. Diemair 153
Holeysovska, H. 97
Hollingsworth, J. W., see Philip, B. A. 149
Holt, L. A., see Leach, S. J. 148, *167*
Holzer, H., see Boll, M. 143
—, see Schreiber, G. 143

Hope, D. B., B. A. Schacter, and B. T. B. Frankland 145, *167*
Hopsu, V. K., see Riekkinen, P. J. 117
Höye, Å. 94
Huang, P. C., see Attardi, G. 156, *168*
Humbel, R. A. 147, *167*
Humbel, R. E., see Bürgi, H. 148, *167*
Hunter, W. M. 146
—, see Greenwood, F. C. 146
—, and F. C. Greenwood 94
Hummel, J. P., and W. J. Dreyer 97, *137*
Humphrey, J. H., see Allison, A. C. 3, *11*
Huth, K., see Wirth, K. 48, *61*, 160

Imanishi, A., see Kakiuchi, K. 118, *138*
Imoto, T., see Hayashi, K. 153
Inglot, A. D., J. Lisowski, and E. Niedzwiedzka 158, *168*
Ingram, V. M., and J. G. Pierce 157
Inman, F. P., and A. Nisonoff 151
Ireland, M., see Ginsburg, M. 145, *167*
Isemura, T., see Kakiuchi, K. 118, *138*
Ishiguro, I., and B. Linzen 165
Ishikura, H. 157
Iwatsubo, M., and A. Curdel 116, *138*

Jackson, A. 38, *61*
Jacobs, H. L., see Harmon, D. J. 128
Jacobsen, S. 149
Jacobsson, L. 160, *168*
—, and G. Widström 94
Jacoby, G. A., see Haber, E. 98, *137*, 150
James, A. T., R. P. W. Scott, and J. R. Ravenhill 39, *61*
—, J. R. Ravenhill, and R. P. W. Scott 39, *61*
James, K., C. S. Henney, and D. R. Stanworth 151
Jarvis, D., see Ferrier, B. M. 134, *140*
—, B. M. Ferrier, and V. du Vigneaud 134, *139*
Jenness, C. P., see Latham, W. C. 162
Jiang, N. S., see Reichert, jr., L. E. 146
Jirgensons, B., see Adams-Mayne, M. E. 150, *169*
—, see Yonezawa, D. 151
—, M. E. Adams-Mayne, V. Gorguraki, and P. J. Migliore 151
Johanson, B. G., see Bengtsson, C. 152, *167*
Johansson, B. G., see Hanson, L. Å. 151
—, and L. Rymo 51, 52, 54, 55, *62*
Johnson, B. L., see Adams, H. E. 126, 127, *140*

Johnson, J. A., see Abbott, D. C. 166
Johnson, J. F., see Cantow, M. J. R. 125, *139*
—, see Pickett, H. E. 125, *138*
Johnson, P., see Rabinowitz, J. L. 161, *168*
Jomain, P., see Contractor, S. F. 130, *140*
Jones, G., S. Moore, and W. H. Stein 143, *166*
Jones, O. W., E. E. Townsend, H. A. Sober, and L. A. Heppel 157, *168*
Joustra, M. K. 46, *61*, 101, 132, *137*
Jung, H., and H. Schüssler 152, *167*
Jungwirth, C., and G. Bodo 117
Jutisz, M., C. Hermier, A. Colonge, and R. Courrier 146
—, see de La Llosa, P. 114, *138*

Kabat, S., see Attardi, G. 156, *168*
Kägi, J. H. R., see Pulido, P. 117, 163
Kakei, M., and G. B. J. Glass 164
Kakiuchi, K., S. Kato, A. Imanishi, and T. Isemura 118, *138*
Kaplan, S. A., see Collipp, P. J. 146
Kärkkäinen, J., see Haahti, E. 27, *61*
Karlsson, R., see Gräsbeck, R. 47, *61*
Karush, F., see Utsumi, S. 151
Kassab, R., see van Thoai, N. 107, *137*
Katchalski, E., see Engel, J. 122, *140*, 164
Kato, S., see Kakiuchi, K. 118, *138*
Kazazian, jr., H. H. 116, *139*
Keilova, H., see Escribano, M. J. 163
Keller, S., and I. Mandl 143, *166*
Kellner, G., see Radola, B. J. 163
Kemp, E., and I. Rubin 116, *138*
Kersten, T. E., see Stouffer, J. E. 39, *61*
Kessen, G., and F. Amelunxen 162
Kickhöfen, B., R. Warth and D. Scheel 50, *62*
Kies, M. W., see Alvord, jr., C. E. 162
Killander, J. 50, *62*, 148, 150, *167*
—, see Flodin, P. 103, *137*, 148
—, see Laurent, T. C. 65, 68, 75, *84*, 108, 113, *137*
—, S. Bengtsson, and L. Philipson 50, *62*
—, and C. F. Högman 148
—, J. Pontén, and L. Rodén 93
King, T. E., see Kuboyama, M. 144, *166*
King, T. P., see Craig, L. C. 2, *11*
—, see Eaker, D. L. 153
—, and P. S. Norman 48, *62*
Kirilov, S., see Bresler, S. 156, *169*
Kisliuk, R. L. 92, *136*

Kjellin, K., see Broman, L. 149
Klieger, E., and E. Schröder 134, *139*
Klink, F., see Dimigen, J. 117
Kniese, G., see Hartmann, G. 98, *137*, 155
Knight, G. W., see Tung, L. 125, *138*
Ko, H., see Reusser, F. 146
Koestler, W., see Signer, R. 2, *11*
Köhler, R., see Determann, H. 101, 120, *137*
Kohlschütter, H. W., K. Unger, and K. Vogel 25, *61*
Kollmansberger, A., see Smith, W. B. 71, 72, 77, *84*
Komorowska-Rycerz, A., A. Brühl, and R. Krauze 162
Konigsberg, W., see Craig, L. C. 2, *11*
—, see Giudotti, G. 153
—, K. Weber, G. Notani, and N. Zinder 27, *61*, 154, *169*
de Koning, P. J. 165
Kössel, H., and S. Doehring 95, *137*, 155
Kotýnek, O., and F. Franěk 151
Krantz, A. B., see Gelotte, B. 143, *166*
Kratz, R. F., see Hess, M. 125, *140*
Krauss, A., see Pfleiderer, G. 153
Krauze, R., see Komorowska-Rycerz, A. 162
Kressman, T. R. E., see Millar, J. R. 11, *12*
Kringstad, E., and Oe. Ellefsen 158, *168*
Krisch, K., see Boguth, W. 116, *138*
Krüger, P. M., see Stouffer, J. E. 39, *61*
Kuboyama, M., S. Takemori, and T. E. King 144, *166*
Kuch, H., see Schlossberger, H. G. 131
Kukacka, L. E., see Colombo, P. 128
Kulakowski, R. A., see Rodriguez, F. 38, *61*, 128
Kunin, R., E. Meitzner, and N. Bortnick 11, *12*, 14, 23, *60*
— —, J. A. Oline, S. A. Fisher, and V. Frisch 11, *12*, 14, 23, *60*
—, and R. J. Meyers 8, *12*
Kurtz, J., see Engel, J. 122, *140*, 164
Kusano, T., see Hasegawa, K. 48, *62*, 163
Kusch, P., and H. Zahn 48, *62*
Kushinsky, S., and I. Otterness 162, *169*
Kutka, M., see Hocman, G. 94
Kvist, B. E., see Granath, K. A. 122, *138*
Kwon, T. W., and H. S. Olcott 164
Kycia, J. H., see Hirs, C. H. W. 153
Kyle, R. A., and W. F. McGuckin 161

de La Llosa, P., C. Tertrin, and M. Jutisz 114, *138*

Labhart, A., see Bürgi, H. 147, *167*

Lamberg, B.-A., see Liewendahl, K. 161, *169*

Lanchantin, G. F., J. A. Friedmann, and D. W. Hart 116, *138*, 143, *166*

Lanckman, M. 151

Lande, S., A. B. Lerner, and G. V. Upton 145, *167*

Lang, H., see Hennrich, N. 160, *168*

Langhammer, G., see Gabert, A. 17, *60*

—, see Seide, H. 128

Largier, J. F., and A. Polson 116, *138*

Latham, W. C., C. P. Jenness, and R. J. K. Timperi 162

Lathe, G. H., and C. R. J. Ruthven 10, *12*

Laurent, E. P., see Laurent, T. C. 71, *84*

Laurent T. C. 75, *85*

—, K. Hellsing, and B. Gelotte 75, *85*

—, and J. Killander 65, 68, 75, *84*, 107, 108, 113, *137*

—, and E. P. Laurent 71, *84*

—, and A. Pietruszkiewicz 75, *85*

La Via, M., see Baglioni, C. 151, *167*

Lea, D. J., and A. H. Sehon 18, *60*

Leach, A. A., and P. C. O'Shea 72, *84*, 115, *138*

Leach, S. J., J. M. Swan, and L. A. Holt 148, *167*

Leaf, G., see Black, J. A. 152, *167*

Leaver, F. W. 146

Le Baron, F. N., see Alvord, jr., C. E. 162

Lee, M., and J. R. Debro 98, *137*, 160

Lee, Y.-Ch., and C. E. Ballou 159

—, and R. Montgomery 154

Lerner, A. B., see Lande, S. 145, *167*

Lester, G., and A. Byers 91, *136*, 144, *166*

Lever, A. F., see Peart, W. S. 132, *169*

Levere, R. D., see Deutsch, B. 59, *62*

Levine, J., see Deutsch, B. 59, *62*

Levitt, J., see Russell, B. 2, *11*

Li, C. H., see Papkoff, H. 146

—, see Sluyser, M. 146

—, see Squire, P. G. 146

Li, Y.-T. 144, *166*

Licko, V., see Hocman, G. 94

Liébecq, C., and M. J. Degueldre-Guillaume 88, *136*

Liersch, M., and G. Hartmann 98, *137*

Liewendahl, K., and B.-A. Lamberg 161, *169*

Liljas, A., see Fridborg, K. 158, *168*

Lin, Y.-C., see Campbell, B. J. 143, *169*

Lindberg, J. J., K. Penttinen, and C. Majani 28, *61*, 165

Lindner, E. B., see Porath, J. 134, *139*

—, A. Elmqvist, and J. Porath 96, *137*, 145, *167*

Lindqvist, B. 165

—, and T. Storgårds 9, *12*

Linzen, B., see Ishiguro, I. 165

Lionetti, F. J., C. R. Valeri, J. C. Bond, and N. L. Forthier 150, *167*

Lipsett, M. N. 157

Lisowski, J. 115, *138*

—, see Inglot, A. D. 158, *168*

—, see Wilcox, P. E. 97

Lissitzky, S. and J. Bismuth 161, *169*

—, see Miranda, F. 132, *139*

—, J. Bismuth, and M. Rolland 94

Liu, W. K., see Papkoff, H. 146

Lloyd, A. M., see Peart, W. S. 143, *169*

Lloyd, W. G., and T. Alfredy, jr. 14, 23, *60*

Lochmüller, H., see Wood, H. G. 144, *166*

Loeschcke, V., see Stegemann, K. 91, *136*

Lüben, G., see Determann, H. 10, *12*, 22, *60*, 108, 120, *137*

Lukens, L. N. 163

Lumsden, C. E., see Carnegie, P. R. 164

Lundberg, B. K. S., see Fridborg, K. 158, *168*

Lundblad, A. 159

—, see Berggard, I. 159

Lynen, F., see Numa, S. 144, *166*

—, see Wood, H. G. 144, *166*

Maass, D., H. Pelzer, and W. Weidel 143

Mach, B., and E. L. Tatum 130, *139*, 163

Madison, L. L., see Tauber, S. 148, *167*

Macchia, V., see Nunez, J. 147

Mahowald, T. A. 134, *139*, 153

Maitland, C. C., see Selby, K. 72, *84*, 115, *138*, 144, *166*

Majani, C., see Lindberg, J. J. 28, *61*, 165

Majoor, C. L. H., see van Tongeren, J. H. M. 97

Makowetz, E., K. Müller, and H. Spitzy 161, *169*

Maley, L. E. 41, *61*, 111, *137*

Mallik, K. L., see Giddings, J. C. 72, *85*

Malkinson, M., see Allan, D. 149

von Malortie, R., see Siebert, G. 143, 153, *166*

Mandel, P., see Virmaux, N. 155, *168*
Mandl, I., see Keller, S. 143, *166*
Manipol, V., and H. Spitzy 147, *167*
Mann, J. D., see Mudd, S. H. 97, *137*
Mansford, K. R. L., see Acred, P. 97
—, see Hardy, T. L. 97
Marin, A. P., see Miller, K. D. 92, *136*, 162
Marks, G. S., R. D. Marshall, A. Neuberger, and H. Papkoff 153
Maroux, S., and M. Rovery 153
Marr, W. E., see Millar, J. R. 11, *12*, 14, 23, *60*
Marsden, N., see Bill, A. 159, *168*
Marsden, N. V. B. 82, *85*
Marshall, Ch. S. 92, *136*
Marshall, R. D., see Marks, G. S. 153
Martenson, R. E., see Alvord, jr., C. E. 162
Martin, R. G., see Ames, B. N. 132, *139*
Martinez-Maldonado, M., see Toro-Goyco, E. 147, *167*
Marx, R., see Beiss, U. 91, *136*, 158, *168*
Mason, J. W., see Mougey, E. H. 161, *169*
Matheka, H.-D., and G. Wittmann 89, *136*, 158, *168*
Matheson, N. A., see Bagdasarian, M. 83, *85*, 134, *139*
Matos, M., see Toro-Goyco, E. 143, *166*
Matos, M. L., see Rivera, J. V. 160
Mauchamp, J., see Nunez, J. 147
Maylay, L. E. 128
Maylie, M. F., see Sarda, L. 116, *138*, 142
McBride, R. A., see Sorof, S. 48, *62*, 117, 163
McEvoy-Bowe, E., and S. Sarojini Thevi 161, *168*
McGuckin, W. F., see Kyle, R. A. 161
McKenzie, J. M., P. R. Fowler, and V. Fiorica 161
McVicar, A. G., see Painter, R. H. 59, *62*
Mead, T. H., see Russell, B. 20, *60*
Mehl, J. W., W. O'Connell, and J. De Groot 150, *167*
Meitzner, E., see Kunin, R. 11, *12*, 14, 23, *60*
Merrett, T. 118, *139*
Mertz, D. P., and H. E. Franz 160, *168*
Mertz, E. T., see Chan, J. Y. S. 149
Metzger, H., and S. J. Singer 151
Meyer, J. G. 155, *169*
Meyerhoff, G. 108, 124, 125, 127, *137*
Meyers, R. J., see Kunin, R. 8, 9, *12*
Michel, W., see Determann, H. 52–54, *62*, 78, *85*, 109, 112, *137*

Miettinen, T. A. 159
Migliore, P. J., see Jirgensons, B. 151
—, see Yonezawa, D. 151
Mikes, J. A. 9, 11, *12*
Millar, J. R., D. G. Smith, W. E. Marr, and T. R. E. Kressman 11, *12*, 14, 23, *60*
Miller, K. D., and A. P. Marin 92, *136*, 162
Milstein, C. 151, *167*
Miranda, F., H. Rochat, and S. Lissitzky 132, *139*
Mitchell, V. E., see Hayes, F. N. 83, *85*, 157, *168*
Mitsuda, H., see Hasegawa, K. 48, *62*, 163
Miyake, H., see Nakayama, F. 99, 117, *139*, 164
Mohring, D., see Gramlich, F. 150
Moldave, K., see Gasior, E. 143
Monfoort, C. H., see van Eijk, H. G. 160
Montgomery, R., see Lee, Y. Ch. 154
—, and Y. Ch. Wu 154
Monty, K. J., see Siegel, L. M. 77, *85*, 107, 113, 116, 117, *137*, *138*
de Moor, P., R. Deckx, and O. Steeno 149
—, K. Heirwegh, J. F. Heremans, and M. Declerck-Raskin 149
— —, and O. Steeno 98, *137*, 149
Moore, J. C. 7, 11, *12*, 23, 24, 25, *61*, 65, 104, *137*
—, see Altgelt, K. H. 73, 76, *84*, *170*
—, see Hendrickson, J. G. 124, *138*
—, see Tung, L. 124, *138*
—, and J. G. Hendrickson 73, *84*, 108, 110, 111, 123, 127, *137*
Moore, S., see Crestfield, A. M. 94, 117, *138*, *139*, 147, *169*
—, see Jones, G. 143, *166*
—, see Ota, S. 143, *166*
Moret, V., see Dixon, H. B. F. 94, *136*
Morris, C. J. O. R. 51, 52, 54, *62*, 112, 117, *137*, 146
—, see Fawcett, J. S. 19, 33, *60*, 76, *85*
—, and P. Morris *170*
Mosbach, R., see Hjertén, S. 7, *12*, 18, *60*
Moschetto, Y., see Biserte, G. 152, *167*
Mougey, E. H., and J. W. Mason 161, *169*
Mould, D. L., and R. L. M. Synge 3, *11*
Mozen, M. M., see White, W. F. 143, *169*
Mücke, D., see Obenaus, R. 165
Mudd, S. H., and J. D. Mann 97, *137*
Muench, K. H., and P. Berg 133, *140*
Müller, H. E., see Gramlich, F. 150
Müller, K., see Makowetz, E. 161, *169*

Müller, K., see Spitzy, H. 84, *85*, 94
Müller, W. A., see Bürgi, H. 147, *167*
Murphey, B. E. P., and Ch. J. Pattee 149, 161, *169*

Naber, J. E., A. M. Schepman, and A. Rörsch 142
Nairn, R. C., see Fothergill, J. E. 93
Nakayama, F. 99, *139*, 164
—, and H. Miyake 99, 117, *139*, 164
Naono, T., and K. Prchal 38, *61*
Nathenson, S. G., see Sanderson, A. R. 159, *168*
—, F. C. Dohan, jr., H. H. Richards, and G. L. Cantoni 133, *140*
Neuberger, A. see Marks, G. S. 153
Neukom, H., see Deuel, H. 9, *12*
Neumann, H., R. F. Goldberger, and M. Sela 93, 95, *136*
Neumann, H.-J., see Obenaus, R. 89, *136*, 164
Nichol, L. W., see Winzor, D. J. 72, *84*
Nicol, A. D., see Frazer, G. P. 142
Niedzwiezka, E., see Inglot, A. D. 158, *168*
Niemann, H., see Boguth, W. 116, *138*
Nieschlag, E., and K. Otto 116, *138*
Nikkari, T., see Haahti, E. 39, *61*
Nilsson, A. 131
Nisonoff, A., see Inman, F. P. 151
Nolan, C., and E. L. Smith 153
Nordin, P. 158, *168*
Nordwig, A., see Grassmann, W. 153
Norins, L. C., see Cohen, I. R. 149
Norman, P. S., see King, T. P. 48, *62*
Norseth, T., see Haavaldsen, R. 130, *140*
Northam, B. E., see Harrison, J. F. 161
Northcote, D. H., see Barrett, A. J. 159
Notani, G., see Konigsberg, W. 27, *61*
Numa, S., E. Ringelmann, and F. Lynen 144, *166*
Nummi, M., and T.-M. Enari 165
—, R. Vilhunen, and T.-M. Enari 165
Nunez, J., J. Mauchamp, V. Macchia, and J. Roche 147
Nyström, E., and J. Sjövall 22, 39, *60*, 132, 133, *139*

Obenaus, R., and H.-J. Neumann 89, *136*, 164
— —, and D. Mücke 165
O'Connell, W., see Mehl, J. W. 150, *167*

O'Donell, I. J., see Thompson, E. O. P. 117, 163
Oeberg, B., S. Bengtsson, and L. Philipson 156, 158, *168*
Oeser, A., see Schreiber, G. 143
Oestling, G. 159, *168*
Ogston, A. G. 14, *60*, 75, *85*
Olcott, H. S., see Kwon, T. W. 164
Olesen, H., and P. O. Pedersen 114, *137*
Oline, J. A., see Kunin, R. 11, *12*, 14, 23, *60*
Ornstein, L. 3, *11*
O'Shea, P. C., see Leach, A. A. 72, *84*, 115, *138*
Ostrowski, W., and J. Rybarska 116, *138*, 142
Ota, S., S. Moore, and W. H. Stein 143, *166*
Otterness, I., see Kushinsky, S. 162, *169*
Otto, K., see Nieschlag, E. 116, *138*
Oxelfelt, P., see Fridborg, K. 158, *168*

Pacheco, G., see Carnegie, P. R. 55, *62*
Page, L. B., see Haber, E. 98, *137*, 150
le Page, M., and H. J. de Vries 22, *61*
Painter, R. H., and A. G. McVicar 59, *62*
Paladini, A. C., see Craig, L. C. 2, *11*
Papkoff, H., see Marks, G. S. 153
—, C. H. Li, and W.-K. Liu 146
Partridge, S. M. 9, *12*
Patrick, R. L., and R. E. Thiers 45, *61*, 160, *168*
Pattee, Ch. J., see Murphey, B. E. P. 149, 161, *169*
Paulis, J. W., see Tipton, C. L. 23, *61*, 164
Payne, N., see Peart, W. S. 143, *169*
Peanasky, R. J., and M. M. Szucs 143, *166*
Pearson, D. J., see Chase, J. F. A. 116, *138*
Peart, W. S., A. M. Lloyd, G. N. Thatcher, A. F. Lever, N. Payne, and N. Stone 143, *169*
Pechère, J. F., see Focant, B. 163
—, and B. Focant 163
Pederson, K. O. 7, *12*, 25, *61*, 76, *85*, 115, *138*
Pedersen, K. O., see Svedberg, T. 1, *11*
Pedersen, P. O., see Olesen, H. 114, *137*
Pelzer, H., see Maass, D. 143
Penttinen, K., see Lindberg, J. J. 28, *61*, 165
Pepper, K. W., D. Reichenberg, and D. K. Hale 15, *60*
Petersen, D. F., see Shepherd, G. R. 155, *167*

Petterson, G., E. B. Cowling, and J. Porath 59, *62*, 144, *166*
Pettit, N., see Chernoff, A. I. 153
Pfeiffer, E. F., see Zahn, H. 148, *167*
Pfleiderer, G., and A. Krauss 153
Pfleiderer, J., see Holbrook, J. J. 153
Philip, B. A., P. Herbert, and J. W. Hollingsworth 149
Philipson, L., see Bengtsson, S. 20, 21, *60*, 105, *137*, 158, *168*
—, see Fridborg, K. 158, *168*
—, see Killander, J. 50, *62*
—, see Oeberg, B. 156, 158, *168*
Phillips, A. W., and P. A. Gibbs 163
Pickett, H. E., M. J. R. Cantow, and J. F. Johnson 125, *138*
Pierce, J. C., see Carsten, M. E. 154
Pierce, J. G., see Ingram, V. M. 157
—, and C. A. Free 2, *11*
Pierson, M. D., see Tipton, C. L. 23, *61*, 164
Pietruszkiewicz, A., see Laurent, T. C. 75, *85*
Piscator, M. 161
Platt, D., see Buddecke, E. 143
Pleiderer, G., and F. Auricchio 144, *166*
Plummer, jr., T. H., and C. H. W. Hirs 48, *62*, 154
Polgár, L., see Harris, J. I. 153
Pollmann, W., see Hohn, Th. 78, *85*, 108, *137*
Polson, A. 10, *12*
—, see Largier, J. F. 116, *138*
—, see Russell, B. 2, *11*
—, and B. W. Russell 51, *62*
Pontén, J., see Killander, J. 93
Popplewell, D. S., see Boocock, G. 97
Porath, J. 10, *12*, 73, 80, 83, *84*, *85*, 108, 136, *137*, *139*, 153, *170*
—, see Björk, W. 10, *12*, 142
—, see Delin, S. 143
—, see Gelotte, B. 33, *61*, 83, *85*, 100, *137*, *170*
—, see Flodin, P. *170*
—, see von Hofsten, B. 142
—, see Lindner, E. B. 96, *137*, 145, *167*
—, see Petterson, G. 59, *62*, 144, *166*
—, see Tiselius, A. 79, *85*, *170*
—, and H. Bennich 33, 51, 55, *62*
—, and P. Flodin 7, 10, *11*, 71, *84*
—, and E. B. Lindner 134, *139*
—, and A. V. Schally 134, *139*
—, and N. Ur 50, *62*
Porter, R. R., see Press, E. M. 152, *167*
—, see Fleischmann, J. B. 150

Porter, R. S., see Cantow, M. J. R. 125, *139*
Posner, A. M. 84, *85*, 164
Potter, G. D., and J. L. Guy 97
Potts, J. T., see Aurbach, G. D. 147
Pradel, L. A., see van Thoai, N. 107, *137*
Prchal, K., see Naono, T. 38, *61*
Preddie, E. C., and M. Saffran 145, *167*
Press, E. M., see Fleischmann, J. B. 150
—, and R. R. Porter 152, *167*
Printz, M. P., and P. H. von Hippel 95, *137*
Pristoupil, T. I. 117
—, and S. Ulrych 149
Pulido, P., Kägi, J. H. R., and B. L. Vallee 117, 163
Pulley, A. O., see Craig, L. C. 2, *11*
Purnell, G. G. 70, *84*

Quincey, R. V., and C. H. Gray 149

Rabinowitz, J. L., see Shapiro, B. 160, *168*
—, B. Shapiro, and P. Johnson 160, *168*
Radola, B. J., G. Kellner, and J. S. Frimmel 163
Rahman, S., see Anderson, D. M. W. 158, *168*
Raible, K., and J. Engelhardt 165
Raisz, L. G., see Friedman, J. 147
Ralph, R. A., see Bergquist, P. L. 133, 134, *139*
Randerath, K. 51, *62*
Raper, J. H., see Virden, R. 116, *139*
Rasmussen, H., see Hawker, C. D. 147
—, see Tenenhouse, A. 147
—, and L. C. Craig 147
—, Y.-L. Sze, and R. Young 147
Ratcliff, A. P., and J. Hardwicke 160
Rauen, H. M., and K. Felix 8, *12*
Ravenhill, J. R., see James, A. T. 39, *61*
Ray, D. K., see Hardman, K. D. 163
Recant, L., see Alp, H. 147, *167*
Reichard, P., see Ringertz, N. R. 89, *136*, 158, *168*
Reichert, jr., L. E., and N. S. Jiang 146
Reisfeld, R. A., B. G. Hallows, D. E. Williams, N. G. Brink, and S. L. Steelman 146
Reiz, K. G., see Habermann, E. 163
Rempel, D., see Wieland, Th. 130, 135, *140*
Renkin, E. M. 77, *85*
Reusser, F., and H. Ko 146
Richard, G. B. 160

Richards, F. F., see Haber, E. 150
Richards, F. M., see Herries, D. G. 99, *137*
Richards, H. H., see Nathenson, S. G. 133, *140*
Richardson, R. W. 9, *12*
Richter, D., see Dimigen, J. 117
Ricketts, C. R. 158, *168*
Riekkinen, P. J., T. O. Ekfors, and V. K. Hopsu 117
Riepertinger, C., see Wood, H. G. 144, *166*
Riesen, W. H., and E. J. Hawrylewicz 142
Rinderknecht, H. 93
Ringelmann, E., see Numa, S. 144, *166*
Ringertz, N. R., and P. Reichard 89, *136*, 158, *168*
Rivera, J. V., E. Toro-Goyco, and M. L. Matos 160
Robbins, J., see Salvatore, G. 147
Roberts, G. P. 55, *62*
Robertson, J. M., see Bergquist, P. L. 133, 134, *139*
Rochat, H., see Miranda, F. 132, *139*
Roche, J., see Nunez, J. 147
Rochlitz, J., see Wilk, M. 81, *85*, 165
Rodén, L., see Flodin, P. 159
—, see Killander, J. 93
Rodriguez, F., and O. K. Clark 126, *140*
—, R. A. Kulakowski, and O. K. Clark 38, *61*, 128
Roger, J., see Sarda, L. 116, *138*, 142
Rogers, K. S., L. Hellerman, and T. E. Thompson 116, *138*
Roos, P., see Hånson, L. A. 146
—, H. R. Fevold, and C. A. Gemzell 146
Rörsch, A. see Naber, J. E. 142
Röschenthaler, R., and P. Fromageot 156, *168*
Rosenfeld, M. 2, *11*
Rosenquist, G. L., and R. V. Gilden 148
Roskes, S. D., and T. E. Thompson 160
Ross, H., see Fritz, G.-H. 155
Ross, J., see Burke, D. C. 117
Roth, L. J., see Barlow, C. F. 97
Rother, H. 166
Rothstein, F. 43, *61*
Rottenburg, W., see Signer, R. 2, *11*
Roubal, W. T., and A. L. Tappel 41, 47, *61*, 111, *137*
Rovery, M., see Maroux, S. 153
—, see van Hoang, D. 152, *167*
Rubin, J., see Kemp, E. 116, *138*
Rubina, Kh. M., see Bresler, S. E. 155

Russell, B. W., see Polson, A. 51, *62*
Russell, B., J. Levitt, and A. Polson 2, *11*
—, T. H. Mead, and A. Polson 20, *60*
Ruthven, C. R. J., see Lathe, G. H. 10, *12*
Ruttenberg, M. A., T. P. King, and L. C. Craig 130, *139*
Rybarska, J., see Ostrowski, W. 116, *138*, 142
Rymo, L., see Hanson, L. Å. 55, *62*, 160
—, see Johansson, B. G. 51, 52, 54, 55, *62*

Sackner, M. A., see Davidson, W. D. 160, *168*
Saffran, M., see Preddie, E. C. 145, *167*
Salenstedt, C. R., see Tirunarayanan, M. O. 162
—, and M. O. Tirunarayanan 162
Salvatore, G., G. Vecchio, M. Salvatore, H. J. Cahnmann, and J. Robbins 147
—, M. Salvatore, H. J. Cahnmann, and J. Robbins 147
Salvatore, M., see Salvatore, G. 147
Saminski, E. see Bresler, S. 156, *169*
Samuelson, O. 8, *12*
Sanderson, A. R., J. L. Strominger, and S. G. Nathenson 159, *168*
Sanfelippo, P. M., and J. G. Surak 107, *137*, 146
Sarda, L., M. F. Maylié, J. Roger, and P. Desnuelle 116, *138*, 142
Saris, N. E. 97
Sarojini-Thevi, S., see McEvoy-Bowe, E. 160, *168*
Saxena, B. B., and P. H. Henneman 146
Schachmann, H. K. 1, *11*
Schacter, B. A., see Hope, D. B. 145, *167*
Schally, A. V., and R. Guillemin 145, *167*
Schane, H. P. 115, *138*
Scheel, D., see Kickhöfen, B. 50, *62*
Schepman, A. M., see Naber, J. E. 142
Scheraga, H. A., see Winzor, D. J. 119, *138*
Scheuermann, E. A. 2, *11*
Schiefer, H., see Wieland, Th. 130, *140*
Schill, H., see Enest, B. 93, 108, *136*
Schimmel, P. R., see Fasella, P. 98, *139*
Schleich, T., and J. Goldstein 155, 156, *168*, *169*
Schlossberger, H. G., H. Kuch, and I. Buhrow 131
Schlubach, H. H., and M. Grehn 90, *136*
—, and R. Ziegler 159, *168*
Schmid, K., see Fireman, P. 150, *167*

Schmidt, M., and A. Dmochowski 158, *168*
Schmidt-Kastner, G. 134, 135, *139*, 163
Schmitt, A., see Siebert, G. 143, 153, *166*
Schneider, C. H., see Aebi, H. 103, *137*, 161
—, and A. L. de Weck 164
Schnetger, J., see Holbrook, J. J. 153
Scholtan, W. 97
Schonne, E. 117
Scholz, A. G. R., see Schulz, G. V. 121, *138*
Schramm, M., see Heller, J. 158, *168*
Schreiber, G., U. U. Eckstein, A. Oeser, and H. Holzer 143
Schröder, E., see Klieger, E. 134, *139*
Schultz, A., see Berger, H. L. 126, *139*
Schulz, G. V., K. C. Berger, and A. G. R. Scholz 121, *138*
Schulz, W. W., J. P. Schelz, and W. C. Purdy 121, *140*
Schüssler, H., see Jung, H. 152, *167*
Schwartz, A. N., A. W. G. Yee, and B. A. Zabin 83, *85*, 157
Scott, R. P. W., see James, A. T. 39, *61*
Segal, S. J., see Talwar, G. P. 149
Sehon, A. H., see Lea, D. J. 18, *60*
—, see Sun K. 18, *60*, 82, *85*
Seide, H., see Gabert, A. 17, *60*
—, and G. Langhammer 128
Sela, M., see Cooke, J. P. 152, *169*
—, see Givol, D. 150
—, see Neumann, H. 94, 95, *136*
Selby, K., and C. C. Maitland 72, *84*, 115, 117, *138*, 144, *166*
Shahani, K. M., see Chandan, R. C. 166
Shainkin, R., and Y. Birk 144, *166*
Shapiro, B., and J. L. Rabinowitz 161, *168*
Shaw, R. W., see Connell, G. E. 88, *136*
Shepherd, G. R., and D. F. Pedersen 90, 91, *136*
—, and D. F. Pedersen 155, *167*
Shibnev, V. A., and V. G. Debabov 164
Shimizu, C. S. N., see Collipp, P. J. 146
Shooter, K. V., see Andrews, P. 116, *138*
Shutov, F., see Bresler, S. 156, *169*
Siebert, G., A. Schmitt, and R. v. Malortie 143, 153, *166*
Siegel, L. M., and K. J. Monty 77, *85*, 107, 113, 116, 117, *137*, *138*
Signer, R., H. Hänni, W. Koestler, W. Rottenburg, and P. v. Tavel 2, *11*
Si Jung Yeh, and H. L. Frisch 81, *85*
Simons, K., and T. Weber 117, 163
Singer, M. F., and G. Tolbert 89, *136*, 142

Singer, S. J., see Metzger, H. 151
Sjöholm, I. 145, *167*
Sjöqvist, J. 151
Sjövall, J., and R. Vihko 164
Skoczylas, B., see Gross, M. 155
Skrube, H., see Spitzy, H. 84, *85*, 94
Sluyser, M., see Bosch, L. 155, *168*
—, and C. H. Li 146
Smith, D. G., see Millar, J. R. 11, *12*, 14, 23, *60*
Smith, E. L., see Nolan, C. 153
Smith, W. B., and A. Kollmansberger 71, 72, 77, *84*
Smithies, O. 3, *11*
Sober, H. A., see Jones, O. W. 157, *168*
Söchtig, H. 131
Solms, J., see Deuel, H. 9, *12*
Somers, T. C. 83, *85*, 165
Sonenberg, M., see Dellacha, J. M. 146
Sorm, F., see Zadražil, S. 157
Šormová, Z., see Zadražil, S. 157
Sorof, S., E. M. Young, R. A. McBride, and C. B. Coffey 48, *62*, 117, 163
Soukup, M. 131, 164
Spitzy, H. 135, *139*
—, see Makowetz, E. 161, *169*
—, see Manipol, V. 147, *167*
—, H. Skrube, and K. Müller 84, *85*, 94
Squire, P. G. 74, *85*
—, B. Starman, and C. H. Li 146
Staehelin, M., see Delikas, N. 48, *62*, 156, *169*
Stahl, E. 51, *62*
Stanworth, D. R., see James, K. 151
Starman, B., see Squire, P. G. 146
Stauff, J. 3, *11*
Steelman, S. L., see Reisfeld, R. A. 146
Steeno, O., see de Moor, P. 98, *137*, 149
Steere, R. L. 158, *168*
—, see Ackers, G. K. 2, *11*, 76, *85*
—, and G. K. Ackers 10, *12*
Steers, jr., E., see Craven, G. R. 47, *61*, 144, *166*
Stegemann, H., see Friedberg, K. D. 162
—, and V. Loeschcke 91, *136*
—, W. Vogt, and K. D. Friedberg 162
Stein, W. H., see Crestfield, A. M. 94, 117, *138*, *139*, 147, *169*
—, see Jones, G. 143, *166*
—, see Ota, S. 143, *166*
Steinberg, M., see Colombo, P. 128
Steiner, R. F. 94, *136*

Stemke, G. W. 150
Stepanov, V., D. Handschuh, and F. A. Anderer 152
Steuerle, H. 130, *140*
Stickland, R. G. 55, *62*, 157
Stinson, E. E., and C. O. Willits 166
Stockmayer, W. H., see Zimm, B. H. 74, *85*
Stoddart, J. F., see Anderson, D. M. W. 77, 78, *85*, 108, *137*, 158, *168*
Stone, N., see Peart, W. S. 143, *169*
Stonehill, E. H., and M. E. Balis 145, *167*
Storgårds, T., see Lindqvist, B. 9, *12*
Stouffer, J. E., T. E. Kersten, and P. M. Krüger 39, *61*
Strandberg, B., see Fridborg, K. 158, *168*
Strauch, L., and W. Grassmann 143, *169*
Streuli, H. 131, 165
Strohmaier, K. 155
Strominger, J. L., see Ghuysen, J.-M. 154, 159, *168*
—, see Sanderson, A. R., 159 *168*
Stumpf, W., see Graul, E. H. 160, *169*
—, and E. H. Graul 161, *168*
Sun, K., and A. H. Sehon 18, *60*, 82, *85*
Surak, J. G., see Sanfelippo, P. M. 107, *137*, 146
Svedberg, T., and K. O. Pedersen 1, *11*
Swan, J. M., see Leach, S. J. 148, *167*
Synge, R. L. M., see Bagdasarian, M. 83, *85*, 134, *139*
—, see Mould, D. L. 3, *11*
—, and M. A. Youngson 2, *11*
Sze, Y.-L., see Rasmussen, H. 147
Szucs, M. M., see Peanasky, R. J. 143, *166*

Takagi, T. 78, *85*, 127, *140*
Takemori, S., see Kuboyama, M. 144, *166*
Talwar, G. P., S. J. Segal, A. Evans, and O. W. Davidson 149
Tan, M., see Epstein, W. V. 136, *139*, 160
—, and W. V. Epstein 151
Tanaka, K., H. H. Richards, and G. L. Cantoni 133, 134, *139*
Tanenbaum, S. W., see Bassett, E. W. 92, *136*, 150
Tappan, D. V. 48, *61*
Tappel, A. L., see Roubal, W. T. 41, 47, *61*, 111, *137*
Tatum, E. L., see Mach, B. 130, *139*, 163
Tauber, S., and L. L. Madison 148, *167*
v. Tavel, P., see Signer, R. 2, *11*

Tenenhouse, A., C. Arnaud, and H. Rasmussen 147
Terr, A. I., and J. D. Bentz 149
Tertrin, C., see de La Llosa, P. 114, *138*
Thatcher, G. N., see Peart, W. S. 143, *169*
Thiers, R. E., see Patrick, R. L. 45, *61*, 160, *168*
van Thoai, N., R. Kassab, and L. A. Pradel 107, *137*
Thompson, A. R. 9, *12*
Thompson, E. O. P., and I. J. O'Donell 117, *163*
Thompsson, T. E., see Rogers, K. S. 116, *138*
Thompson, T. E., see Roskes, S. D. 160
Thureborn, E. 99, *137*, 164
Timperi, R. J. K., see Latham, W. C. 162
Tipper, D. J., see Ghuysen, J.-M. 159, *168*
Tipton, C. L., J. W. Paulis, and M. D. Pierson 23, *61*, 164
Tipton, K. F. 116, *138*, 143, *166*
Tirunarayanan, M. O., and C. R. Salenstedt 162
—, see Salenstedt, C. R. 162
Tiselius, A. 9, *12*
—, J. Porath, and P.-Å. Albertsson 79, *85*, *170*
Tokumaru, T. 93
Tolbert, G., see Singer, M. F. 89, *136*, 142
Tombs, M. P. 3, *11*
Tompkins, V. N., see Gordon, M. A. 93
van Tongeren, J. H. M., and C. L. H. Majoor 97
Tongur, V., see Bachvaroff, R. J. 156, *169*
Toro-Goyco, E., see Rivera, J. V. 160
—, M. Martinez-Maldonado, and M. Matos 147, *167*
—, and M. Matos 143, *166*
Townsend, E. E., see Jones, O. W. 157, *168*
Trautmann, R. 1, *11*
Trautschold, J., see Fritz, H. 111, 119, *137*
Tubbs, P. K., see Chase, J. F. A. 116, *138*, 143
Tung, L. H. 125, *138*
—, J. C. Moore, and G. W. Knight 125, *138*
Turba, F., see Fasold, H. 7, *11*
Turski, W., see Gross, M. 155

Ulfendahl, H. R., see Bill, A. 159, *168*
Ullmann, U., see Wirth, K. 48, *61*, 160
Ullner, H., see Heitz, W. 22, 23, *60*
Ulrych, S., see Přistoupil, T. I. 149
Unger, K., see Kohlschütter, H. W. 25, *61*

Updike, S. J., see Hicks, G. P. 45, *61*
Upton, G. V., see Lande, S. 145, *167*
Ur, N., see Porath, J. 50, *62*
Urban, P. F., see Virmaux, N. 155, *168*
Utsumi, S., and F. Karush 151
Uziel, M., and W. E. Cohn 90, *136*, 157

Vallee, B. L., see Coleman, J. E. 144, *166*
—, see Pulido, P. 117, 163
Valeri, C. R., see Lionetti, F. J. 150, *167*
Valmet, E., see Ekman, L. 97
Varandani, P. T. 148, *169*
Vasil'eva, N. N., see Bresler, S. E. 155
Vaughan, M. F. 10, *12*, 25, *61*, 82, *85*
Vecchio, G., see Salvatore, G. 147
Ventruto, V., see Baglioni, C. 151, *167*
Vergani, C., see Agostini, A. 55, *62*, 161
Vernay, J. L., see Bourrillon, R. 154
du Vigneaud, V., see Ferrier, B. M. 134, *140*
—, see Drabarek, S. 134, *139*
—, see Jarvis, D. 134, *139*
—, see Yamashiro, D. 134, *140*, 145, *167*
Vihko, R. 131, 164
—, see Sjövall, J. 164
Vilhunen, R., see Nummi, M. 165
Virden, R., D. C. Watts, R. L. Watts, D. B.
    Gammack, and J. H. Raper 116, *139*
Virmaux, N., P. Mandel, and P. F. Urban
    155, *168*
Vogel, K., see Kohlschütter, H. W. 25, *61*
Vogt, W., see Friedberg, K. D. 162
—, see Stegemann, H. 162
Vollmert, B. 120, 121, *138*
de Vries, A. J. 128
de Vries, H. J., see le Page, M. 22, *61*

Wagner, M. 59, *62*, 93
Walter, I., see Determann, H. 82, 83, *85*
Walton, K. W., see George, W. 93
Ward, D. N., and M. S. Arnott 114, *137*, 146
Warth, R., see Kickhöfen, B. 50, *62*
Watts, D. C., see Virden, R. 116, *139*
Watts, R. L., see Virden, R. 116, *139*
Weber, K., see Konigsberg, W. 27, *61*, 154,
    169
Weber, T., see Simons, K. 117, 163
de Weck, A. L., see Schneider, C. H. 164
Weidel, W., see Maass, D. 143
Weil, J. H., see Dirheimer, G. 155, *168*
Wellner, D., see Glazer, A. N. 132, *139*
Wells, M. A., and J. C. Dittmer 135, *139*
van der Wende, G., see Bosch, L. 155, *168*

Werle, E., see Fritz, H. 111, 119, *137*, 143,
    166
Werner, M. 149
Westenbrink, H. G., see van Eijk, H. G. 160
Wheaton, R. M., and W. C. Baumann 9, *12*,
    67, 68, *84*
Whitaker, J. R. 48, *62*, 68, *84*, 108, 111, 115,
    137
—, see Feinstein, G. 117
White, W. F., G. H. Barlow, and M. M.
    Mozen 143, *169*
Wicke, E. 69, *84*
Wicken, A. J., and J. Baddiley 159, *168*
Widén, R., and K. E. Eriksson 43, *61*
Widström, G., see Jacobsson, L. 94
Wieland, Th., see Determann, H. 10, *12*, 22,
    60, 108, 120, *137*
—, and H. Bende 134, *139*
—, H. Determann, and E. Albrecht 2, *11*
—, P. Duesberg, and H. Determann 108,
    116, *137*
—, G. Lüben, and H. Determann 132, *139*,
    164
—, D. Rempel, U. Gebert, A. Buku, and
    H. Boehringer 130, 135, *140*
—, H. Schiefer, and U. Gebert 130, *140*
Wiesmann, U., see Aebi, H. 103, *137*, 161
Wilcox, P. E., and J. Lisowski 97
Wilding, P. 48, *61*, 132, *139*
Wilk, M., J. Rochlitz, and H. Bende 81, *85*,
    165
Williams, D. E., see Reisfeld, R. A. 146
Williams, R. J. P., see Baker, C. A. 121, *138*
Willits, C. O., see Stinson, E. E. 166
Winterhalter, K. H. 118, *140*
Winzor, D. J. 119, *138*, *140*
—, and L. W. Nichol 72, *84*
—, and H. A. Scheraga 119, *138*
Wirth, K., U. Ullmann, K. Brand, K. Huth,
    and B. Hess 48, *61*, 160
Witkop, B., see Gross, E. 152, *167*, *169*
Witte, J. J., see van Eijk, H. G. 161
Wittmann, G., see Matheka, H.-D. 89, *136*,
    158, *168*
Wood, H. G., H. Lochmüller, C. Rieper-
    tinger, and F. Lynen 144, *166*
Woof, J. B. 131, 165
Wright, jr., H. E., W. W. Burton, and R. C.
    Berry, jr. 131, 166
Wu, Y. Ch., see Montgomery, R. 154
Wucherpfennig, K., and I. Franke 131, *165*
Wuthier, R. A. 135, *140*

Yamashiro, D. 133, 134, *139*
—, H. L. Aanning, and V. du Vigneaud 145, *167*
—, D. Gillesen, and V. du Vigneaud 134, *140*
Yee, A. W. G., see Schwartz, A. N. 83, *85*, 157
Yonezawa, D., P. J. Migliore, S. C. Capetillo, and B. Jirgensons 151
Young, E. M., see Sorof, S. 48, *62*, 117, 163
Young, N. M., see Barker, S. A. 158, *169*
Young, R., see Rasmussen, H. 147
Youngson, M. A., see Bagdasarian, M. 83, *85*, 134, *139*
—, see Synge, R. L. M. 2, *11*

Zabel, R., see Zahn, H. 148, *167*
Zabin, B. A., see Schwartz, A. N. 83, *85*, 157
Zachau, H. G. 155, 156, *168*
Zadražil, S., Z. Šormová, and F. Sorm 157
Zahn, H., H. Bremer, and R. Zabel 148, *167*
—, B. Gutte, E. F. Pfeiffer, and J. Ammon 148, *167*
Zeleznick, L. D. 134, *139*, 159
Ziegler, R., see Schlubach, H. H. 159, *168*
Zikan, J., see Franěk, F. 151
Zimm, N. H., and W. H. Stockmayer 74, *85*
Zinder, N., see Konigsberg, W. 27, *61*, 154, *169*
Zipp, O., see Determann, H. 163
Zwaan, J., and A. F. van Dam 93

Subject Index

N-acetylglucoseaminidase 143
acid phosphatase 116
acrylamide 17, 18
actinomycin C 98, 135, 155, 163
adapter for centrifuge tubes 57
adenosine deaminase 116
— triphosphocreatine phosphotransferase 153
adrenaline 91
adsorption 81
—, aliphatic 82
—, reversible 80
— chromatography 79
aerogels 4, 25, 73
affinity 79
— to the gel phase 82, 83, 129
agar gels 50, 105, 149, 158
— —, chemical composition 19, 20
— —, granulated 10
— —, properties 21
— —, spherical particles 20
agarose, granulated gels, properties 29, 30
—, isolating from agar 20
— beds 20
— gels 142, 149, 156
— —, fractionation range 30
agavain 116, 143
alanine transaminase 116
albumin, barley 165
—, determination 98
alcohol dehydrogenase 107
aldolase 103, 107
alkali chlorides, partition chromatography on Sephadex 134
— protease 117
amanita phalloides, toxic cyclopeptides 130, 135
americium 97
amino acid derivatives 80
amino acids 80
— —, dialysis rate 82
— —, separation from protein 9
— —, DNP-derivatives 83
aminoacyltransfering enzymes 143
aminopeptidase 116
ammonium persulfate 18
amylase 132

α-amylase 118, 119, 144
β-amylase, barley 165
anaphylatoxin 162
angiotensin 98
anterior lobe hormones 146
anthracene 81
antigen-antibody, separation 92
— — complexes 98, 150
antigens 150
applicator thinlayer 52
arginine kinase 116
aromatics, polycyclic 165
arthritis, rheumatoid 160
aspartataminotransferase 143
asphalts 128
asphaltenes 128
association equilibria 118
autoanalyzer 47
azoglobins 153
azoisobutyronitrile 24

basket centrifuge 56
— —, filter insert 57
bee venom 163
beer constituents 165
Bence-Jones proteins 55, 151, 160, 161
benzene 71, 81
bile acids 132
Bio-Gel 90
— —, fractionation range 29
— —, preparation 19
— —, properties 28
— —, retardation of aromatics 83
— —, stability 29
biotin enzymes 144
biuret-complex with radioactive copper 47
blood group antibodies 148
Boltzmann equation 78, 81
bovine serum, modified 117
brewing materials 165
bromelain 117, 143, 160
buffer exchange 89
buffers, volatile 89

calibration 105
capillary, flowing particles 76
caramel colour 166

carboxyl group 84, 88
carboxypeptidase 144
carotene 132
carnitine acetyltransferase 116, 143
casein 152, 160, 163
catalase 103, 107, 160
catecholamines 91
cathepsin 143, 153
cations, retardation 84
Cd-poisoning, proteinuria 161
cell wall 154
cellulase 117, 144
— activity, concentrating 59
cellulose nitrate, molecular weight 108
— trinitrate 124
centrifuge technique with gels 56, 98
— techniques, equipment 56
— tube, adapters 58
ceruloplasmin 149
cetyl pyridinium chloride 20
cheese, peptides 165
chlorophyll 132
cholesterin 99, 133
chromatography, definition 6
— columns, commercially available 34
a-chymotrypsin 107, 152, 153
chymotrypsin-inhibitor 143
chymotrypsinogen A 107
clinical chemistry 159, 160, 162
clupein 8
coat protein 154
coffee constituents 165
collagen 153
— hydroxyproline 163
collagenase 143
collodium membrane 3
column designs, simple 33
— for gel chromatography 32–34
— for recycling chromatography 33
— packing procedure 42
— — with compressible gels 43
— — — organophilic gels 43
— with adjustable plungers 33
complex formation 96
complexes, composition 97
—, degree of binding 97
compounds, aromatic, retardation
    80, 82, 129
—, heterocyclic 80
concavalin A 132
concentrating, continuous 50

concentration isotherm 80
— of the sample 72
concentrator 51
cone model 73
corticoids 149
cortisol 149
creatine phosphokinase 109
cromium-51 97
cross-linkages 13
cross-linking 73
— —, degree 76
cytochrome oxydase 144
—, fragments 152
— c 107, 143, 153
— c-551 130

dehydrogenases 107, 144
delay of elution 80
deoxyribonucleic acid 90
desalting 88
— in a basket centrifuge 58
desoxycholic acid 99
detector, conductivity 38
—, dielectric differences 38
—, flame ionization 39
—, IR 38
—, optical density 36, 37
—, refractive index 38
—, temperature 79
—, temperature effect 38
dextran 15, 16, 17, 58, 159
—, concentrating 59
—, contamination 158
—, labeled with $^{131}I_2$ 158
— gels, preparation 15, 16
— —, swelling properties 16
— preparations, molecular weight
    distribution 122
— sodium chloride 58
dextrins from glycogenes 158
— from starch 158
dialysis 2, 87, 92, 98
—, differential 2
p-dibromo-benzene 71
diffusion, longitudinal 71, 125
—, restricted 76
— equilibrium 4, 70
— inhibition 76
— principle 77
— rate 76
— time 73
dilute solutions, concentration 56

dilution 56, 87, 88, 91
— steps 69
β-dimethylaminopropionitrile 18
dipalmitin 100
dipeptidase 143
dipeptides, partition chromatography on Sephadex 134
diphteria toxin 162
dipol-dipol interaction 3
dispersion forces 3
distance of migration 112
distilled water 88
distribution, calculation 123
—, counter current 4
divinyl benzene 24
DNP-amino acids, partition chromatography 134
— aspartic acid 6
dodecylsulfate 99
DPNH-binding 144
drug-protein binding 97
dye, cotton 9
—-protein conjugates 93

effluents, analysis of 47
egg albumin 107
EHTP 69
—-values 71
electrophoresis 3, 161
elution 46
— parameters 65, 68
— pattern 66
— volume 66, 111
endonuclease 142
enolase 109
enzyme-cofactor, separation 92
—/inhibitor complex 120
— labeling 38
— reactions 144
—-substrate complex 120
— traces 144
enzymes, isolation 141
—, molecular weights 116
—, pancreatic 142
epichlorohydrin 15, 16, 17
equilibrium dialysis 75
estrogens 131, 162
estradiol 149
ethyleneglycoldimethacrylate 22
ethylene glycols 79
excess of reagents 93
exclusion 81

exclusion chromatography, terminology 7
— limit 64, 78
— mechanism 75, 79
— principle 73, 77, 78
exonucleases 145

ferritin 113, 163
fibrinogen 113
fish meals 160
flavanes 131
flow rate 46, 47, 70, 72
— — control 46
fluorescent antibody 93
— antisera 93
— labeling 92, 93
— protein conjugates 93
foam 3
Folin-Lowry color reaction 47
fraction collectors 39
fractionation ranges 99
— methods, comparison 126

galactomannan, cross linked 9
D-galactose 20
β-galactosidase 144
gall bladder bile 99, 117, 164
gastrin 148
gel, definition 3
—, density 64
—, general synthesis 13
—, macroporous 14
—, permeability 123
—, schematic structure 14
—, structure 82
— bed 64
— —, volume 88
— chromatography, history 8
— —, model 72
— —, schematic representation 5
— —, terminology 7
— column, calibrated 122
— —, effectivity 69
— —, long 48
— filtration 86
— —, choice of gel 87
— —, terminology 7
— model 3
— — by OGSTON-LAURENT 75
— packing 87
— —, dimensions 71
— particles, deformation 46

gel permeation chromatography, terminology 7
— phase 79, 80
— —, affinity 78
Gilbert theory 119
glass beads, size separation by 25
— powder, porous 25
globulin 152
—, human 153
γ-globulin, fragments 150, 151
γ-globulins 107, 149, 153, 160
(7 S) globulins 103
(19 S) globulins 103
β-glucoronidase 116
glucose 6, 160
—-6-phosphate dehydrogenase 116
glutamate dehydrogenase 116, 118
—-pyruvate transaminase 116
glutathione 163
glyceraldehyde 3-phosphate dehydrogenase 116, 153
glycerides 81, 100, 132
glycerine aldehyde phosphate 107
glycerol 9
glycol 9
glycopeptides 153
glycoproteins 114
GPC, calculation methods 125
—-apparatus 40, 41, 123
—- —, calibration 111
grain size 71
grass extract 90
group separation 90
growth hormone 94, 117, 118, 145, 146

height equivalent of one theoretical plate 70
hemicelluloses 158
hemoglobin 6, 58, 89, 118, 153, 154, 160, 161
—, concentrating 59
—, pure, from erythrocytes 102
—-binding capacity 160
—-haptoglobin complex 150
—- — —, isolation 50
histones 117, 163
hose connections 35, 36
humic acid 164
— —, desalting 89
— substances 131
hyaluronic acid gel 75
hyaluronidase 143

hydrochloric acid 71
hydrocarbons, molecular weight 108
—, polycylic 81
hydrogen bond 3
hydroxylamine reductase 116
α-hydroxysteroid dehydrogenase 109, 143
β-hydroxysteroid dehydrogenase 143

immuno-chemical tests 55
immunocomplexes, soluble 150
immunoglobulins 149
impure enzyme preparations, molecular weight 115
indol-derivatives 131
inhomogenity 121
inner volume, fraction 67
insulin 94, 147
—, A- and B-chains 148
— inhibitor 147
interaction 78—81, 83
— between aromatic compound 83
— of solutes 79
interactions, quantitative description 98
interferon 117
intermediate lobe hormones 145
inulin 160
iodine, labeled 129
ion exchange 80
— — effect 93
— — side effects 132
ion exchangers, macroreticular 9, 11
— —, size separation 8
— exclusion 131, 132

junction points 3
junctional regions 4

kallikrein inhibitor 109
kidney function test 160
K_{av}-value 68
K_d-value 67

α-lactalbumin, immunologically active fragment 152
lactate dehydrogenase 103, 116, 143, 153
— —, concentrating 59
lactoglobulin 118
β-lactoglobulin, immunologically active fragment 152
lactose synthetase 144
lanthanons 97
lignin 8, 165
lipase 116, 117, 142

lipid complex 164
lipids 135, 164
lipoproteins 103, 149
lysozyme 132, 144, 153

macroglobulin 50, 149, 150
macroglobulinemia 160, 161
macromolecule, labeled 84
macromolecules, concentrating 59
—, modification 92
macroporous polystyrene gels, properties
    24, 25
macroporosity, definition 14
malate dehydrogenase 109
malonaldehyde 164
manganous irons 97
mannobiose 159
mannosidase 144
mannotetraose 159
mannotriose 159
manufacturers of equipment 41
membranes, semipermeable 2
— of agar, agarose 2
mercaptoethanol 93
metallothionein 117, 163
methemoglobin 109
methionine activating enzyme 98
N, N'-methylen-bis-acrylamide 17, 18
methylmethacrylate 22
micelle-forming substance 98
micelles 99
micro-column 55
milk, lactose-free 165
—, separation of strontium 166
— lipase 166
molecular sieve chromatography,
    terminology 7
— — filtration, terminology 7
— sieves 1, 2
— size 105
— weight 106
— —, average 120
— —, number average 121
— —, weight average 120
— — determination, columns size 111
— — distribution 41, 121, 122
— — —, integral 123
— — from impure preparations 55
— — values, comparison of average 127
— weights and elution behavior 108
model separation 6
monostearin 100

β-MSH-activity 145
mucosaccharides 159
—, thinlayer gel chromatography 55
mucopolysaccharides 96, 159
myoglobin 107, 163
—, fragments 152
myeloma 160, 161
myogens 163

naphtalene 81
noradrenaline 91
nucleic acid, complexes 98
— — components 83
— acids, removal of low molecular
    weight substances 155
— —, shape 114
nucleosides, strongly phosphorylated 83
nucleotide, desalting 90

oligamides, cyclic 48
oligonucleotides 79, 155
—, degree of phosphorylation 156
—, molecular weight 108
—, separation 157
oligopeptides, molecular weight 108
—, separation 152
oligosaccharides 79, 90, 120
—, separation 159
oligostyrenes 120
—, molecular weight 108
ovalbumin 154
ovomucoid 154
oxytocin 96, 145
—, partition chromatography 133
—-analogs, partition chromatography on
    Sephadex 134

packing devices 43
— of the gel bed 42
pancreas extract, enzymatic activities 101
pantothenic acid synthetase 116
paraffins, molecular weight 108
parathyroid hormone 147
partial specific density 113
— — volume 65
particle, separation 105
partition 80, 81
— chromatography 79, 133
— principle 78
peaks, broadening 69
pectic substances 159
penicillin 164

penicillin, protein-binding 97
pentapeptides, oligomeric 101
pepsin 107, 143
—, concentrating 59
S-peptide 152
peptides 80
—, desalting 90
—, —, partition chromatography 134
—, labeled isolation 153
—, oligomeric 120
—, relation between molecular weight
   and elution volume 83
—, thinlayer gel chromatography 55
—, tryptic from RNase 48
peptide synthetase 117
permeability 126
peroxydase 109
phase, mobile 79, 80
—, stationary 79
phenol 90
— oxydases 91
— red 98, 160
—, retardation, comparison of Sephadex
   and Bio-Gel 83
phosphatase, acid 142
—, alkaline 116, 142
— isoenzymes 142
phosphodiesterase 142
6-phosphogluconate dehydrogenase 116
phosphoglyceromutase 109
phospholipids 99, 132
photometer, flow-through 37
—, — - — cells 38
phosphomonoesterase 142
picric acid 83
pinguinain 143
plasma proteins 50
— —, complexes with steroid hormones
   149
— —, fractionation 148
plasminogen 149
plastein 101
—-subunits 163
plate size, thinlayer 52
polarity 81, 82
pollen proteins 48
polyacrylamide gels 3, 76, 82
— —, designation 18
— —, macroporous 19
— —, preparation 17, 18
polyacrylnitrile 128
—, cross-linked 23

polybutadiene 126, 127
cis-1,4-polybutadiene 123
polydisperse polymers 126
polyethers, molecular weight 108
polyehtylene 127, 128
—, molecular weight 108
— glycol 20, 100
polyfructosan-S 160
polygalacturnic acid 9
polyisobutane 127
polyisobutylene, molecular weight
   distribution 122
— fractions 79
polylysine 98
polymer chains 75
polymers, statistically coiled 78
—, stretched, chain length 124
polymethacrylate 108, 120, 124
—, cross-linked 10
— gel 132
— gels, preparation 22
polynucleotides, hydrolyzed 157
polypeptides 152, 164
polyphenols 83
polyphosphoric acid 9
polysaccharides 75, 90
—, bacterial 158
—, desalting 89
—, molecular weight 108
— chain 75
polystyrene 108, 123, 124, 127
—, molecular weight distribution 122
— gels 10
— —, macroporous 11
— —, preparation 23
— —, preparation of macroporous 23–25
— standards 104, 106
polytripeptide, molecular weight
   distribution 122
polyvinylpyrrolidon 128
pore radius, effective 77
pores 73
pore size distribution 99
porosity 99
—, determination 15
posterior lobe hormones 145
potatoe juice 91
precipitation, fractional 121
pregnancy test 162
pressure, hydrostatic 46
progesterone 98, 149
protease 117, 143

protein denaturation 114
— association 115
— carriers 96
—-iron binding 97
—-metal complexes 97
— molecules, shape 113
— purification 141
— standards 107
proteins, elution volume and molecular
    weight 109
—, frontal analysis 72
—, globular 113
—, molecular weights 52, 55, 108, 113, 117
—, partial hydrolyzate 134
—, pathological 160
—, radio-iodination 93
—, soybean 48, 163
—, structural 162
—, temperature influence on the elution
    114
—, toxic 162
—, tritiation 96
— from liver 48
S-protein 152
prothrombin 116, 143
pseudoglobulins 136
pyruvate kinase 109

random coils 124
recorder 37
recycling chromatography 49, 50
refractometer 38
regions, accessible 74
renin 116, 143
riboflavin 18
ribonuclease 93, 94, 107, 117, 132, 153, 154
—, fragments 152
—, ribosomal 142
ribonucleic acids, ribosomal 155, 156
— —, soluble 48, 95, 155, 156
ribonucleotides, prepurification by thin-
    layer gel chromatography 55
rigid fibers, network 75
RNA, bacteriophage 156
—, polio virus 156
—/DNA-hybrides 156
s-RNA 156
— partition chromatography 133, 134
— peptidyl 156
rubber 128
—, granulated 10
—, synthetic 79

sample application 43
— —, automated 44
— — by flow adaptor 45
— — — underlayering 45
— solution, concentration 56
— —, viscosity 56
— volume 88
separation, interpretation 63
— power 71
— time 52
— volume 68, 69, 99
— without differences in size 86
Sephadex 78, 90
—, acylation 21
—, discovery 10
—, growth of microorganisms 27
—, hydroxyalkyl ether 22
—, methylation 22
—, preparation and chemical structure 15
—, properties of the commercial product
    26
—, reaction with isocyanates 22
—, recepies 17
—, regeneration 27, 28
—, retardation of aromatics 82
—, rules for application 27
—, separation range 26
—, volume values 65
— gels, equations 111
— —, separation range 114
— —, swelling time 27
— LH-20 22, 28, 81, 92, 132
serum 88
—, fractionation 148
—, iodo-compounds 94
— albumin 71, 97, 98, 103, 107, 117, 132
— proteins 52, 97, 104
— —, interaction 98
shape, molecular 124
sieving 1
silica gel 25
— —, bead form 25
silicones 128
snake venom 142, 153
sodium chloride 89
solubility 81
solvent layer 77
— regain 64
— —, determination 15
— reservoir 33
solvents in the GPC-apparatus 128
sorbit 9

spectrophotometer 47
—, flow-through 37
staining of proteins 55
starch 5, 91
— gel electrophoresis 3
— grains, sieving properties 9
starting a column 44
steroid separations 131, 164
sterols 164
Stokes' radii 77
— radius 113, 118
Styragel 41, 77, 78, 81, 104
—, fractionation range 31
—, properties 30, 31
styrene 24
sugar 91
— purification 166
—, partition chromatography 134
sulfanilic acid, diazotized 95
sulfite reductase 116
sulfonamide, protein bound 97
sulfonic acids, aromatic 143
synovial fluid 158

teichoic acids 159
temperature effect 72, 79
terminology 6
tetanus toxoid 162
theoretical plates 69
thickness of layer 52
thinlayer gel chromatography 51, 111
— — —, control 54
— — —, detection of proteins 54
— — —, drying of plates 54
— — —, equipment 53
— — —, techniques 52
— plates, preparation 51
thiophosphate 94
thrombin 116, 143
thymidylic acid 79
thyrocalcitonin 147
thyroglobulin 147
thyroid function test 161
— glands, extracts 147
thyronine 161
thyroxine 161
TMV-RNS 155
tobacco 131, 166
— mosaic virus 152
toxins, extracellular 92, 162

transferrin 103
triacetin 100
tributyrin 100
tricaprin 100
trichosiderins 131, 165
triglycerides 100, 133
triiodothyronine 129
3,5,3'-triiodotyrosine 161
tripeptide, desalting 83
tristearin 100
tritium uptake and release 94
trypsin 107, 132
—-inhibitor 94, 107, 109, 119, 143
tryptophan 83, 129, 131
tubing 35
tyrocidines 130, 163

ultracentrifuge 1, 115
—, density gradient 1
urea 93
urease 113, 117
uridylic acid 71
urokinase 116, 143

vasopressin 96, 145
venom, cobra 142
virus, polio 105
—, influenza 105
— separation 157
viruses, desalting 89
— from red beats 91
viscosity 58
vitamine B_{12} 59, 117, 163, 164
volume, accessible 75
— ratios 87
volumes in the gel bed 64

wheat flour 166
wine tannins 165
wool 117, 152, 163

xanthine oxydase 109, 116
xantophyll 132
Xerogel 4

yttrium-91 97

Zeolites 1, 2
zinc ions 118

Type-setting and printing : Mandruck München Theodor Dietz KG